M000072732

Polypropylene Handbook

This book is dedicated to the spirit of creativity, discovery, and innovation that has made polypropylene technology and the consequent business growth so vigorous and exciting for four decades, and to the researchers who personify that spirit, represented by Prof. Giulio Natta, who gave birth to PP technology in 1954.

1903–1979

Giulio Natta   March 11, 1954

Prof. Giulio Natta was born on February 26, 1903. He received a degree in chemistry from Milan Polytechnic in 1924. In 1933, he became a professor of chemistry at Pavia, then in Rome in 1935. In 1938, Natta moved to Milan Polytechnic and became Director of the Institute of Industrial Chemistry. Following Ziegler's successful preparation of linear polyethylene in 1953, Natta prepared polypropylene on March 11, 1954. He promptly identified the crystal structure of PP and the stereospecific nature of the catalyst. Karl Ziegler and Giulio Natta shared the Nobel prize in chemistry in 1963.

Polypropylene Handbook

Polymerization, Characterization, Properties, Processing, Applications

Edited by
Edward P. Moore, Jr.

With Contributions by

Enrico Albizzati, Stephen E. Amos, Ronald F. Becker, Omar M. Boutni
Lester P.J. Burton, Gianni Collina, Dario Del Duca, Stephen M. Dwyer, Umberto Giannini,
Gregory A. Larson, Richard T. LeNoir, Richard T. Lieberman,
Edward P. Moore, Luciano Noristi, Charles G. Oertel, Roger A. Phillips,
Luigi Resconi, Catherine E. Ruiz, Chichang Shu, Michael Wolkowicz

HANSER

Hanser Publishers, Munich Vienna New York

Hanser/Gardner Publications, Inc., Cincinnati

The Editor:
Edward P. Moore, Jr., Montell USA, Inc. (retired), 718 Cheltenham Road, Wilmington, DE 19808, USA

Distributed in the USA and in Canada by
Hanser/Gardner Publications, Inc.
6600 Clough Pike, Cincinnati, Ohio 45244-4090, USA
Fax: (513) 527-8950
Phone: (513) 527-8977 or 1-800-950-8977

Distributed in all other countries by
Carl Hanser Verlag
Postfach 86 04 20, 81631 München, Germany
Fax: +49 (89) 98 12 64

The use of general descriptive names, trademarks, etc., in this publication, even if the former are not especially identified, is not to be taken as a sign that such names, as understood by the Trade Marks and Merchandise Marks Act, may accordingly be used freely by anyone.

While the advice and information in this book are believed to be true and accurate at the date of going to press, neither the authors nor the editors nor the publisher can accept any legal responsibility for any errors or omissions that may be made. The publisher makes no warranty, express or implied, with respect to the material contained herein.

Library of Congress Cataloging-in-Publication Data
Polypropylene handbook : polymerization, characterization, properties,
applications/edited by Edward P. Moore, Jr.
   p. cm.
Includes bibliographical references and index.
ISBN 1-56990-208-9
1. Polypropylene. I. Moore, Edward P.
TP1180.P68P65   1996
668.4'234–dc20   96-15822

Die Deutsche Bibliothek – CIP-Einheitsaufnahme
Polypropylene handbook : polymerization, characterization,
properties, applications / ed. by Edward P. Moore. – Munich ;
Vienna ; New York : Hanser ; Cincinnati : Hanser/Gardner,
1996
  ISBN 3-446-18176-8
NE: Moore, Edward P. [Hrsg.]

© Carl Hanser Verlag, Munich Vienna New York, 1996
Typeset in England by Techset Composition Ltd., Salisbury
Printed and bound in Germany by Friedrich Pustet GmbH & Co. KG, Regensburg

Foreword

Professor Dr. Paolo Galli is President of the Montell Technology Company

More than forty years have elapsed since the discovery of the stereospecific polymerization of polypropylene (PP). It is now widely recognized that the discovery not only represented the first and most significant step in the synthesis of crystalline PP at the scientific and industrial level, but, even more important, it meant the beginning of a new challenging adventure still in progress today. In the years following its discovery, PP went through such a dynamic industrial development that it is today one of the most widely used polymeric materials, and still has a very bright future.

The world market for PP has grown from around 1.5 mio tons in the 1970s, to about 13 mio tons in the 1990s, and is expected to be over 19 mio tons in 1995. In the year 2000 it could exceed 25 mio tons. Such explosive and unarrestable growth is due to the outstanding combination of cost performance, excellent physical properties, strong and continuous expansion of process versatility, and environmental friendly processes and materials, during manufacturing, use, and recycling stages. Nevertheless, this unique and enviable position was not expected nor foreseen, even up to the early '70s. Before this period, polypropylene was a marginal, low quality commodity, with little versatility. The process was complex, expensive and inflexible. It was also environmentally challenging, because of the complexity of its manufacturing and purifying cycles.

This unexpected surge, which started in the early '70s, and is still surprisingly vigorous, was made possible by focusing and investing in the thorough scientific understanding of the catalytic system, and its subsequent development.

After the discovery of polypropylene, obtained for the TiCl$_3$-based first generation catalyst, at the Polytechnic of Milan in 1954, nothing revolutionary happened until the discovery of the active MgCl$_2$-supported high yield Ziegler-Natta catalysts at the Ferrara Giulio Natta Research Center in 1968. That event was the beginning of the revolution that brought about the creation of the third and fourth generation catalysts. This represented a real "breakthrough" for PP technology. It was possible to design new, versatile, clean, and economical processes to create a new family of materials, including:

- PCMA* (polymeric composite material and alloys),
- Copolymers (random and heterophasic),
- Catalloy* (PP-based polyolefin alloys),
- Hivalloy* (PP-based engineering plastic alloys).

Figure 1 well illustrates how these new catalysts brought about the dramatic evolution of polypropylene technology, the processes, the product families, and consequently, the market.

* Montell Polyolefin Trade Marks.

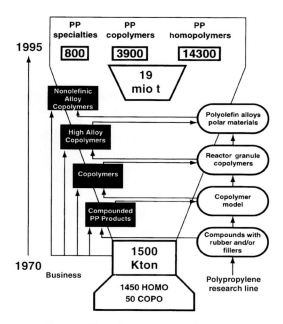

Figure 1 The polypropylene product cornucopia

The research line has continuously developed a systematic scientific understanding of the basic technology. The prompt and aggressive industrialization of all the technological results gave a rapid confirmation of its validity. The research was also driven by the market, which required particular needs, and demanded better and deeper scientific understanding. These needs gave impetus to the development of new basic research projects on catalysis and polymerization processes. The new scientific understanding showed the existence of new technological potentials, disclosing new opportunities in terms of new catalytic system performance, new product properties, and eventually new businesses.

The new understanding has been a continuous, autocatalytic process, whose dynamic development has been the real key to the outstanding polypropylene growth. This is a technological success that is based on the full exploitation of the close synergistic cooperation of catalyst and polymerization scientists, process engineers, and marketing experts in a real interdisciplinary action. In short, the research approach has generated and supported the revolution that brought about the dynamic development of the catalyst systems from the first to the fourth generations. This success gave rise to the creation of a rich cornucopia of the new product families shown in Fig. 2.

Where is PP going? The adventure is not over yet. As a matter of fact, the new catalyst generations, having always been the key to the process and product improvements, are impacting the technologies of two strong new families.

First, the superactive fourth generation catalysts are introducing an innovative and revolutionary new dimension to heterogeneous catalysis. Thanks to the specific, tailored "architecture" of the catalyst, it is now possible to give the catalyst the capability of determining the physical shape of the polymer generated and the external and internal

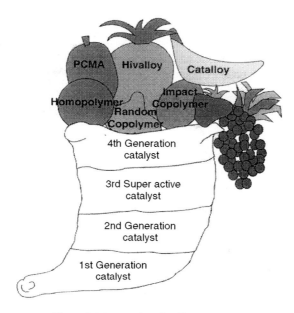

Figure 2 New product families Cornucopia

morphology, i.e., to control the type of specific distribution within the single granule. This capability is going to have a significant impact on our concepts of the process and the product.

Second, the metallocenes offer a new dimension in control, at the molecular level, of the molecular weight and monomer distributions with relevant impact on the final material properties. We forecast that over the next decade, the combination of the fourth generation catalyst linked to the metallocene catalysts will generate an explosive growth with a great impact on the processes and the products. It is becoming natural to expect a continuation of the dynamic evolution of polypropylene.

As a researcher in the company that more than any other trusted in PP, supported, drove the catalyst, process, product research, and commercialization, I am proud to participate in this precise and vivid presentation of polypropylene history and its continuing development. Montecatini SpA was the company that supported in the early fifties, the research of Prof. Natta who brought about the discovery of isotactic PP at the Polytechnic of Milan in 1954. In 1957 the first commercial production was achieved in the Ferrara plant only three years after the scientific discovery. The discovery of the revolutionary high yield catalyst in 1968 in Ferrara allowed Montecatini to once again provide a major advance in PP technology, which has driven the scientific and industrial evolution that followed in the 80s and 90s, and characterizes the PP history. This dynamic evolution, continuously surpassing itself, has been made possible by the continuous growth of scientific understanding of catalyst, process, and product developments, and the integration of these technologies into the market development process. This has been the approach that has driven the technology and the market evolution since the early 70s.

The most visible commercial consequence is that today over 80% of the global PP production capacity (over 19 M tons in 1995), is operated under Montedison patent or know-how licenses. Montecatini became Montedison in 1967, and then joined with Hercules to form Himont in November 1983. Himont merged with Shell, becoming Montell in April 1995.

Montell supports the publication of this book on PP, which contains the contributions from many of its researchers and engineers, and is happy to have participated in this documentation of the vigorous PP industry. It is truly exciting to have been, and to continue being, a part of this adventure.

March 1996   *Paolo Galli*

Preface

The focus of interest in polypropylene has shifted over the last four decades from the first catalysts, to the nature of those early polymers, to the growing applications, then accelerating interest in the manufacturing process, leading to several new rounds of catalysts, processes, polymers, and applications, much of the latest round occurring in the last decade. The pace and magnitude of the recent changes, which became visible in the early '80s, have constituted a virtual revolution. While some recent books and articles have captured some of these activities, notably Van der Ven's excellent 1990 treatment of PP polymerization, none have been all-inclusive. This book is an attempt to present, in one comprehensive document, the new state of the PP industry, and to record and explain those fast-moving technological and business events that have resulted from that recent revolution, all in the light of the four-decade PP experience.

My own involvement with PP, while extensive, has been more broad than deep. From the secret project (polymerizing propylene) that an engineer friend was assigned at Hercules in 1955, through my operation of a continuous loop reactor in the late '50s, development, manufacture, and understanding of biaxially oriented films in the '60s, development of new polypropylene resins in the '70s, and finally, market development and assisting at managing the new technologies from the mid-'80s until retirement in 1993, I was, as a jack of all polypropylene trades, well qualified to ask penetrating questions of our authors. Perhaps more important, retirement gave me the time needed to attend to the editing chores for this book.

Although all of the authors are from Himont and Montell backgrounds, we have tried to present an industry-wide view of polypropylene, while including Montell developments that are, we believe, pertinent examples of the vigor that exists in the polypropylene industry today.

Thanks for helping make this book a reality go first to Hanser's Dr. Ed Immergut, who suggested that Himont take the lead in preparing this volume. Second, thanks to the Himont management for accepting that challenge, then persevering in that commitment when the difficulties of forming the Montell joint venture demanded so much attention. Third, to those who bore the true burden of creating this book, the authors who provided these chapters in a timely manner, and the many other contributors to those chapters, I and the future readers of this book are most grateful. Fourth, special thanks go to a few individuals whose contributions were above and beyond the call of duty: Luciano Noristi, for assembling and correcting, after our computer scrambled it, the extremely complex catalyst chapter; Roger Phillips, for his untiring pursuit of the scientifically correct explanation; Larry Thurrell and Chuck Oertel, for giving us the quick response when the need was critical; Dave Szasz, for converting so many of our rough scribbles into clear illustrations; and Enrico Zanoli, for providing rapid approvals at deadline time.

Finally, for her unswerving support of this project, and for cheerfully tolerating the many lonely hours it caused in the last few months, I thank my lovely and loving wife, Georgie.

Wilmington, DE   *Edward P. Moore, Jr.*
March 1996

Contents

4 Additives 177

Ronald F. Becker, Lester P. J. Burton, Stephen E. Amos

5 Compounded Polypropylene Products 211

Stephen M. Dwyer, Omar M. Boutni, Chichang Shu

6 End-Use Properties 237

Dario Del Duca, Edward P. Moore, Jr.

Edward P. Moore, Jr., Gregory A. Larson

Contributors

Albizzati, Enrico, Montell Italia S.p.A., G. Natta Research Center, P.le Donegani 12, 41000 Ferrara, Italy

Amos, Stephen E., 3M Company, 5215 Logan Ave. South, Minneapolis, MN 55419-1021, USA

Becker, Ronald F, Montell USA, Inc., R & D Center, 912 Appleton Rd., Elkton, MD 21921, USA

Boutni, Omar M., Montell USA, Inc., 2727 Alliance Dr., Lansing, MI 48910, USA

Burton, Lester P.J., Montell USA, Inc., R & D Center, 912 Appleton Rd., Elkton, MD 21921, USA

Collina, Gianni, Montell Italia S.p.A., G. Natta Research Center, P.le Donegani 12, 41000 Ferrara, Italy

Del Duca, Dario, Montell Italia S.p.A., G. Natta Research Center, P.le Donegani 12, 41000 Ferrara, Italy

Dwyer, Stephen M., Montell USA, Inc. 2727 Alliance Dr., Lansing, MI 48910, USA

Giannini, Umberto, Montell Italia S.p.A., G. Natta Research Center, P.le Donegani 12, 41000 Ferrara, Italy

Larson, Gregory A., Montell Polyolefins, P.O. Box 625, Hoeksteen 2130 AP, Hoofddorp, The Netherlands

LeNoir, Richard T., Montell USA, Inc., R & D Center, 800 Greenbank Rd., Wilmington, DE 19808 5961, USA

Lieberman, Richard B., Montell USA, Inc., R & D Center, 912 Appleton Rd., Elkton, MD 21921, USA

Moore, Edward P., Montell USA, Inc. (retired), 718 Cheltenham Road, Wilmington, DE 19808, USA

Noristi, Luciano, Montell Italia S.p.A., G. Natta Research Center, P.le Donegani 12, 41000 Ferrara, Italy

Oertel, Charles G., Montell USA, Inc. (retired), 1000 Oriente Ave., Wilmington, DE 19807, USA

Phillips, Roger A., Montell USA, Inc., R & D Center, 912 Appleton Rd., Elkton, MD 21921, USA

Resconi, Luigi, Montell Italia S.p.A., G. Natta Research Center, P.le Donegani 12, 41000 Ferrara, Italy

Ruiz, Catherine E., Allied-Signal Corp., 101 Columbia Rd., Morristown, NJ 07962, USA

Shu, Chichang, Montell USA, Inc., 2727 Alliance Dr., Lansing, MI 48910, USA

Wolkowicz, Michael D., Montell USA, Inc., R & D Center, 912 Appleton Rd., Elkton, MD 21921, USA

Part I

Polypropylene: The Material

1   Introduction

Edward P. Moore, Jr.

1.1   Scope

This volume is intended to be a primary reference for anyone wishing to learn about some aspect of polypropylene (PP). In addition to providing a detailed reference on the conventional PP materials and the current business, we also explore the origins of PP, PP-related activities, and the implications for the future of this extraordinary polymer.

Following some basic chemical considerations and historical background, the material section is divided into the catalysis, polymerization, and structure of conventional commercial PP products, which are based on isotactic, crystalline PP homopolymers, random copolymers, and impact (or heterophasic) copolymers. We discuss additives for, and compounded products of, the above, which include rubber-modified, mineral-filled, and glass fiber reinforced PPs. The properties acheived with these materials, and the principal factors determining them, follow.

The business section includes the manufacture, processing, and applications of PP, along with regulatory and environmental aspects.

Although the principal chapters focus on appropriate aspects of conventional PP, we also comment on some of the major new PP materials, such as high melt strength PP and highly substituted copolymers, which are already available in commercial quantities. Looking to the future, we discuss the impact of metallocene catalysts on PP, such as syndiotactic PP, and some of the materials that are based on polypropylene but which are clearly beyond any definition of PP, including the non-olefinic alloys polymerized in situ in a PP matrix.

1.2   Chemistry

What is polypropylene? Strictly defined, PP would simply be whatever was obtained by polymerizing propylene. Prior to 1950, propylene polymer was a branched low molecular weight oil, of no interest then, or now. We prefer to use a more practical definition of PP here: the materials and related businesses that grew out of the Ziegler–Natta discovery of catalysts capable of producing stereoregular PP.

Let's explore in more detail the concept of stereoregularity, which distinguishes present PP from the pre-Ziegler–Natta variety. Three factors control the stereo arrangement of the propylene polymer:

1. *The degree of branching:* Is it linear; does the next monomer unit always add at the chain end, or does it sometimes add onto the backbone, forming a branch? Figure 1.1 shows schematically the two possibilities, excluding the hydrogen atoms, and highlighting the pendant carbon atom as white.

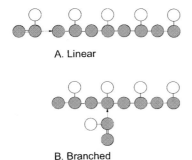

A. Linear

B. Branched

Figure 1.1 Linear (A) and branched (B) addition of propylene monomer to the growing PP chain

2. *The pendant methyl sequence:* Is it regiospecific; is the monomer unit always added in a head-to-tail manner, or is it sometimes inserted head-to-head or tail-to-tail? See Fig. 1.2.
3. *Right or left hand:* Is it stereospecific; does the monomer unit always add in the same stereo arrangement—either d or l—or does it sometimes insert in the opposite hand? Figure 1.3 shows the two addition possibilities (tertiary hydrogen included to show hand).

When the answer to all three questions is yes, the result is isotactic PP, illustrated in Fig. 1.4.A. Figure 1.4.B shows syndiotactic PP, which results from *consistent* insertion of the monomer in the opposite hand from the previous monomer unit, a different type of stereoregularity that is not yet commercially significant. Atactic PP results from inconsistency of, in the case shown in Fig. 1.4.C, the hand of the monomer insertion, but atactic PP would result from inconsistency in any of the three factors mentioned above.

Let us go one step further in describing our stereoregular PP. The regularity of the isotactic PP allows it to crystallize. Figure 1.5 shows the schematic arrangement of the carbon atoms in the crystallized isotactic PP chain, viewed obliquely from one end. This diagram shows how the alignment of the backbone (gray) and pendant methyl carbons (white) provide a shape, in this case forming a left-handed helix, that permits close nesting of chains for crystallizing, when matched with an equal number of chains in the form of a right-handed helix. The length of chain shown, five turns of the helix, represents about 1/4 to 1/3 of the length normally found traversing the crystal lamella thickness. More detail regarding these morphological aspects appears in Chapter 3. Almost all of the PP materials we will discuss contain some significant fraction of the isotactic PP described above, and display substantial crystallinity. The exceptions are, of course, syndiotactic PP and atactic PP.

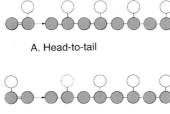

A. Head-to-tail

B. Tail-to-tail

Figure 1.2 Head-to-tail (A) and tail-to-tail (B) addition of propylene to the growing PP chain

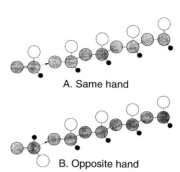

A. Same hand

B. Opposite hand

Figure 1.3 Addition of propylene to the growing PP chain in the same (A) and opposite (B) hand

The degree of stereoregularity (and consequent crystallinity) among conventional PPs varies considerably. Even homopolymers, where the room temperature xylene solubles level approximates the atactic content, are available from as little as 1% xylene solubles to about 20%. These variations are usually due to the effectiveness of the polymerization catalyst, but the production process also can have some effect. One of the major driving forces in the PP industry has been the ability to improve the process as a result of improvements in the catalysts. That is addressed in Chapters 2 and 8.

Beyond homopolymers, there is a wide range of copolymers and terpolymers, usually of ethylene and butene, of two types: random and impact. Random copolymers typically contain up to 6% (by weight) of ethylene or other comonomers inserted at random within the chain, which reduces the crystallinity and the melting point by introducing irregularities into the chain. Random copolymers are used where clarity, lower melting point, or lower modulus is desirable. Impact copolymers, also known as heterophasic copolymers, usually contain up to about 40% ethylene-propylene rubber (EPR), intimately dispersed within the matrix, usually homopolymer. As the EPR is usually about 50% ethylene, this translates into a 20% ethylene level on the total product, a more widely used description. As implied in the name, those copolymers are used where impact strength is important, especially at low temperatures. The compositions, molecular weights, amounts, and morphologies of the dispersed EPR and continuous homopolymer phases are crucial to having an effective impact copolymer. Chapters 3, 5, and 6 provide more details.

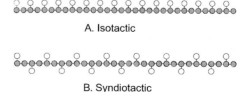

A. Isotactic

B. Syndiotactic

Figure 1.4 Schematic illustrations of isotactic (A), syndiotactic (B), and atactic (C) PP

C. Atactic

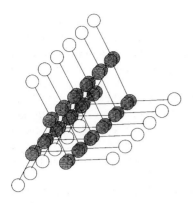

Figure 1.5 Arrangement of carbon atoms in the 3_1 helix of PP, as they appear in the crystal

1.3   History

1.3.1   Before Ziegler and Natta

The early history of PP is about more than the discovery of crystalline PP and the catalysts for producing it. It involves a major change in thinking about polymers, especially regarding stereoregular polymerization. Prior to 1950, scientists were still struggling with the nature of polymers, and few had any appreciation for the potentialities of stereoregular polymerization. Disbelief and skepticism were common responses, even to major discoveries, which made the brilliance of the Ziegler–Natta achievements even more dramatic. Early hints at the role of stereoregularity were ignored or misunderstood.

To appreciate the difficulties, it is worth reviewing some of the developments in polymer science. It wasn't until the 1920s that the high molecular weight of polymers and their chain structure were first recognized, and these concepts met strong resistance. During the 1930s, numerous plastics reached commercial status: poly(vinyl chloride), polystyrene, poly(methyl methacrylate), low density polyethylene, and nylon. Consequently, characterization tools improved greatly, but they were still primitive compared to today's standards. Much skepticism and ignorance remained. In 1935, when Fawcett suggested at the Faraday Society meeting that ICI might have made polyethylene, he was ridiculed by Staudinger, who "knew" that ethylene would not polymerize. However, ICI began commercial production in 1939.

The very concept of stereoregular polymerization was largely ignored in the relatively infant polymer chemistry science. Discussions of stereoregularity occurred only among a few of the more theoretical chemists. In an elegant 1942 paper, Bunn predicted the helical form of crystalline PP, but his paper was essentially forgotten until Natta's publications on crystalline PP, 13 years later. It was in the 1940s that a stereoregular polymer from an asymmetric monomer was first observed: natural rubber. Essentially all head-to-tail cis-1,4 isoprene polymer, no means of synthesizing such a stereospecific material (out of the twelve stereo possibilities) was available or even imagined that might do the job that nature had done so well. In 1947, when Schildknecht suggested that a highly crystalline poly(isobutyl vinyl ether) could have been the result of stereoregular polymerization, even Herman Mark expressed skepticism.

In the 1930s, low levels of crystallinity were observed in several polymers, but further investigation was hampered by the prevailing concept of stereoblock structures. The crystalline sections were believed to reside in segments of the chain also containing the noncrystalline material. Consequently, no one considered trying to fractionate the polymers to study the more crystalline fractions in more detail.

By 1950, chemists were familiar with crystalline PE, for even highly branched LDPE had enough linear sections for moderate levels of crystallinity. In contrast, crystalline PP had never been observed on any scale. At that time, the polymerization of propylene proceeded without any consistent head-to-tail or right/left hand (d/l) insertion, produced nonlinear polymers, and could not acheive even moderate molecular weights. The result, a low molecular weight amorphous oil, exhibited no attractive properties.

Because ethylene is symmetrical, no regulation of head-to-tail or d/l insertion is needed to produce the consistent zig-zag, and therefore crystallizable, PE chain. Only branching affects crystallizability in the high molecular weight ethylene homopolymer. Consequently, the preparation of linear PE by Ziegler proved the lack of branching but did not constitute proof of stereoregular polymerization. In contrast, the observation of the isotactic PP chain in the PP crystal obtained from the asymmetric[1] polypropylene molecule, was *a priori* proof of stereoregular polymerization: head-to-tail insertion, in the same "hand," with no branching. Although some researchers encountered crystalline PP prior to Natta, most were apparently unaware of the presence of crystallinity, and none recognized the connection to stereoregular polymerization. In spite of those oversights, one of them proved to be very significant later.

1.3.2   Ziegler

Ziegler's 1950 work on the "Aufbau" reaction, the growth of alkyl chains by insertion of ethylene into the Al—C bond of trialkyl aluminum, without ever forming a branch, was largely ignored by the chemical community. Only a few perceptive individuals, such as Herman Mark, appreciated with Ziegler the uniqueness of the totally linear products and anticipated the ultimate possibility of high molecular weight linear polyethylene. The information, disseminated largely by Mark, stimulated the interest of several individuals: Sir Robert Robinson of PCL, Ltd., a group at Hoechst, and Giulio Natta of the Milan Polytechnic Institute, sponsored by Montecatini. Hercules Powder Company was also interested in the new chemistry, but primarily as a potential route to para-xylene, for making DMT, a precursor to polyesters. This small group took out early licenses to the Ziegler discoveries.

It was Natta who reacted most decisively, placing three of his assistants in Ziegler's lab, as part of the agreement reached for the Italian rights to Ziegler's results. They were present when the major breakthroughs in high-density PE occurred in 1953.

Ziegler was conducting a routine set of experiments on the Aufbau reaction in June 1953. It proceeded only to the first insertion step; only butene was formed, instead of the usual higher alkenes. Investigation revealed that the presence of nickel in the reactor inhibited the reaction. Ziegler reasoned that if one metal could slow the reaction, others could accelerate it.

---

[1] Although the propylene molecule itself does not contain an asymmetric carbon atom, the propylene unit within the PP chain does.

He began a systematic search of other transition metal compounds to determine their effects on the Aufbau reaction, which was being run at 100 °C and 70 bar (1000 psi). Chromium gave the first positive result: a small amount of high molecular weight polymer. Then, in October 1953, zirconium caused the formation of so much polymer that the catalyst was quickly fouled. By altering the conditions, a moderate quantity of polymer was prepared and molded for examination. It was immediately established that this was a highly crystalline and linear polyethylene. One assistant was assigned the task of determining how to speed up the reaction.

The day after the zirconium success, propylene was tried. It did not respond with a pressure drop, as was normal with ethylene. The researcher did not consider that the high solubility of propylene in the solvent used could produce such an effect even when the reaction was proceeding. He concluded that propylene would not work and was reckless enough to record in his notebook, "Propylene cannot be converted to high molecular weight PP," an entry that was to become both an embarrassment and a liability during later patent proceedings.

Meanwhile, the metal search had arrived at titanium, and the result was spectacular: The reaction proceeded so rapidly that the reactor heated up uncontrollably, and the polymer that was formed was highly charred. The assistant's task of speeding up the reaction immediately became one of slowing the reaction. The most optimistic possibility, the use of no external heat or pressure, was tried first, and to the delight and amazement of all, the reaction proceeded readily. The chemist is reputed to have burst into Ziegler's office, a most uncharacteristic behavior for a European researcher, and proclaimed, "Es geht in Glas!" (It goes in glass!). Word of the new achievements, high molecular weight linear PE, with very attractive process conditions, soon spread to the small group of Ziegler licensees.

1.3.3   Natta

Of course, Natta's assistants kept him appraised of these events as they occurred. Given Montecatini's interest in practical results, Natta's response was swift and focused: notwithstanding Ziegler's negative results with propylene, he moved immediately to try propylene, and succeeded in March 1954. His expectation was such that, upon that success, his notebook entry simply stated, "Fatto il polipropilene" (Made polypropylene). A copy of that historical entry appears in Fig. 1.6.

The Natta group fractionated the largely amorphous product by solvent extraction and isolated an insoluble fraction constituting about 40% of the product. Because they had anticipated a more rubbery material, they were startled when the insoluble fraction was a hard, high-melting solid, with high extensibility, and within days they had characterized the polymer. When they found the high crystallinity and identified the crystal structure, including the helical chain, they also recognized the role of stereoregular polymerization in achieving this structure.

Natta went on to define the three stereo conformations of PP, and his wife, an accomplished linguist, suggested the appropriate Greek terms for them: isotactic, syndiotactic, and atactic. As did Ziegler, Natta published quickly, and the world was on its way to discovering a new type of chemistry, now known as Ziegler–Natta catalysis.

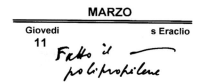

MARZO

Giovedi   s Eraclio
11

Figure 1.6 Natta notebook entry of March 11, 1954, "Made polypropylene;" Courtesy Prof. L. Porri, Polytechnical Institute of Milan, and the family of Giulio Natta

Unaware of Natta's results, Ziegler had modified his equipment and prepared PP in June 1954. However, he soon found that Natta had beaten him to the patent office. This event precipitated a major conflict between these two talented but ambitious men, and it ended a friendship that had developed with their previous close collaboration. The motives of both have been much discussed but little resolved. Suffice it to say that they shared the Nobel prize for chemistry in 1963 and had praise for each other's work in their acceptance speeches. Ziegler eventually conceded the initial patent rights to PP to Natta and Montecatini. Of course, neither was aware of any contemporary work on PP outside of their own, and the U.S. rights to crystalline PP were not settled for another 29 years. That patent battle is described further in Chapter 7.

By 1955, the Milan researchers were able to achieve polymers containing over 80% isotactic chains, compared to 40% in the first 1954 product.

1.4   Commercial Significance

With the demonstration, in the form of crystalline PP, that stereoregular polymerization was a reality, the scientific floodgates opened, and an explosion of new chemistry, new processes, and new products engulfed the world, virtually overnight. While, in 1950, no one had ever seen crystalline PP, there were, by 1960, several commercial producers, delivering some 50,000 tons of PP into several rapidly expanding applications. PP changed from a useless material, impossible to polymerize to high molecular weight, into an exciting combination of new science with practical applications. This was truly a revolution.

At the same time, a whole new family of commercial materials were created, including, besides high-density polyethylene (HDPE) and PP, poly(4-methyl pentene-1), ethylene-propylene rubber (EPR), ethylene-propylene-diene monomer rubber (EPDM), polybuta-diene, and polyisoprene. Even crystalline polystyrene and syndiotactic PP were prepared, although they have not yet become commercial successes. That could change quickly as a result of the new metallocene catalyst developments (See Chapters 2 and 12).

Those with early interest in the Ziegler chemistry quickly became the leaders in the new HDPE and PP businesses that appeared, due to the licensing arrangements they made with Ziegler (and in the case of PP, Montecatini), and have remained major suppliers of HDPE or PP. Hercules and Montedison (Montecatini's successor) eventually merged into Himont. PCL Ltd became part of Shell, and is now joined with Himont in Montell. Hoechst has continued to be prominent in both HDPE and PP. In contrast, those who encountered crystalline PP in the lab, but did not participate directly in the Ziegler–Natta revolution in catalysts and stereospecific polymers, played minor roles in the growth of the PP business.

Of course, neither the new HDPE nor PP had any assured applications when the first plants were built, but the high melting points, strength, and orientable natures convinced business executives to invest millions of dollars in pursuit of the potential benefits of these materials. PP was found to be an excellent molding resin, and by 1960, a wide range of injection molded items, monofilaments for rope and chair webbing, and films, both oriented and unoriented, were consuming substantial quantities of polymer from numerous producers around the world. In the early 1960s, luggage, carpet yarn, wire coating, auditorium and home seating, closures, medical ware, television set backs, bread wrap film, and coated biaxially oriented PP (BOPP) film for overwrap and laminates were added to the outlets for PP. By 1963, competition had increased, and the introductory price of 65¢/lb had dropped to 36¢/lb. While that does not seem unusual by today's standards, keep in mind that monomer was only 5¢/lb at that time.

While capacity grew rapidly in the 1960s, the names of the major players remained little changed, as new suppliers were reluctant to join in the increasingly competitive business. The growth continued unabated until 1969, when the capacity of the industry was ten times that of 1961, a growth rate of 35% per year. The atmosphere of change and renewal has continued in PP. The Solvay catalyst advances of the 1970s, the Montedison high-yield, high-stereo-specificity supported catalysts, which led to the Himont processes of the 1980s, and several new developments in the 1990s indicate that this industry remains full of vigor. More detailed discussions of the current PP business and its future potential appear in Chapters 7 and 12.

General References

Seymour, R.B., and Cheng, T.: History of Polyolefins, D. Reidel Publishing Company, Dordrecht, Holland, 1986.
McMillan, F.M.: The Chain Straighteners, The MacMillan Press Ltd, London, 1979.
Pino, P., Moretti, G.: Polymer 28 (1987) 683.

The above references contain excellent accounts of those early discoveries of HDPE, PP, and related polymers. They are recommended for the reader seeking more detailed, yet highly readable, accounts of the above events that space prevented us from including here.

2   Catalysts and Polymerizations

E. Albizzati, U. Giannini, G. Collina, L. Noristi, L. Resconi

2.1   Introduction

A Ziegler–Natta catalyst can be defined as a transition metal compound bearing a metal-carbon bond able to carry out a repeated insertion of olefin units. Usually, though not necessarily, the catalyst consists of two components (i.e., a transition metal salt (most frequently a halide) and a main-group metal alkyl (activator) which serves the purpose of generating the active metal-carbon bond).

As anticipated in Chapter 1 and as thoroughly described by Boor [1], it was Natta in 1954 who, following the previous discovery by Ziegler of the ability of $TiCl_4/AlR_3$ mixtures to polymerize ethylene [2], first succeeded in preparing polypropylene (PP) having an isotactic content around 30% to 40% [3] by using the same catalyst system. He also very soon realized that much higher isotactic yields (80% to 90%) could be obtained by using crystalline $TiCl_3$ modifications instead of soluble $TiCl_4$ [4].

Since then "isotactic" PP has become one of the most important polyolefin plastics, and a huge amount of work has been done in both the industrial and the academic worlds to develop ever more efficient catalyst systems, as well as to elucidate the mechanisms by which the stereospecific polymerization is governed.

The aim of this chapter is to provide a short but nonetheless exhaustive description of the different catalysts which have been or are currently used for PP manufacturing, as well as of the fundamental aspects related to the polymerization mechanisms, stereochemistry, and kinetics. Particular emphasis will be given to the following topics:

- Historical development of the catalysts and future perspectives;
- synthesis, chemistry, structure, and performance of the main catalyst systems so far developed;
- mechanism and stereochemistry of the polymerization reaction, including the most widely accepted views on the structure of the catalytic sites and the role of the stereospecificity promoters (Lewis bases or electron donors);
- kinetic features of propylene homo- and copolymerization in connection with the different catalysts considered.

2.2   History and Development of Stereospecific Catalysts

Since Natta's discovery in 1954 of the possibility of preparing highly isotactic PP with $TiCl_4$, and later $TiCl_3$, as catalyst, and AlR_3 or preferably AlR_2Cl as cocatalyst [3, 4], the development of more efficient and more sophisticated catalysts has been relentless and is still in progress today.

2.2.1   First Generation Catalysts

The $TiCl_3/AlEt_2Cl$ catalyst used in the earlier industrial processes for PP manufacturing, in fact, showed a low productivity and stereospecificity, the Isotactic Index (II) (i.e., the fraction of isotactic polymer) being around only 90%. Consequently, both removal of the catalytic residues (deashing) and separation of the atactic polymer fraction were required [5].

The research carried out both in Natta's group and in other industrial laboratories led very soon to the discovery that catalysts obtained by prolonged ball milling of either Al-reduced $TiCl_3$ (thus containing co-crystallized $AlCl_3$) or mixtures of $TiCl_3$ and $AlCl_3$ were much more active than pure $TiCl_3$ [6]. A catalyst of this type, named AA-$TiCl_3$ (where AA stands for Al-reduced and activated), was made commercially available by Stauffer Chem. Co. in 1959 [7] and is usually considered as the first generation Ziegler–Natta catalyst for PP. AA-$TiCl_3$, together with similar catalysts prepared in different ways but having similar performance, has been used, in combination with $AlEt_2Cl$ (DEAC) as cocatalyst, for PP production by many companies, at least up to the mid '70s, and is probably still used today by some minor PP producers.

Its productivity and stereospecificity, however, were still rather low, and the need for deashing and atactic removal, together with the poor polymer morphology, rendered the production process complicated and expensive [5]. Considering that in $TiCl_3$ only the surface Ti atoms, which represent only a small fraction of total Ti, were likely to be accessible to the Al-alkyl and thus available for making active polymerization sites [8, 9], several efforts were soon started to improve the Ti efficiency. Three main approaches appear to have actually been followed to increase the fraction of accessible Ti atoms:

1.   Reduction of the size of the catalyst microparticles (crystallites),
2.   dispersion of Ti compounds on high surface carriers,
3.   use of soluble transition metal compounds.

2.2.2   Second Generation Catalysts

Efforts to increase accessibility to Ti atoms led to the development by Solvay [10], in the early '70s, of a $TiCl_3$ catalyst having a much higher surface area than the usual AA-$TiCl_3$ (150 + instead of 30 m^2/g to 40 m^2/g), a fivefold productivity and an isotactic index around 95%. This catalyst, usually referred to as "Solvay" $TiCl_3$, can be considered as the first example of the second generation catalysts for PP and, after several improvements [11], is still employed today, together with DEAC as cocatalyst, in some production processes. As will be shown later, many other catalysts of this type, also referred to as "low-Al" catalysts, have been developed during the '70s and '80s by several companies.

2.2.3   Third Generation Catalysts

Attempts to develop supported catalysts started very early in the '60s by making use of conventional high surface supports bearing surface functional groups (mainly $-OH$) able to chemically anchor the transition metal compound (e.g., silica, alumina, Mg-hydroxides or

-hydroxychlorides). These attempts, however, though leading in some cases to highly active catalysts for polyethylene (PE), were not very successful for PP (because of the low activity) until the discovery in the late '60s [12] that catalysts based on "activated" $MgCl_2$ were highly active for PE and PP as well. Owing to their low stereospecificity (II < 50%) [13], the use of these catalysts was initially limited to PE (actually in 1972 Montedison started a plant for PE running with a high-yield catalyst based on comilled $MgCl_2/TiCl_4$). In a few years, however, this problem was overcome by the addition of appropriate Lewis bases [14] which made it possible to obtain highly active and stereospecific catalysts by comilling $MgCl_2$, $TiCl_4$, and a Lewis base (LB), usually referred to as "internal donor" (D_i), combined with an Al-trialkyl as cocatalyst and a second Lewis base, usually called "external donor" (D_e).

Later, an improved version of this catalyst was developed [15] and used in a plant started by Montedison in Ferrara in 1978, in which the Lewis bases were ethylbenzoate (EB) as D_i and methyl-p-toluate (MPT) as D_e.

This $MgCl_2$-supported, donor-modified catalyst is the parent of a large family of catalysts which have been called the third generation. Though sufficiently active to avoid the need for deashing, these catalysts still required the removal of the atactic polymer which, depending on the conditions used, still constituted from 6% to 10% of the total. The research was thus focused on both more efficient routes for the catalyst synthesis and more efficient combinations of electron donors.

2.2.4   Fourth Generation Catalysts

Further research led to highly active and stereospecific catalysts, called by the inventors super high activity catalysts (SHAC), which, though still making use of benzoic acid esters as electron donors, were claimed to display a superior productivity and isotacticity [16, 17]. The latter resulted, in the early '80s, in the discovery of a new combination of electron donors, namely alkylphthalates as D_i and alkoxysilanes (or silyl-ethers) as D_e, able to afford a much better productivity/isotacticity balance than benzoic acid esters [18].

The above catalyst systems, which are currently used in most of the modern industrial processes for PP manufacturing, were named "super-active third generation" by Galli et al. [19], but to avoid confusion with the SHAC above and also because they are based on a totally different electron donors pair, we think that "fourth generation catalysts" is more appropriate.

2.2.5   Fifth Generation Catalysts

In the second half of the '80s, a new type of electron donors was discovered (1,3-diethers) which, if used as internal components, provided extremely high activities and isotacticities without the need of any external Lewis base [20]. These catalysts, though not yet brought into industrial use, potentially form a new class of catalysts for PP which we will call of the fifth generation.

2.2.6   Metallocenes—Sixth Generation Catalysts

At the same time, the approach to homogeneous stereospecific catalysts, which had proven disappointing for many years, began to advance with the discovery that stereorigid metallocenes of transition metals, such as Zr and Hf, when combined with methylalumi-noxane (MAO), were able to provide highly stereoregular isotactic or syndiotactic PPs in extremely high yields [21 - 23]. This discovery aroused an enormous interest in both the industrial and the academic worlds, not only because of its scientific value but also because it appears to open the way to materials with unprecedented properties. The metallocene systems can, thus, be fully thought to represent the "sixth generation" of stereospecific catalysts for propylene polymerization, and they will probably undergo a great development in the near future.

Comparisons of the performance achievable with the different catalyst generations, up to the fourth one, have been often reported in the literature. Table 2.1 shows an updated comparison, based on data from Himont (now Montell) obtained under hexane slurry or bulk polymerization conditions, including all the above catalysts generations. Although the figures are only valid relative to one another, they clearly show the great progress in catalysts over forty years of unceasing research efforts.

Table 2.1 Performance of the Different Catalyst Generations

Generation	Composition	Productivity[a] (kgPP/g Cat)	I.I. (wt%)	Morphology control	Process requirements
1st	δ-TiCl$_3$0.33AlCl$_3$ + DEAC	0.8–1.2	90–94	not possible[b]	Deashing + atactic removal
2nd	δ–TiCl$_3$ + DEAC	3–5 (10–15)	94–97	possible	Deashing
3rd	TiCl$_4$/Ester/MgCl$_2$ + AlR$_3$/Ester	5–10 (15–30)	90–95	possible	Atactic removal
4th	TiCl$_4$/Diester/MgCl$_2$ + TEA/Silane	10–25 (30–60)	95–99	possible	
5th	TiCl$_4$/Diether/MgCl$_2$ + TEA	25–35 (70–120)	95–99	possible	
6th	Zirconocene + MAO	(5–9·10^3) (on Zr)[c]	90–99[d]	to be achieved	

[a] Polymerization: hexane slurry, 70 °C, 0.7 MPa, 4 hrs, H$_2$ for MW control (values in brackets are from bulk polymerization for 2 hrs at 70 °C, with H$_2$)
[b] Only possible with Al-alkyl reduced TiCl$_3$, at 200–300 μm size level
[c] One hour polymerization time
[d] *mmmm*% (by ^{13}C NMR)

2.3   Catalysts: Synthesis, Chemistry, Structure

In this section, the most important catalyst systems will be described in some detail regarding their synthesis, chemistry, and structure. Polymerization performance will be discussed as well, but mainly in connection with the catalyst structure, whereas the theoretical aspects concerning the polymerization mechanisms and kinetics will be treated in the subsequent sections 2.4, 2.5 and 2.6.

2.3.1   Heterogeneous Catalysts

We will discuss first the heterogeneous catalysts, which have provided all of the commercial PP materials generated during the four-decade lifetime of the PP industry.

2.3.1.1   First Generation TiCl₃ Catalysts

2.3.1.1.1   Synthesis and Structure   According to the preparation method used, Ti-trichloride shows four different crystalline modifications (i.e., α, β, γ, and δ) and may or may not contain cocrystallized $AlCl_3$ or $AlRCl_2$. According to Natta [24, 25], the violet α, γ, and δ modifications display a layer structure arising from a regular stacking of structural Cl-Ti-Cl triple layers containing Ti ions between two layers of Cl ions (Fig. 2.1).

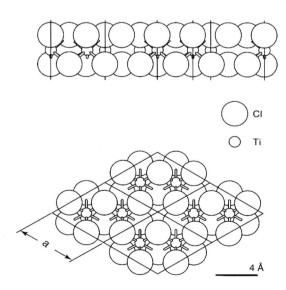

Cl

Ti

Figure 2.1 Stereochemical model of the structural layer which characterizes the layer modifications (α, γ and δ) of $TiCl_3$. Reproduced with permission from Ref. [24], John Wiley & Sons, Inc.

The three modifications only differ in the mode of Cl packing, which is hexagonal in the a form and cubic in the γ form. On the other hand, the δ form displays a random succession of hexagonal and cubic close packings (Fig. 2.2).

The brown β modification, on the contrary, exhibits a fiber-like structure [24] as shown in Fig. 2.3.

In all the above modifications, the Ti^{3+} coordination is octahedral. When $AlCl_3$ is present, the Al^{3+} ion simply replaces a Ti^{3+} ion in the crystal lattice without significantly modifying the unit cell parameters.

Several methods are known for the synthesis of the various $TiCl_3$ modifications, both with and without cocrystallized $AlCl_3$, a summary of which is given in Table 2.2. Among them the most significant ones for the industrial production of $TiCl_3$ catalysts have been the reduction of $TiCl_4$ by means of either Al metal or Al-alkyls, and these methods will thus be discussed in some detail.

2.3.1.1.2 Aluminum Metal Reduction   The $TiCl_4$ reduction with Al metal is usually carried out at nearly stoichiometric conditions in inert solvents (decane, cyclohexane, etc.) at $150\,^{\circ}\text{C}$ to $180\,^{\circ}\text{C}$, with the aid of $AlCl_3$ as catalyst. The reaction product is a γ-$TiCl_3 \cdot 0.33\,AlCl_3$, which is subsequently transformed into the more active δ form by prolonged dry milling. This appears to have been the route followed by Stauffer for its commercial AA-$TiCl_3$ previously mentioned.

As thoroughly discussed by Kissin [38], milling, especially in the dry state, has two main effects:

1. To convert the γ, or even the α form, into the δ form by inducing sliding and rotation of the structural layers with respect to one another, and
2. to reduce the crystallite size and increase the surface area up to 40 m^2/g to 50 m^2/g, at least as long as the milling time is short enough to prevent reagglomeration.

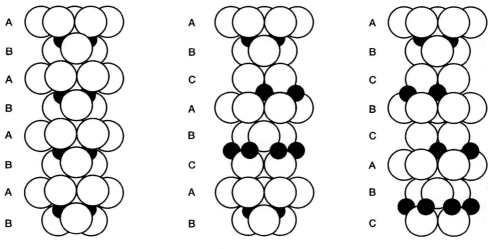

Figure 2.2 Models of chlorine packing in the different $TiCl_3$ modifications: α (left), γ (center), δ (right). Reproduced with permission from Ref. [25], La Chimica & Industria (Milano)

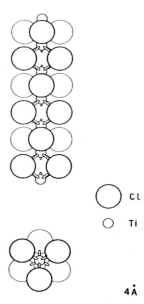

Figure 2.3 Stereochemical model of the linear β modification of TiCl$_3$. Reproduced with permission from Ref. [24], John Wiley & Sons, Inc

As will be shown later, these modifications are of great importance in determining the catalyst performance.

2.3.1.1.3 Aluminum Alkyl Reduction   The reduction of TiCl$_4$ with Al-alkyls or chloro-alkyls at low temperatures affords a β-TiCl$_3 \cdot x$AlCl$_3 \cdot y$AlRCl$_2$ composition which needs to be thermally activated to the γ/δ modification by heating at 160 °C to 200 °C. This method has the advantage over the previous one of leading to a catalyst with controlled shape and narrow particle size distribution, provided the reduction conditions are carefully controlled, and appears to have been used by several companies for this reason [39].

Table 2.2 Preparation Methods for the Different TiCl$_3$ Modifications

No.	Modification	Composition	Preparation	Reference
1	α	TiCl$_3$	TiCl$_4$ + H$_2$ (500–800 °C)	[26, 27]
2	α	TiCl$_3$	TiCl$_4$ + H$_2$ on W wire (1000–1100 °C)	[28]
3	α	TiCl$_3$	Heating β-TiCl$_3$ at 300–400 °C	[29]
4	α	TiCl$_3 \cdot 0.5$AlCl$_3$	TiCl$_4$ + Al(+ AlCl$_3$) at 200 °C	[30]
5	α	TiCl$_3 \cdot 0.02$AlCl$_3$	TiCl$_4$ + Ti + Al at > 200 °C	[6]
6	β	TiCl$_3$	TiCl$_4$ + electric discharge at low T, or + γ radiations	[31]
7	β	TiCl$_3$	Heating CH$_3$TiCl$_3$ at > 25 °C	[32]
8	β	TiCl$_3 \cdot 0.33$AlCl$_3$	TiCl$_4$ + Al at < 100 °C	[6b, 33]
9	β	TiCl$_3 \cdot x$AlCl$_3$	TiCl$_4$ + TEA, DEAC or EAD at < 25 °C	[34]
10	γ	TiCl$_3$	Heating β-TiCl$_3$ at > 150 °C	[35]
11	γ	TiCl$_3 \cdot 0.33$AlCl$_3$	TiCl$_4$ + Al (+ AlCl$_3$) at $\sim$ 160 °C in inert solvents	[6b, 33]
12	δ	TiCl$_3$	Milling α or γ-TiCl$_3$	[6b, 36]
13	δ	TiCl$_3 \cdot 0.33$AlCl$_3$	Milling α or γ-TiCl$_3 \cdot 0.33$ AlCl$_3$	[37]
14	δ	TiCl$_3 \cdot x$AlCl$_3$	Milling TiCl$_3$ with AlCl$_3$	[6b, 24, 37]

This technique has been discussed in detail by Goodall [40], who pointed out that the shape, size, and particle size distribution (PSD) of the catalyst are closely related to the reduction, and consequently to the precipitation rate. To obtain particles of adequate average size, a low rate is necessary, and this can be obtained either by using low temperatures ($\ll 0\,°C$) if the Al-alkyl is $AlEt_3$ (TEA) or a milder reducing agent such as $AlEt_2Cl$, in which case the use of higher temperatures ($>0\,°C$) is allowed. Other important parameters for the control of the particle size and PSD are the solvent type, the mode and sequence of reactant addition, and the stirring power.

2.3.1.1.4 Polymerization Performance   According to the studies carried out by Natta and co-workers [8, 25, 41], two factors mainly appear to affect the polymerization performance of $TiCl_3$-based catalysts: 1) the nature of the cocatalyst, and 2) the crystalline modification of $TiCl_3$.

Among the possible cocatalysts, the only ones of practical interest were the Al-alkyls or chloroalkyls, and among them the following values for isotactic index (II) were quoted by Natta [41] for the α, γ, and δ forms of $TiCl_3$:

$AlEt_3 = 80\%$ to 85%,
$AlEt_2Cl = 91\%$ to 94%,
$AlEt_2Br = 94\%$ to 96%,
$AlEt_2I = 96\%$ to 98%,

whereas activity with the γ-form was shown to decrease in the following order [8]:

$$AlEt_3 > AlEt_2Cl > AlEt_2Br > AlEt_2I.$$

The best activity/isotacticity balance is shown by $AlEt_2Cl$ (DEAC), which has thus been the cocatalyst invariably used in commercial processes with this type of catalyst.

As far as the differences among the crystalline $TiCl_3$ modifications are concerned, the α, γ, and δ forms display substantially the same II, as shown above, whereas a much lower II ($\sim 55\%$ with TEA and $\sim 70\%$ with DEAC) is shown by the β modification [42, 43]. As regards the activity, the following sequence reported by Natta [25] ($\delta \gg \gamma > \alpha$) is generally accepted.

Additional parameters which appear to play a significant effect on the polymerization performance are the presence of co-crystallized $AlCl_3$ and the extent of milling. As far as the effect of $AlCl_3$ is concerned, while it does not seem to appreciably affect the catalyst stereospecificity, activities from 2 to 7 times higher than for pure $TiCl_3$ have been reported [7, 37, 44], the optimum Al:Ti atomic ratio being 0.33:1. This activating effect has been attributed either to electronic factors or to an increase in the true catalyst surface area due to the solubilization of $AlCl_3$ by TEA or DEAC in the course of polymerization, with a consequent increase of the number of accessible Ti atoms [38]. A further effect of $AlCl_3$, according to Goodall [40], is to decrease the average molecular weight (MW) of the polymer and to broaden to some extent its molecular weight distribution (MWD).

Regarding the effect of milling, an up to tenfold increase of activity with the milling time has been documented [37] and has been attributed both to the progressive transformation into the disordered δ form and to the parallel increase in the surface area from less than 10 m^2/g to more than 40 m^2/g. As shown by Yermakov [45], however, the activity increase is more likely to be related to the decrease of the crystallite size rather than to the surface area. A linear

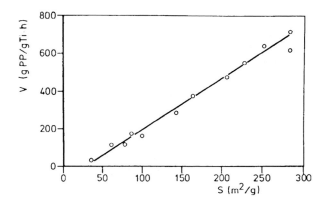

Figure 2.4 Dependence of the catalytic activity of TiCl$_3$ (V) on the crystallites surface (S). Reproduced with permission from Ref. [71], Hüthig & Wepf Verlag

relationship, in fact, can be observed when plotting the activity as a function of the theoretical surface area calculated from the average crystallite dimensions (Fig. 2.4).

The polymerization kinetics also depend on the TiCl$_3$ modification and on the cocatalyst type. As a matter of fact, a constant polymerization rate has been generally observed with the α and γ form irrespective of the cocatalyst used. With the more active δ modification, on the contrary, a decay type kinetic curve (i.e., an initial rate increase followed by a rapid decrease) is usually observed with TEA, whereas constant or acceleration type kinetics (i.e., rate increase followed by a steady or slowly declining rate period) are more usual for DEAC [8]. A typical kinetic profile for the commercial AA-TiCl$_3$/DEAC system is shown in Fig. 2.5.

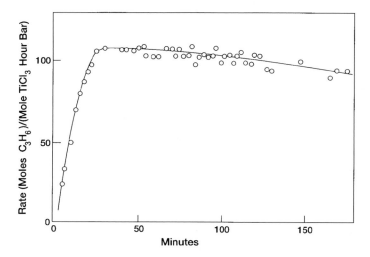

Figure 2.5 Typical kinetic profile for the AA-TiCl$_3$/DEAC system at 60 °C. Reproduced with permission from Ref. [46], Harwood Academic Publishers

Besides the Al-alkyl, a third component (modifier) has been often added either to the catalyst or to the cocatalyst to improve either the isotacticity or the activity, or both. Typical examples are carboxylic acid esters [47], amines [1], cycloheptatriene [48], and fluoride ions [49]. Ethers, ketones, phosphines, and organophosphorous derivatives have been used, as well [50 and references therein]. According to Goodall [40], their role is possibly to complex, or to prevent, the formation of the $AlEtCl_2$ (EADC) from the interaction between DEAC and the $AlCl_3$ present in the catalyst, as EADC is thought to be a catalyst poison. On the other hand, other effects, as pointed out by Tait [50], could be to complex the active sites and render them more stable and more stereospecific, or to complex the cocatalyst and so reduce its effective concentration. As pointed out by Pasquon [13], however, the effect of all the above components is very limited and hardly exceeds that which can be achieved by a proper purification of $TiCl_3$.

2.3.1.2   Second Generation TiCl₃ Catalysts

2.3.1.2.1   Synthesis and Structure   The procedure described in the earlier Solvay patents claiming the synthesis of an improved $TiCl_3$ catalyst includes the following stages:

1. Preparation of a "reduced solid" by reducing $TiCl_4$ in hydrocarbon solvent by slow addition of a slight excess of DEAC at 0 °C to 2 °C, then heating the mixture to 65 °C in 1 hr and keeping it at this temperature for 1 hr. The obtained brown solid is a β-$TiCl_3$ modification having the composition $TiCl_3 \cdot xAlCl_3 \cdot yAlEtCl_2$ (where $x \approx 0.15$ and $y \approx 0.20$) and a very low surface area (S.A.) as well as catalytic activity.
2. Treatment of the reduced solid with *i*-amyl ether at 35 °C for 1 hr in an ether/Ti molar ratio of 0.8 to 1.0. In this stage, almost all the Al is removed from the solid, while some ether remains complexed (~ 0.06 mol/mol Ti). This product, referred to as "treated solid," also shows a low S.A. and low activity.
3. Treatment of the above solid with excess $TiCl_4$ diluted in hydrocarbon at 60 °C to 70 °C for 1 hr to 3 hr to give a δ-$TiCl_3 \cdot x(AlEt_nCl_{3-n}) \cdot y(i\text{-}Am_2O)$ composition in which $n = 0$ to 2, $x < 0.2$, and $0.01 < y < 0.11$. After extensive washings with hydrocarbon to remove the adsorbed $TiCl_4$ and other by-products, a "catalytic complex" is obtained with a high surface area (150 m²/g to 200 m²/g) and porosity (> 0.2 cm³/g) and a very high catalytic activity.

The catalyst is claimed to possess a nearly spherical shape, a mean size between 20 μm and 40 μm and a narrow PSD, and appears to consist of aggregates of subparticles having a microporous sponge-like structure and made of very small primary crystallites 50 Å to 100 Å in size. The particle porosity is mainly due to micropores ($d_p < 200$ Å) located inside the above subparticles. In the catalyst preparation, steps 1 and 2 can also be carried out simultaneously.

This basic "Solvay" catalyst was subsequently improved for storage stability [51] and later for stereospecificity by means of the addition of third components (e.g., alkoxysilanes) to the cocatalyst DEAC [52].

Catalysts similar to the "Solvay" one were also developed by Chisso by means of two different procedures:

1. Reduction of TiCl$_4$ with a DEAC/ether mixture at 35 °C for 3 hrs followed by heating at 75 °C for 1 hr to give a solid which is then treated by a TiCl$_4$/ether mixture to give the catalyst [53];
2. reduction of TiCl$_4$ as above under vigorous stirring to give a TiCl$_3$ composition, which (optionally prepolymerized) is then treated first with ether and then with a Lewis acid to afford the catalyst [54].

In this way, nearly spherical catalysts with narrow PSD can be obtained, which when used with DEAC and a Lewis base (benzoic acid esters, alkoxysilanes) are claimed to afford high activity and isotacticity.

Analogous catalysts, sometimes referred to as "low-Al" catalysts, have been developed by other companies, as well [55]. The procedures used differ from the Solvay one mainly in that the reduction stage (by means of DEAC, TEA, or even EADC) is usually performed in the presence of the ether, generally added to both the TiCl$_4$ and the Al-alkyl, and at higher temperatures (50 °C to 100 °C) and often in aromatic solvents. By this procedure, sometimes including a further thermal treatment, a δ-TiCl$_3$ with less than 5% Al can be obtained very simply. A slight excess of TiCl$_4$ is generally used to ensure the presence of enough TiCl$_4$ to catalyze the $\beta \rightarrow \delta$ transformation. On the other hand, the ether in the reducing step appears to play a twofold role [40] (i.e., a) to remove the AlCl$_3$ (as in the Solvay procedure), and b) to decrease the reducing power of the Al-alkyl, so allowing a higher temperature to be used).

From the structural point of view, both the "Solvay" and the other similar second generation catalysts appear characterized by a lower crystallite size and a much higher surface area than the first generation TiCl$_3$. Chemically they contain a much lower amount of cocrystallized AlCl$_3$ or AlRCl$_2$. The presence of some epitaxially adsorbed TiCl$_4$ on the TiCl$_3$ surface also has been postulated [56] to explain the superior performance of these catalysts, but, as discussed by Goodall [40], this assumption has not been demonstrated and appears debatable.

2.3.1.2.2 Polymerization Performance The performance claimed in the earlier Solvay patents, at 60 °C, 1.03 MPa, DEAC/Ti molar ratio $= 5$ in 2 hrs time is as follows:

*   Productivity $= 1900$ g PP/g TiCl$_3 \times h$ (to be compared with 400 for AA-TiCl$_3$),
*   wt% of polymer soluble in the polymerization solvent $= 2$,
*   percentage of m diads in the insoluble PP (by NMR) $= 96.2$,
*   polymer PSD: 92.6 wt% between 250 μm and 500 μm,
*   polymer shape: spheroidal.

Compared with the earlier generation, both the productivity and the isotacticity are considerably higher and the polymer morphology much improved. Even better performances are claimed by Solvay for its more recent catalyst SB 12, with DEAC and a third (not specified) component as cocatalyst [11]:

*   Productivity in bulk propylene at 70 °C, 1.5 hrs $= 12$ kg PP/g to 15kg PP/g catalyst, and
*   II $= 98$% (with mm triads $= 95$%).

The polymer MWD appears broader than with supported catalysts (Mw/Mn $= 8$ to 9 vs. 5 to 6) [11], but, according to Goodall [40], somewhat narrower than with AA-TiCl$_3$ owing to the absence of AlCl$_3$.

Though little is known about this subject, the polymerization kinetics of these catalysts appears to be of the decay type [11], the deactivation being slow but somewhat faster than with the conventional AA-TiCl$_3$ catalyst. According to Goodall [40], the yield/time relationship can be described by the following equation:

$$Y_t = Y_1 \cdot t^p \tag{2.1}$$

where Y_t is the polymer yield at time t, Y_1 is the yield after 1 hr and p is a measure of the rate decay ($p = 1$ means no decay, $p < 1$ means rate decay, the smaller the p value the higher the decay rate).

2.3.1.3   MgCl$_2$-Supported Catalysts

2.3.1.3.1   Preparation Methods   Though other supports with layer structure also may, in principle, be used to make stereospecific catalysts for PP (e.g., MgBr$_2$, MnCl$_2$, and others), MgCl$_2$ has been almost invariably used for all the supported catalysts of practical interest, because it allows the realization of catalysts with the highest activity and stereospecificity.

A variety of routes to prepare these catalysts have been used, differing either in the type of MgCl$_2$ precursor, in the way it is converted to "active" MgCl$_2$, or in the procedure followed for the incorporation of the Ti compound (most often TiCl$_4$) and of the "internal" Lewis base (D$_i$).

Three main general procedures have been followed, the first being based on a purely mechanical technique (usually ball milling), the second on a mechanical plus chemical technique (ball milling followed by a chemical reaction), and the third being entirely chemical. Within each of these techniques a further subdivision can be made according to the reagents and the reaction conditions used. a short description is given below, together with appropriate patent references.

1. *Mechanical routes* normally include a stage in which the catalyst components (usually MgCl$_2$, TiCl$_4$, and a Lewis base) are milled together in suitable ratios for several hours, usually in ball mills [14, 57]. Sometimes a MgCl$_2$ precursor is used together with a chlorinating agent, in which case a chemical reaction occurs that leads to the formation of MgCl$_2$ in the course of milling.

2. *Mechanical plus chemical routes* have used two procedures alternatively:
    a. Comilling of MgCl$_2$ or MgCl$_2$ precursors with the Lewis base, followed by one or more treatments with excess TiCl$_4$ (optionally diluted in aromatic or halogenated solvents) at temperatures above 80 °C and washings with hydrocarbons to remove unreacted TiCl$_4$ [15, 58]. In the treatment with TiCl$_4$, part of the Lewis base is removed and replaced by TiCl$_4$. Most of the reaction by-products are also solubilized and removed in this stage.
    b. Comilling of the catalyst components as in route 1, followed by one or more treatments with halogenated or aromatic solvents, which serve the purpose of rendering the catalyst active and stereospecific [59].

3. *Chemical routes* are used both to generate active MgCl$_2$ and to incorporate the Ti compound and the Lewis base. According to the reactants and the reaction type involved, four main types are recognized:

a. Reaction of MgCl$_2$ and a Lewis base (e.g., an alcohol) to form a complex, subsequently treated (either together or in separate stages) with the D$_i$ and excess TiCl$_4$, sometimes diluted in aromatic or halogenated solvents, at temperatures above 80 °C, followed by extensive washing with hydrocarbon solvents [60]. The initial complex also may be decomposed thermally or chemically (with Al-alkyls, SiCl$_4$, etc.) to generate active MgCl$_2$, which is then loaded with TiCl$_4$ and D$_i$ as above.

b. Treatment of solid Mg(OR)$_2$ or Mg(OR)Cl (sometimes prepared in a preliminary stage, e.g., from Grignard + Si(OR)$_4$) with D$_i$ and excess TiCl$_4$ diluted in aromatic or halogenated solvents as above [16, 17, 61]. In this case, MgCl$_2$ is obtained from the reaction between the Mg compound and TiCl$_4$, its by-products (Ti-alkoxides) being eliminated during the treatment and the subsequent washings.

c. Reaction of MgR$_2$ or MgRCl (optionally dispersed on SiO$_2$, Al$_2$O$_3$ or other carriers) with chlorinating agents to form active MgCl$_2$, followed by hot treatment with D$_i$ and excess TiCl$_4$ as above [62]. The intermediate MgCl$_2$ can be sometimes reacted with a Lewis base (e.g., an alcohol) before the final treatment.

d. This route involves first the formation of a solution of MgCl$_2$ or other Mg-compounds such as Mg(OR)$_2$, Mg(OCOR)$_2$, MgR$_2$, or Mg-silylamide, etc., in suitable solvents such as ROH, trialkylphosphate, Ti(OR)$_4$, epoxychloropropane, and others, often with the aid of CO$_2$. The solution is then either treated with a chlorinating agent to precipitate MgCl$_2$, which is then loaded with Ti and D$_i$ in one of the ways described above, or directly treated with D$_i$ and excess TiCl$_4$ [63].

Among the above techniques, those based on purely mechanical or mechanical-plus-chemical treatments appear to have been mainly used in the early stages of the MgCl$_2$-supported catalysts development, owing to their simplicity and low cost. Subsequently, the chemical routes have been preferred, as they proved to be more suitable for the synthesis of catalysts and, thus, thanks to the well-known "replication" phenomenon [64, 65], of polymers with controlled shape, size, and PSD.

Among the more effective techniques used to obtain catalysts with a controlled morphology are the following:

1. Careful control of the support precipitation rate,
2. use of spray-drying or spray-cooling techniques starting from Mg-compound solutions or molten Mg-compounds,
3. impregnation of MgCl$_2$ or MgCl$_2$ precursors into supports having regular shape and size, and
4. cooling of emulsions of molten MgCl$_2 \cdot n$ROH adducts in a paraffin oil, thus obtaining an almost perfectly spherical support, which is then converted into the catalyst.

For chemically prepared catalysts, essential factors required to obtain high performance appear to be purity of the reagents, their ratio and order of mixing, the time/temperature profile, and the stirring speed [66, 67]. In particular, the temperature and the time of the support treatment with TiCl$_4$ must be carefully controlled to avoid undesired reactions which could result in the presence in the catalyst of either inert complexes between TiCl$_4$, D$_i$, and even MgCl$_2$, or undesired by-products arising from the reaction between the components (e.g., benzoyl- or phthaloyl-chlorides, phthalic anhydride, chloroTi-alkoxides, etc.).

On the other hand, for catalysts obtained through purely mechanical or mixed routes, the milling time and efficiency and the ratio among the catalyst components appear to be the most critical factors [68 - 70].

2.3.1.3.2   Structure of MgCl₂   As reported by many authors [13, 50, 68, 71 - 73], two crystalline modifications are known for $MgCl_2$, the commercial α form and the less stable β form. Similar to the γ-TiCl₃ previously described, the α-form has a layer structure of the $CdCl_2$ type and shows a cubic close-packed stacking (ABC ... ABC ...) of double chlorine layers with interstitial Mg^{2+} ions in sixfold coordination [74]. The β-form, on the contrary, shows a hexagonal close packing like that of α-TiCl₃ [75]. The layer structure of α-MgCl₂ displays an X-ray diffraction spectrum with a strong (104) reflection at $d = 2.56$ Å as a result of the cubic close-packed arrangement of the Cl ions (Fig. 2.6).

The key ingredient of the catalysts we are dealing with, however, is the "activated" or δ-MgCl₂, which exhibits a disordered structure arising from the translation and rotation of the structural Cl-Mg-Cl layers with respect to one another that destroy the crystal order in the stacking direction [71]. As a consequence, the X-ray spectrum shows a gradual disappearance of the (104) reflection and its replacement by a broad "halo" centered at $d = 2.65$ Å (i.e., in an intermediate position between the cubic (2.56 Å) and the hexagonal (2.78 Å) close packing) (Fig. 2.7).

Models for the structural disorder of $MgCl_2$ and other layer metal-chlorides, based on a stochastic succession of structural layers still maintaining a close packing of the Cl ions, have been proposed by Zannetti and his group [76, 77]. In these models, three probability parameters are used to describe the sequence between two structural layers (i.e., P_{cub}, P_{hex}, $P_{rot(+/-60)}$) with their sum being 1. Three more parameters are included to take into account the crystallite size along the crystallographic directions, expressed as number of unit cells N_a, N_b and N_c. The ability of these models to fit the experimental X-ray spectrum provides evidence in favor of the above description of the structural disorder. Accordingly, an extremely activated $MgCl_2$, showing the X-ray spectrum of Fig. 2.8, can be thought of as made up of very small lamellae with a thickness close to just one structural layer (i.e., $N_c \sim 1$) (Fig. 2.9).

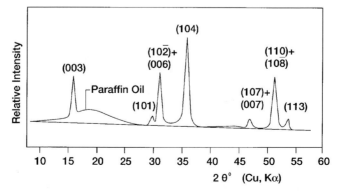

Figure 2.6 X-ray powder spectrum of α-MgCl₂. Reproduced with permission from Ref. [71], Hüthig & Wepf Verlag

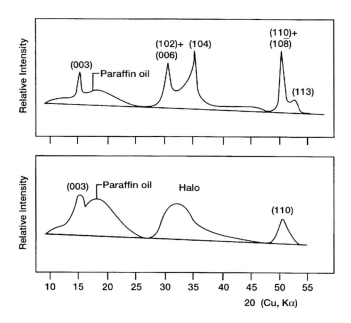

Figure 2.7 X-ray powder spectra of MgCl₂ with different degrees of activation. Reproduced with permission from Ref. [71], Hüthig & Wepf Verlag

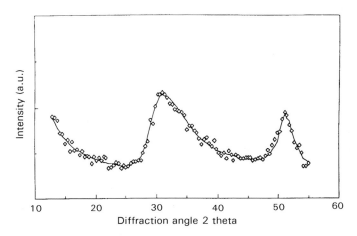

Figure 2.8 X-ray diffraction patterns of highly activated MgCl₂: (◇) experimental; (—) calculated. Best fit parameters (hexagonal cell): a = 3.60 Å, c = 5.86 Å; Na = Nb ≈ 10; Nc ≈ 1. Reproduced with permission from Ref. [77], John Wiley & Sons, Inc.

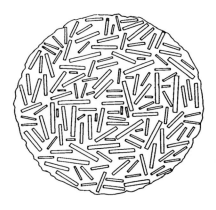

Figure 2.9 Possible model of a catalyst particle constituted of $MgCl_2$-based lamellae. Reproduced with permission from Ref. [77], John Wiley & Sons, Inc.

Under usual preparation conditions, the crystallite size reduction is not so drastic, however. As indicated by the broadening of the (110) and (003) reflections, dimensions such as 50 Å to 100 Å for width (D_{110}) and 30 Å to 50 Å for thickness (D_{003}) appear quite normal [71].

Experimental data suggest that preferential lateral cuts correspond to the (100) and (110) planes [71], and though their relative amounts have not been experimentally evaluated, theoretical calculations of the lattice electrostatic energies give a lower energy for the (110) cut, which should therefore prevail in the activated $MgCl_2$ [78]. These two lateral cuts, for electroneutrality reasons, contain coordinatively unsaturated Mg^{2+} ions, with coordination number 4 on the (110) cut and 5 on the (100) cut, as shown in Figs. 2.10 and 2.11 [79].

The situation on crystal edges and corners could present additional differences, so that the presence on the $MgCl_2$ surface of Lewis acidic sites with different acid strength and steric requirements is likely to occur and actually has been verified through interaction with Lewis bases of different strength and steric hindrance [78, 80], as well as by IR and ESR studies [81]. The "activated" $MgCl_2$ support, as it exists in the catalyst, can thus be envisaged as an agglomerate of very small crystallites (primary units) bearing on their side surfaces a variety of exposed Mg^{2+} ions with different degrees of unsaturation, Lewis acidic strength, and steric hindrance, and thus potentially able to coordinate with the other catalytic components. How this actually occurs is discussed in the following section.

2.3.1.3.3 Catalyst Chemistry   A survey of the patent literature reveals that the catalyst composition most often falls within the following ranges (on weight basis):

$TiCl_4 = 4$ to 20%,
internal donor (D_i) $= 5$ to 20%,
$MgCl_2 = 55$ to 80%.

On a molar basis, these figures lead to the following ratios:

$TiCl_4/MgCl_2 = 0.02$ to 0.16,
$D_i/MgCl_2 = 0.04$ to 0.22,
$D_i/TiCl_4 = 0.30$ to 1.6.

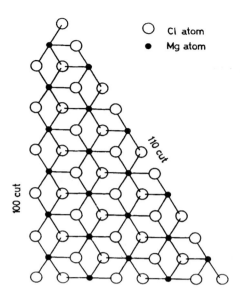

Figure 2.10 Model of $MgCl_2$ layer showing the (100) and (110) cuts. Reproduced with permission from Ref. [79], La Chimica & l'Industria (Milano)

Thus, $MgCl_2$ always largely exceeds $TiCl_4$ and D_i. In addition a reciprocal relationship between the Ti and D_i content has been frequently observed, at least for chemically prepared catalysts [82-85], so that the total $Ti + D_i$, if not truly constant, usually does not change much, provided any inert $TiCl_4/D_i$ or $TiCl_4/D_i/MgCl_2$ complex is carefully removed. Also, it is well known that neither $TiCl_4$ nor the internal donor can be easily removed from the catalyst [68, 86, 87] unless severe thermal treatments or strongly coordinating solvents are used. Thus, it seems that the catalyst components lose their identity and become strongly linked together, forming new complexes.

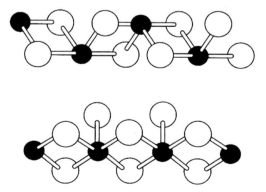

Figure 2.11 Mg coordination on the (110) (upper) and (100) (lower) faces of $MgCl_2$: (O) Cl^-, (●) Mg^{2+}. Reproduced with permission from Ref. [79], La Chimica & l'Industria (Milano)

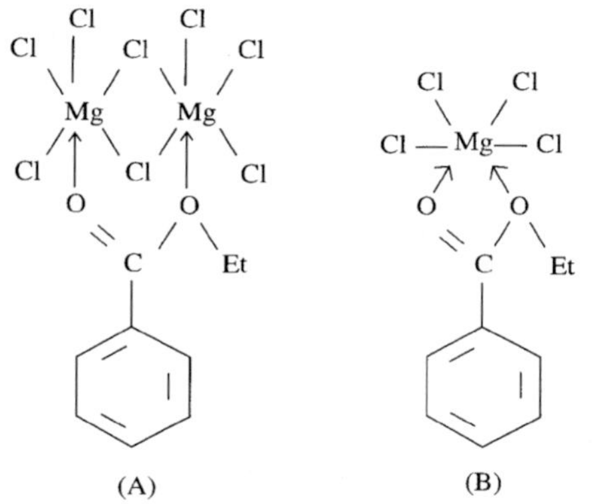

Figure 2.12 Possible models for EB coordination on the (100) (A) and (110) (B) faces of MgCl$_2$. Reproduced with permission from Ref. [94], John Wiley & Sons, Inc.

A considerable amount of work has consequently been aimed at elucidating the nature of this bonding, mainly by means of spectroscopic observations (IR, NMR) and thermogravimetric (TG) analyses carried out on both the true catalyst and model combinations of its components (i.e., MgCl$_2$/D$_i$, TiCl$_4$/D$_i$, TiCl$_4$/MgCl$_2$, TiCl$_4$/D$_i$/MgCl$_2$ complexes or comilled mixtures).

A great deal of IR data is available for catalysts containing ethylbenzoate (EB) as internal donor [40, 82, 88 - 93], for which a shift of the C=O stretching frequency from 1725 cm^{-1} in the free ester to 1680 cm^{-1} to 1700 cm^{-1} is most commonly observed in both the catalyst and the comilled EB/MgCl$_2$ mixtures. This result has been interpreted as an indication that a complexation of EB through the carbonyl oxygen takes place to Mg and not to Ti. The concomitant broadening of the C=O absorption band has been attributed to the presence of a variety of coordination complexes with different bond strengths [40, 80].

Solid state CP MAS (cross polarization with magic angle spinning) ^{13}C NMR investigations on both the catalyst [94, 95] and model TiCl$_4$·EB complexes or MgCl$_2$/EB comilled mixtures [96] also led to the conclusion that EB is prevailingly complexed to MgCl$_2$. Possible structures for EB complexed to the (100) and (110) faces of MgCl$_2$ have been proposed by Chien [94] and are shown in Fig. 2.12.

According to some authors [91, 97, 99], however, a slight difference can be noticed in the infrared C=O absorption frequency of the catalyst ($\sim$1680 cm^{-1}) and that of the EB/MgCl$_2$ mixture ($\sim$1690 cm^{-1}), and this would suggest that in the former, EB is in some way complexed to both Mg and Ti. On the other hand, from electron spin resonance (ESR) analysis of the catalyst after interaction with TEA, some evidence for the presence of small amounts of EB or phthalates complexed to Ti^{3+} has been reported, as well [98, 100].

The information concerning bifunctional donors (phthalates, diethers) is not as abundant. For phthalic acid esters, however, IR observations [65, 101 - 105] show a shift of the C=O stretching frequency from $\sim$1730 cm^{-1} in the free ester to 1685 cm^{-1} to 1700 cm^{-1} in both the catalyst and the MgCl$_2$/ester complex. Similarly, the C-O stretching frequency of diethers (1113 cm^{-1}) is shifted to a doublet at 1059 cm^{-1} and 1024 cm^{-1} in both the catalyst and the MgCl$_2$/diether mixture, with no bands from the TiCl$_4$·diether complex being detectable in the former [106]. The same indication is provided by ^{13}C NMR observations on catalyst containing either diethers [106] or phthalates [107], though in the latter case a considerable line narrowing observed in binary $MgCl_2$/ester mixture after treatment with $TiCl_4$ would suggest, according to the authors [107], that a separate crystalline phase is formed on the support surface.

From all the above, it seems possible to conclude that both monofunctional and bifunctional donors are essentially complexed to Mg rather than to Ti. The structure of the complexes could, however, be different for the different donor types. As a matter of fact, bifunctional Lewis bases could form either 1:1 chelate complexes with tetracoordinated Mg ions on the (110) face or 1:2 complexes with adjacent pentacoordinated Mg ions on the (100) face [106, 108, 109].

As far as the $TiCl_4$ bonding is concerned, in the absence of meaningful spectroscopic evidence, the most widely accepted models, supported by energy calculations, are those based on epitaxial adsorption on the different $MgCl_2$ faces. According to Corradini and his group [110, 111], for instance, the (100) cut is more basic than the (110) one as far as $TiCl_4$ coordination is concerned. Also, calculations suggest that $TiCl_4$ coordination as a Ti_2Cl_8 dimer on the former face and as a monomer on the latter is energetically favored. Fig. 2.13 shows these situations before and after $TiCl_4$ reduction with the Al-alkyl.

Similar models were proposed by Chien [112] who, however, assumed the presence of tetracoordinated rather than hexacoordinated monomeric species on the (110) face, both in clusters and in isolated form. As a consequence of the preference of $TiCl_4$ to coordinate on the (100) face, the situation in the catalyst, before and after reduction with the Al-alkyl, can be roughly represented [78] as in Fig. 2.14, with the (100) face being prevailingly occupied by Ti_2Cl_8 dimers and the (110) face by the Lewis base.

As will be shown later, these models represent the basis for the most widely accepted explanation of the stereoregulating effect of the Lewis bases, which is an essential feature of this type of catalyst.

2.3.1.3.4 Catalyst Structure   As mentioned earlier, highly activated $MgCl_2$ usually displays a very small crystallite size. Though this increases to some extent, owing to recrystallization, during hot treatment with $TiCl_4$, it remains still very low in the catalyst, as well ($D_{110} = 50$ Å to 300 Å, $D_{003} \leqslant 50$ Å). High surface areas and pore volumes are thus to be expected, and are actually observed, in $MgCl_2$-supported catalysts.

The actual values, however, greatly depend on the catalyst nature and the technique used for its preparation. Reported Brunauer-Emmet-Teller (BET) surface area and porosity values range from 100 m^2/g to 350 m^2/g and from 0.15 cm^3/g to 0.4 cm^3/g respectively, whereas mean pore radii from 20 Å to 80 Å have been quoted [70, 83, 84, 86, 110, 113 - 116].

According to our experience, catalysts obtained via chemical routes generally show a BET surface area around 300 m^2/g and pore volumes around 0.3 cm^3/g to 0.4 cm^3/g, slightly lower values usually being found in catalysts obtained by comilling or comilling plus $TiCl_4$ treatment.

2.3.1.3.5 Cocatalyst Chemistry   The cocatalysts used with $MgCl_2$-supported catalysts are invariably Al-trialkyls, triethyl-Al (TEA) and tri*iso*-butyl-Al (TIBA) being by far the most preferred ones. Al-alkyl-chlorides, in fact, afford a much poorer performance and can be used only in combination with trialkyls [68].

On the other hand, the external donor which can be used appears to be dependent on the type of internal donor. If D_i is an aromatic monoester (EB is the most usual), esters of the

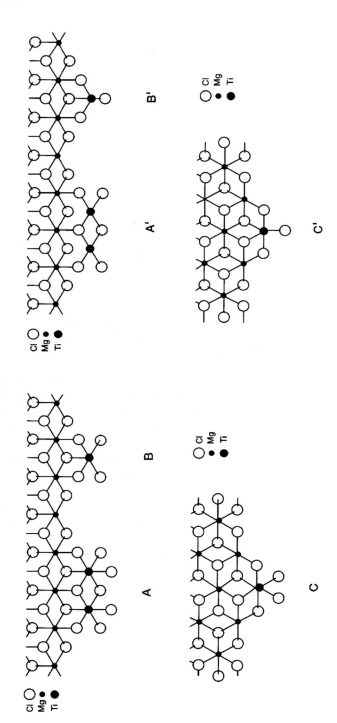

Figure 2.13 Possible models of TiCl$_4$ complexes on the (100) cut (A and B) and on the (110) cut (C) of MgCl$_2$; the same after activation by the Al-alkyl (A', B' and C'). Reproduced with permission from Ref. [125], Hüthig & Wepf Verlag

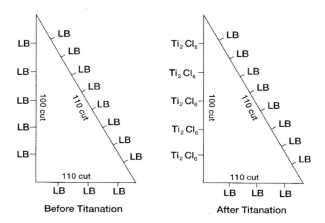

Figure 2.14 Schematic drawing of the Lewis base and Ti halide distribution on the (110) and (100) cuts of MgCl$_2$: (left) = support, (right) = catalyst activated with the Al-alkyl. Reproduced with permission from Ref. [78], Reidel Publishing Company

same type are normally required, such as methyl-*p*-toluate (MPT), ethylanisate (EA), *p*-ethoxy-ethylbenzoate (PEEB) and the like, whereas alkoxysilanes are required with phthalates (or diethers). Hindered piperidines, such as 2,2,6,6-tetramethylpiperidine (TMP), on the other hand, seem to work well with diesters, but not as well with monoesters. Whichever is the external donor, however, owing to its basic nature and the acidic nature of the AlR$_3$, a more or less complex interaction between the two components takes place.

   Most of the literature deals with the interaction between TEA or TIBA and aromatic monoesters, whose chemistry has recently been reviewed by several authors [68, 40, 73, 80]. According to most of the findings, the interaction involves first the formation of an acid–base complex through the carbonyl oxygen, as demonstrated by the shift of the infrared C=O stretching frequency from ~ 1725 cm^{-1} in the free ester to 1655 cm^{-1} to 1670 cm^{-1} in the AlR$_3$/D$_e$ mixture. The complex is most often assumed to exist in a 1:1 ratio, but, on the basis of spectroscopic evidence [117] and calorimetric studies [80], complexes involving two moles of AlR$_3$ per mole of D$_e$ also have been hypothesized. Structures such as those represented in Fig. 2.15 have been proposed by Spitz [117], while not very different structures

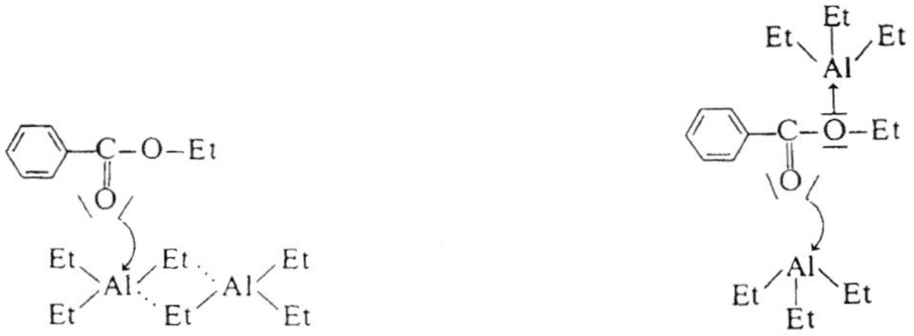

Figure 2.15 Possible structures of 1:2 EB/TEA complexes. Reproduced with permission from Ref. [68], Springer-Verlag Berlin

were assumed by Chien [118] and Tashiro [119]. The complex formation is very fast even at low temperature and in dilute solutions [80].

As regards alkoxysilanes, the formation of a 1:1 complex between TEA and phenyltriethoxysilane (PES) has been indicated by means of ^{13}C NMR spectroscopy, at least at relatively high TEA concentrations (0.5 mol/L) [120, 121]. The complex seems to involve the O atom from only one OR group, irrespective of the number of OR groups attached to Si.

The above complexes can undergo a further reaction, especially in the presence of excess AlR$_3$ as is usual for polymerization. In the case of aromatic monoesters, such as EB, a nucleophilic attack of free AlR$_3$ on the carbonyl group complexed with AlR$_3$ has been postulated. The reaction leads finally to the formation of two moles of dialkylaluminumalkoxide per one mole of ester, according to the following scheme [68 - 70]:

$$
\begin{array}{ccccc}
& & R & & R \\
& & | & & | \\
\text{Ph}-\text{C}-\text{OEt} & \xrightarrow{\text{(AlR}_3)} & \text{Ph}-\text{C}-\text{OEt} & \xrightarrow{+\text{AlR}_3} & \text{Ph}-\text{C}-\text{OAlR}_2 + \text{R}_2\text{AlOEt} \\
\| & & | & & | \\
\text{O}\rightarrow\text{AlR}_3 & & \text{OAlR}_2 & & R
\end{array}
$$

Reduction of the C=O group, rather than alkylation, prevails with TIBA with the concomitant elimination of isobutene. The reaction rate is higher for TEA than for TIBA and is greatly enhanced in concentrated solutions. Even at the mild conditions used in the polymerization and in the presence of the monomer, however, the reaction proceeds to a considerable extent. An example, taken from ref. 80, is shown in Fig. 2.16 for the reaction between TEA and MPT.

Silyl ethers, in turn, can undergo an exchange reaction with the Al-alkyl, with the formation of alkylated silylethers and dialkyl-Al-alkoxides. The reaction rate is appreciable

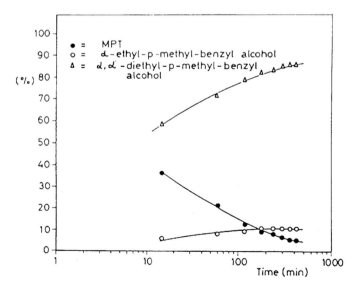

Figure 2.16 Reaction between TEA and MPT during polymerization: TEA = 0.5 g/L, TEA/MPT molar ratio = 3.33, T = 60 °C. Reproduced with permission from Ref. [80], Hüthig & Wepf Verlag

for silanes containing three or four OR groups and at high concentrations of the Al-alkyl [121 - 123]. Starting from PhSi(OMe)$_3$ and TEA, for instance, the reaction at 75 °C can proceed up to the formation of PhEt$_2$SiOMe, according to the scheme of Fig. 2.17 [121, 123].

Under the much more diluted polymerization conditions, however, the reaction is much slower [80, 120] and only 20% of PES, for example, is converted in 1 hour at 70 °C, with TEA = 5 mmol/L and PES = 0.5 mmol/L [80].

The reaction is even slower, and sometimes absent, for dialkoxysilanes and practically absent at all for monoalkoxysilanes [121]. On the other hand, in the case of trialkoxysilanes, the main reaction product, besides the Al-alkoxide, is a dialkoxy-Si derivative which, differently from the aromatic ester derivatives, still behaves as a good stereoregulating agent.

In conclusion, it can be stated that all types of external donor easily form complexes with the AlR$_3$ cocatalyst. These complexes are rather stable for silanes, whereas in the case of aromatic esters, they further react, leading to the partial destruction of the ester and its replacement with significantly less stereoregulating products. The true cocatalyst is, in this case, a mixture including free AlR$_3$, unconverted AlR$_3$/ester complex, and a mixture of Al-alkoxides of different bulkiness. Some free D$_e$ also can be present if the Al/D$_e$ ratio is very low [124].

2.3.1.3.6   Catalyst-Cocatalyst Interactions   MgCl$_2$-supported catalysts are much more complex systems than the TiCl$_3$-based ones, not only because of the presence of Lewis bases, which can interact with both the catalyst and the cocatalyst, but also owing to the different type of Ti compound used, which is normally in a tetravalent state and prone to undergo reduction upon interaction with the Al-alkyl. On the other hand, the latter is normally a trialkyl and thus possesses a higher reducing power than DEAC used along with the earlier generation catalysts.

The aim of this section is to review the modifications occurring in the catalyst composition and structure when it is put into contact with the cocatalytic mixture, as these

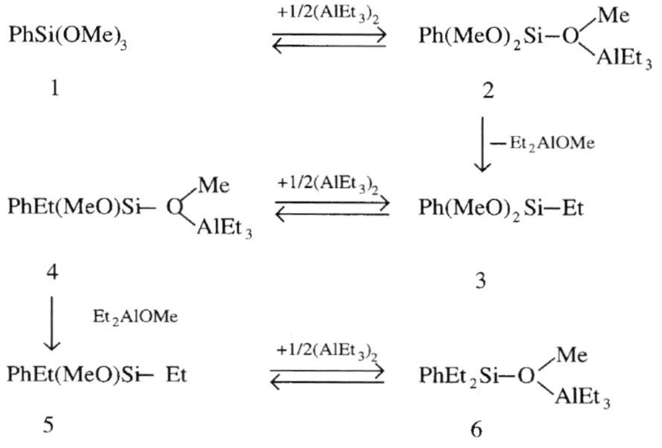

Figure 2.17 Pathway of the reaction between TEA and PhSi(OMe)$_3$. Reproduced with permission from Ref. [121], John Wiley & Sons, Inc.

changes are likely to be closely related to the polymerization performance. Two aspects are mainly considered: the transformations concerning the catalyst composition, and the change in the oxidation state of the Ti component.

2.3.1.3.7 Catalyst Composition   Catalysts involving aromatic monoesters as both D_i and D_e have recently been reviewed by Barbè et al [68]. Their findings, subsequently confirmed by other authors [125 - 129], were that in the absence of any D_e the following modifications take place in the catalyst through exchange equilibria with the cocatalyst:

- Extensive removal of the internal donor due to complexation or reaction with the AlR_3,
- incorporation of substantial amounts of Al-alkyl, and
- slight loss of $TiCl_4$.

In the presence of MPT as D_e, this migrates to the catalyst, apparently in competition with the Al-alkyl, but at the same time the removal of EB is to some extent prevented, whereas the loss of Ti is almost unchanged (Fig. 2.18).

The conclusion was that the Al-alkyl is able to displace the D_i by forming a soluble complex, whereas both Al-alkyl and D_e are able to complex on the free surface $MgCl_2$ sites. The ability of AlR_3 to remove D_i is, however, decreased by its complexation with the external donor.

As far as phthalates and alkoxysilanes as D_i/D_e system are concerned, much less experimental data are available. Nonetheless, the reported results suggest a qualitatively similar behavior. A comparison between the two systems under the same reaction conditions and with catalysts prepared according to the same procedure [129] demonstrated that, qualitatively, the same changes occur in both catalysts (Fig. 2.19).

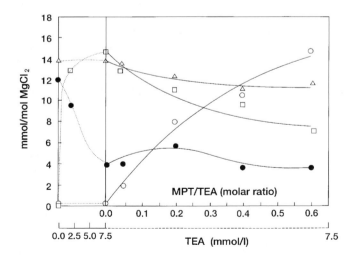

Figure 2.18 $MgCl_2/EB/TiCl_4$ catalyst + TEA and TEA/MPT: catalyst composition versus TEA concentration and MPT/TEA molar ratio ($\triangle$ = Ti, $\square$ = Al, $\bullet$ = EB, $\circ$ = MPT) Reproduced with permission from Ref. [129], Hüthig & Wepf Verlag

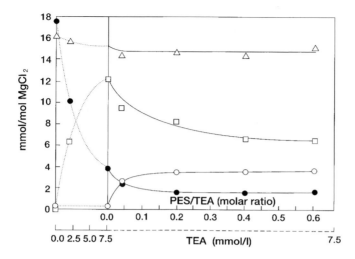

Figure 2.19 MgCl$_2$/DBP/TiCl$_4$ catalyst + TEA and TEA/PES: catalyst composition versus TEA concentration and PES/TEA molar ratio ($\triangle$ = Ti, $\square$ = Al, $\bullet$ = DBP, $\bigcirc$ = PES). Reproduced with permission from Ref. [129], Hüthig & Wepf Verlag

Some remarkable quantitative differences, however, appear to hold:

- The initial rate by which the content of D$_e$ in the catalyst increases as a function of the D$_e$/TEA ratio is much higher for silanes, though the level attained at high ratios is higher for MPT; and
- the silanes appear to favor the removal of the internal donor (phthalate), whereas the contrary is, to some extent, observed with the EB/MPT system.

This finding, confirmed by other authors as well [106, 127, 130], has been explained by assuming that silanes coordinate more strongly to MgCl$_2$ than to TEA, whereas the opposite is true for benzoic acid esters [80, 106, 129]. The higher level of MPT found in the catalyst at high D$_e$/TEA ratios, in turn, can be explained on the ground of Kezler's reports [131, 132] about aromatic esters being able to interact not only with the MgCl$_2$ surface but with its bulk as well.

On the other hand, it also has been shown that the internal/external donor exchange is much less easy when cross combinations of the above donors (i.e., EB/silane and phthalate/MPT) are considered [106, 127]. This fact seems to support the "key and lock" concept formulated by Spitz [133] to explain why only certain donor combinations are able to afford high II's.

1,3-Diethers behave very similarly to alkoxysilanes if used as external donors. When used as D$_i$, however, they show the unique property of virtually not being removed at all by the Al-alkyl [106, 134].

Practically nothing has been reported about how the external base, incorporated into the catalyst through the above exchange, is linked to the solid. However, according to results obtained by the authors by means of FTIR and solid state NMR, the Lewis base appears to be almost exclusively bonded to Mg in the same way previously described for the internal base.

Besides the above exchanges, other reactions involving the Lewis bases and other species are likely to occur in the course of polymerization. As a matter of fact, Ti-alkyl and Ti-polymer bonds can react with the carbonyl group of aromatic esters, leading to the formation of bulky (probably inactive) alkoxy-Ti chlorides, as shown by means of MPT labeled with ^{14}C [135]. Bulky alkoxy-Ti-chlorides also can arise from the reaction between esters and Ti—H bonds coming from the chain transfer with H_2, whereas in the case of silanes the possible exchange reaction products, Ti-OMe or Ti-OEt, contain small alkoxy groups and thus would be easily realkylated by the AlR_3 [80]. On the other hand a reaction between Ti-polymer bonds and silanes has been excluded on the basis of experiments with ^{13}C enriched silanes [136].

2.3.1.3.8   Ti Oxidation State   While it is generally accepted that in the $TiCl_3$/DEAC system Ti^{3+} species are almost exclusively present [40], a more extensive reduction of Ti from the initial $4+$ oxidation state is likely to occur in supported catalysts.

Literature reports are often contradictory, owing to the different catalysts and analytical methods used. Actually a reduction to both Ti^{3+} (20%) and Ti^{2+} (80%) has been reported by Kashiwa [137] for a $TiCl_4$/EB/$MgCl_2$ catalyst after 2 hours contact with TEA at 60 °C and Al/Ti $= 50$. With a similar catalyst but at milder reaction conditions (10 min., 50 °C, 3:1 TEA/MPT as cocatalyst), Chien observed that 85% of the initial Ti^{4+} was reduced to Ti^{3+} and 15% to Ti^{2+} [138]. With the same catalyst Weber found, after contact with TEA at 25 °C, 70% of Ti^{3+} and 30% of Ti^{2+}, whereas with TEA/MPT and in the presence or absence of an olefin both Ti^{4+} (35%), Ti^{3+} (25%) and Ti^{2+} (40%) could be detected [139].

Almost exclusively Ti^{3+}, on the contrary, was quoted by Sergeev [98] when working with a similar catalyst combined with TIBA with or without EB as D_e at 60 °C, Al/Ti $= 50$ and 2 minutes contact time. About 30% of Ti^{3+} ions were directly detectable by ESR, the remaining 70% only after interaction with pyridine. According to the author the presence of some Ti^{2+} ions cannot be completely ruled out, but its amount should be reduced by the presence of the Lewis base.

More recently, a combination of ESR and titration techniques was used by Chien to estimate the Ti oxidation states in catalysts based on the phthalate/silane system [100]. After interaction with TEA/PES (50 °C, 1 hr) he found the following distribution: $Ti^{4+} = 28.1\%$, $Ti^{3+} = 38.5\%$ (24% detectable by ESR, the remaining ESR silent), and $Ti^{2+} = 33.4\%$, whereas in the absence of PES the following values were found: $Ti^{4+} = 7\%$, $Ti^{3+} = 73.7\%$ (34% detectable by ESR), and $Ti^{2+} = 19.3\%$.

From the above results, despite the different catalysts and conditions investigated, it seems reasonable to conclude that under polymerization conditions a considerable reduction of Ti takes place, not only to Ti^{3+} but to Ti^{2+} as well.

2.3.1.3.9   Polymerization Performance   Due to their greater chemical and structural complexity, $MgCl_2$-supported catalysts show a much more complicated polymerization behavior than the $TiCl_3$-based ones, the number of parameters potentially able to affect the catalyst performance being higher. In addition, the literature reports are often contradictory, probably because of the catalysts being prepared by different techniques and the use of different polymerization conditions. Consequently the identification of unequivocal trends and laws for the polymerization behavior of these catalysts is rather difficult.

Nonetheless, both patent and the open literature clearly show that the main factors determining the catalyst performance are related to the presence, the chemical structure, and the concentration of the electron donors, both internal and external. Other factors such as the catalyst composition and its physical structure, though of minor importance, may contribute as well.

2.3.1.3.10 Lewis Base Effects   Although the literature reports on this subject often appear conflicting, some fundamental trends seem to be well-established. First, it seems clear that to obtain a high stereospecificity, a Lewis base must be added to both the catalyst and the cocatalyst, the only exception being the fifth generation catalysts for which a single base, as D_i, can be used [106, 140]. This is clearly shown in Table 2.3, obtained from literature data [68, 106, 127, 128, 136, 141, 142], from which it is evident that neither D_i nor D_e, if used alone, is able to provide acceptable isotacticity.

Once stated that two donors are required, it is clear that a proper matching of their chemical nature is necessary, as well [127, 133, 136, 141]. This is already evident from Tables 2.1 and 2.3, which clearly show that both the activity and the stereospecificity are remarkably higher in the fourth generation catalysts, based on the couple phthalate/silane, than in the third generation containing aromatic monoesters as both D_i and D_e. On the other hand, an even higher activity can be seen in the fifth generation catalysts containing only one donor, but of completely different chemical structure. Additional differences can be found if the polymer molecular properties are considered. As a matter of fact, while no significant differences are usually observed in microtacticity, the molecular weight (MW) is known to decrease, at the same H_2 concentration, on passing from the third to the fourth and then to the fifth generation. As far as the MWD is concerned, unequivocal GPC values can hardly be found in the literature; nonetheless, it can be said that a progressive narrowing takes place in the same order.

Within each donors pair, the D_e/AlR_3 (or D_e/Ti) ratio is without doubt the most critical parameter determining the catalyst performance, and particularly the productivity and the stereospecificity. The specific effect of this parameter, however, varies according to the particular D_i/D_e combination used and will be discussed in detail with reference to the most

Table 2.3 Performance of MgCl$_2$ Catalysts with Different Lewis Bases

Catalyst	Cocatalyst	Maximum isotatic index (wt%)	Remarks
MgCl$_2$/TiCl$_4$	AlEt$_3$	50	–
	AlEt$_3$/MPT	90	$D_e/Al \geq 0.3$
MgCl$_2$/TiCl$_4$/EB	AlEt$_3$	60	Normal Al/Ti
		90	Very low Al/Ti
	AlEt$_3$/MPT	95	$D_e/Al \geq 0.3$
MgCl$_2$/TiCl$_4$/DIBP	AlEt$_3$	70 to 80	All Al/Ti's
	AlEt$_3$/DPMS	95 to 99	$D_e/Al \geq 0.02$
MgCl$_2$/TiCl$_4$/DE	AlEt$_3$	95 to 99	Depending on DE/Ti

EB = Ethylbenzoate; MPT = methyl-p-toluate; DIBP = diisobutylphthalate; DPMS = diphenyldimethoxy-
silane; DE = 1,3-diether

widely used systems (i.e., EB/MPT (or other similar aromatic monoesters) and phthalate/alkoxysilane).

In both systems, the increase of the D_e/Al molar ratio brings about a progressive increase of the isotactic index (II), the extent of which, however, greatly depends on the donor system. With the EB/MPT system, in fact, the II increases slowly as the D_e/Al ratio increases, and values around, or higher than, 90% can only be attained at D_e/Al ratios higher than 0.2 [68, 141, 143 - 145], as shown in Fig. 2.20.

With the phthalate/silane system, on the contrary, the II increase is sharp, and, as shown in Fig. 2.21, values of 95% or more can be easily attained at Al/D_e ratios as high as 20 or more (i.e., at D_e/Al ratios equal to or lower than 0.05) [120, 133, 144, 146].

Parallel to the II increase, the catalyst productivity also changes remarkably with the D_e/Al ratio, and again in different ways for the two systems considered. For the EB/MPT system, the total productivity is most often reported to undergo a progressive decrease [68, 79, 89, 126, 129, 147 - 151], though a flat maximum at low ratios has sometimes been described as well [99, 152, 153]. As a consequence a reciprocal yield/II relationship has often been shown to hold [40, 86, 151].

On the contrary, with the phthalate/silane systems, the productivity most often shows an initial sharp increase up to a maximum, especially in the presence of H_2, followed by a slow decrease [79, 133, 153 - 156]. This different behavior of the two donor systems is clearly shown in Figs. 2.22 and 2.23, from which it is also evident that in both systems, despite the different trend for the total productivity, the isotactic polymer productivity increases up to a maximum and then decreases, whereas the atactic productivity decreases monotonically as the D_e/Al ratio increases.

The superiority of the phthalate/silane system over the EB/MPT one appears due to its higher efficiency in both increasing the productivity of the isotactic polymer and decreasing the productivity of the atactic one as a function of the D_e/Al molar ratio. As a consequence, the former system shows a much better isotacticity/productivity balance and entails a much lower D_e consumption than the latter, as shown in Fig. 2.24.

On the other hand, the different trends for productivity appear closely related to the different effect the D_e/Al ratio has on the polymerization kinetics in the different systems. All $MgCl_2$-supported catalysts display a marked decrease of the polymerization rate with time, but the decay rate varies according to the donor system used.

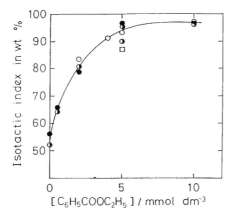

Figure 2.20 Isotactic index versus EB concentration at constant TEA concentration with $MgCl_2$/EB/$TiCl_4$ catalysts having different Ti contents ($\bigcirc$ = 0.84 wt%, ◑ and $\square$ = 0.67 wt%, ● = 4.65 wt%). Reproduced with permission from Ref. [145], Harwood Academic Publishers

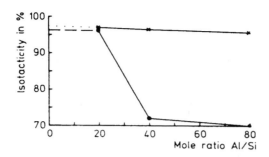

Figure 2.21 Isotacticity versus TEA/PES molar ratio for a phthalate-based catalyst: (●) PES = 0.15 mmol/L, (x) PES = 0.3 mmol/L. Reproduced with permission from Ref. [133], Hüthig & Wepf Verlag

Though a generalization is difficult, the rate decay for EB/MPT or other similar systems is frequently reported to obey a second-order law [110, 111, 138, 157 - 159] (though a multi-site first-order model is perhaps more appropriate [160, 161]), whereas a mono- or two-site first-order decay is mostly observed with the phthalate/silane systems [142, 154, 162, 163]. A comparison of the rate/time profile for the two systems is shown in Fig. 2.25.

The shape of the kinetic profile is said not to change with the addition of the silane to a phthalate-based catalyst [142, 154, 162], whereas in EB-containing catalysts the addition of increasing amounts of MPT brings about, at first, essentially a decrease of the initial rate, and then an increase of the decay rate (Fig. 2.26).

In all systems the polymer molecular properties also appear to depend to some extent on the amount of the external donor. For instance, the average MW of the polymer, and especially that of the isotactic fraction, reportedly increases with the D_e/Al ratio in both the EB/MPT [40, 107, 143, 144, 151, 164 - 166] and the phthalate/silane [120, 136, 142, 144, 154, 155, 167] systems, the increase being particularly evident in the absence of H_2. The effect is less clear for the MWD, for which either no effect [40, 125, 143, 164, 168] or at most a slight broadening [151, 165] of the isotactic fraction has been reported.

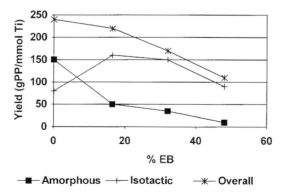

Figure 2.22 Effect of %EB (versus Al) for a MgCl$_2$/EB/TiCl$_4$ catalyst. Reproduced with permission from Ref. [79], La Chimica & l'Industria (Milano)

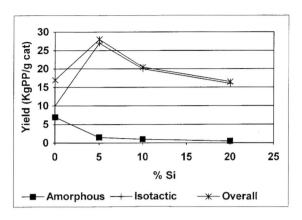

Figure 2.23 Effect of %Si (versus Al) for a MgCl$_2$/phthalate/TiCl$_4$ catalyst. Reproduced with permission from Ref. [79], La Chimica & l'Industria (Milano)

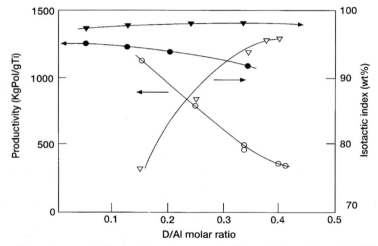

Figure 2.24 Effect of Donor/Al-alkyl molar ratio on productivity and isotacticity with different catalysts. Polymerization in bulk propylene, 70 °C, 2 hours: ▼, ● = 4th generation catalyst; ∇, ○ = 3rd generation catalyst

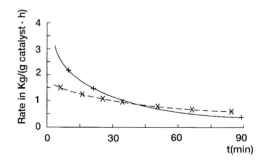

Figure 2.25 Typical kinetic profiles for 3rd (+) and 4th (x) generation catalysts. Reproduced with permission from Ref. [133], Hüthig & Wepf Verlag

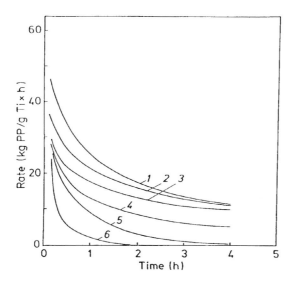

Figure 2.26 Kinetics of propylene polymerization with a 3rd generation catalyst at different MPT/TEA molar ratios. 1: MPT/TEA = 0.0; 2: MPT/TEA = 0.05; 3: MPT/TEA = 0.2; 4: MPT/TEA = 0.3; 5: MPT/TEA = 0.4; 6: MPT/TEA = 0.6. Reproduced with permission from Ref. [68], Springer-Verlag Berlin

Another polymer property that appears to be affected by the D_e/Al ratio is the polymer stereochemical composition, as determined by fractionation and ^{13}C NMR analysis of the fractions (expressed as % of *mm* triads or *mmmm* pentads). Also in this case, however, the literature reports are not always in agreement. According to Wu [169], an increase of the EB/Al ratio brings about not only an increase of the percentage of isotactic polymer but also of the probability of selecting isotactic configuration at the isospecific sites (i.e., micro-tacticity). Kashiwa [126, 170], on the contrary, found no change in the *mm*% ($\sim$ 93) of the isotactic fraction upon increasing the EB/Al ratio from 0 to 0.6. Almost a constant *mmmm* level (90 ± 2%) was observed by Busico [141] in the heptane insoluble polymer obtained both in the absence of any D_e and with various D_i/D_e combinations. A considerable increase of the *mmmm* content of the octane insoluble fraction on going from no base to D_e/Al = 0.2 was, on the contrary, observed by Barbè [144] for both the EB/MPT and the DIBP/PES systems. Small microtacticity enhancements were also reported by Sacchi [128] and Härkönen [174] for phthalate/silane systems, and by Kakugo [171 - 173] for various catalysts (with or without D_i) and external donors. It thus seems, on the whole, that not only the percentage of prevailingly isotactic polymer but also its microtacticity, at least to some extent, can be increased by increasing the concentration of the external donor or its ratio to the Al-alkyl.

The external donor structure, too, appears to have a significant effect on the catalyst performance, as well as on the polymer structure. As previously mentioned, within the monoester systems the most frequently used external donors are methyl- or ethyl benzoates bearing in para position an electron-releasing group (CH_3, OCH_3, OEt, *t*-Bu, etc.) to decrease their reactivity toward the Al-alkyl. Not many data are available about the effect of these different esters on polymerization performance. However, Guyot [153] recently reported some polymerization results obtained with a $TiCl_4/EB/MgCl_2$ catalyst combined with TEA and EB, EA, EPT (ethyl-*p*-toluate) and PTBMB (*p-t*-butylmethylbenzoate) as external donors, at a D_e/Al ratio of 0.2. From his data, it appears that EB, EA, and EPT give the same II ($\sim 93\%$), whereas the productivity is somewhat higher for EPT. On the contrary, PTBMB affords the highest productivity but a rather low II ($\sim 80\%$), which is attributed to its higher steric hindrance that limits its ability to form a complex with TEA, which, according to the author, is the true stereoregulating component.

A superior performance of MPT over EB as D_e has been claimed by Kashiwa [175], especially as far as productivity is concerned (about three times higher). He also showed that best overall results are obtained when MPT is used as both D_i and D_e.

More results are available for the effect of the silane structure in phthalate/silane systems. According to Proto [136], Sacchi [128], Seppälä [167] and Härkönen [174, 176, 177], the performance of silanes is affected by the number and size of the alkoxy group as well as by the bulkiness of the moiety attached to Si (most often a hydrocarbyl radical). Two, or at most three, small OR groups (methoxy or ethoxy) are required for high performance. As regards the non-alkoxy moiety, the II appears to increase with its bulkiness in the following order [136]:

$$Me < n\text{-Bu} < i\text{-Bu} \approx C_6H_5 < i\text{-Pr}.$$

The MWD, at the same time, is said to become narrower, though an opposite trend (i.e., a broadening with increasing the bulkiness of Si substituents) is perhaps more likely [178]. On the other hand, no correlation between MWD and the silane structure has been observed by Seppälä [167]. MW is generally reported to increase with the steric hindrance of silanes [136, 167, 174].

In the same way, the microtacticity of the heptane insoluble fraction was shown to increase on passing from $MeSi(OMe)_3$ to the bulkier $i\text{-BuSi(OMe)}_3$ [171]. Härkönen [176] concluded that optimum silanes are those bearing two small alkoxy groups and branched hydrocarbyl substituents on the Si atom. On the other hand, according to the patent literature [179, 180], cycloalkyl- and amino-substituents afford high performance, as well. Within dimethoxysilanes, Okano [181], by means of Modified Neglect of Diatomic Overlap (MNDO) calculations, concluded that the isotactic productivity increases with the overall molecular volume, whereas the atactic productivity decreases as the electron density on the oxygen atoms decreases. He thus speculated that both electronic and steric factors are important in determining the performance of the external donor. Similar conclusions were drawn by Härkönen as well [177].

If, as suggested by the above results, the structure and the concentration of the external Lewis base are critical for the catalyst performance, the role of the internal one, though less clear, cannot in any way be neglected. As a matter of fact, as already shown in Table 2.3, II's higher than 90% can hardly be obtained in the absence of D_i, irrespective of the type and amount of the D_e used [68, 89, 128, 141, 143, 182], whereas II's as high as 98% can be obtained even without D_e if a proper internal donor (1,3-diether) is used [20, 106, 140]. The internal donor seems, thus, to be at least as important as the external one. In addition, as mentioned earlier, the structure of the internal donor also appears to be the factor which determines the need for the external base and the type to be used, the selection rule being roughly as follows:

D_i type	Best D_e type
• Monofunctional (aromatic monoester)	• Monofunctional (aromatic monoester)
• Bifunctional (aromatic diester)	• Polyfunctional (silylethers) or monofunctional (TMP)
• Bifunctional (1,3-diether)	• None or bifunctional (silane, diether)

Thus, a monofunctional D_e appears to be required for monofunctional D_i's, whereas with a bifunctional D_i, a bifunctional D_e seems more appropriate, though a monofunctional one, like TMP, also works fairly well.

This behavior can be explained by assuming that to afford a high stereospecificity a certain amount of Lewis base, possessing the proper requisites, must be present in the catalyst in the course of polymerization, and this can be obtained either by using as D_i a Lewis base that shows a strong preference for coordination to $MgCl_2$ or through the exchange equilibrium between the internal and the external donor discussed earlier. In more detail, the situation appears to be as follows:

1. If D_i is highly reactive toward AlR_3, it usually tends to be displaced from the catalyst. If, in addition, it is highly stereoregulating, as are aromatic esters, stereospecificity becomes lower as the donor extraction proceeds. Two possibilities are then opened to preserve the stereospecificity, either
   a. the D_i extraction is prevented, as for instance by lowering the AlR_3 concentration [183] or by using hindered Al-alkyls [184], or
   b. an equally effective external base is used to replace the internal one in the catalyst thus preserving its stereospecificity (this actually appears to be the case for aromatic monoester donors such as EB and MPT).
   On the other hand, if D_i is not so highly stereoregulating, as for instance phthalates, the use of a highly efficient external donor able to quickly replace it on the catalyst is absolutely required. This is what appears to happen with silanes.
2. If, on the contrary, D_i possesses a high stereoregulating ability and no or little reactivity toward AlR_3, it cannot be removed from the catalyst, and thus no external donor is required. This appears to be the case with 1,3-diethers. Clearly, Lewis bases not reactive toward AlR_3 but not having a sufficient stereoregulating power cannot provide a high stereospecificity.

Besides these direct effects, the D_i also appears to improve the catalyst performance indirectly (e.g., by favoring the support activation during milling [68] and by helping the elimination of undesired by-products, such as Cl_3TiOR, which are formed during the catalyst synthesis from $Mg(OR)_2$ or $MgCl_2 \cdot nROH$ precursors) [70, 83, 84, 185].

Not much has been reported about the effect of the D_i structure. On the whole, EB is the preferred donor for the third generation catalysts, though MPT has been recently claimed to give better overall performance [175]. As far as phthalates are concerned, the following ranking was established by Soga [142]:

$$Bu > Et > Me.$$

From both the patent and the open literature, however, similar performance are obtained with phthalates containing from ethyl to isodecyl OR groups.

As far as 1,3-diethers are concerned, it has been shown that the polymerization behavior is closely related to the diether conformation, the optimum performances being obtained when the most stable conformation, which is determined by the size of the substituents at the central C atom, is such that the distance between the two oxygen atoms falls in the range 2.5 Å to 3.3 Å [106, 140].

2.3.1.3.11 Effect of Catalyst Composition and Structure   Parameters related to the catalyst composition are mainly the Ti and D_i content. As mentioned earlier, these quantities are often related by a reciprocal relationship, and, in addition, the base content may also affect the degree of the $MgCl_2$ activation and its porosity and surface area, which, in turn, can affect the polymerization performance. A separate evaluation of the effects of the compositional parameters is, thus, very difficult, if not impossible.

Catalysts obtained by comilling $MgCl_2$ with the $TiCl_4 \cdot EB$ complex show no change in productivity per unit weight of Ti for Ti contents from 0.5% to 3%, whereas higher Ti levels bring about a productivity drop, probably because some Ti remains complexed to EB and is, thus, inactive [186]. The same explanation was given by Keii [157] for the observed activity decrease beyond 2% Ti contents in catalysts obtained by treating a comilled $MgCl_2$/EB support with hot $TiCl_4$. Analogous results have been reported by Kezler [148] for similar catalysts. Yano [82], on the contrary, found a slight increase in Ti productivity and a parallel decrease of isotacticity with catalysts showing a Ti content increasing from 1.9% to 3.6% and a parallel decrease of the EB content.

A slight decrease of both Ti productivity and II in catalyst prepared at different temperatures and having increasing Ti content (from 1.9% to 2.33 wt%) and decreasing phthalate content (from 0.3 wt% to 0.13 wt%) was observed by Yang [85]. On the other hand, with similarly prepared catalysts, Chadwick [187] found a maximum activity for the catalyst prepared at intermediate temperature and having intermediate Ti and DIBP contents, whereas the percentage of xylene insoluble (isotactic) polymer was the highest at the highest levels of both Ti% and DIBP%. The percentage of octane insoluble (thus highly isotactic) polymer and its *mmmm* content, however, were shown to increase as the DIBP content decreased. With a catalyst prepared from $Mg(OEt)_2$, DBP, and excess $TiCl_4$ at variable DBP/Mg ratios, Gupta [84] observed in turn a slight decrease of Ti productivity and increase of II as the Ti and DBP contents changed from 4% to 3% and from 14% to 23%, respectively.

The above reports clearly show that no unequivocal relationships between catalyst performance and its composition can be identified. On the other hand, performance could also be affected by factors related to the synthesis conditions and not having any detectable effect on the catalyst composition.

Impurities originated during the catalyst synthesis may also be important in determining the catalyst performance. Inert or poisonous by-products, such as chloro-Ti-alkoxides, phthaloylchlorides, and $TiCl_4$-D_i complexes, must be carefully removed for maximum performance [66, 67]. On the other hand, the effect of acylchlorides appears controversial, as either a negative [104] or no effect [105] was found by Yang for phthaloylchloride, whereas Jeong [103] claimed a positive effect of benzoylchloride on isotacticity.

In conclusion, a moderate effect of both the Ti and (probably more) the D_i content on catalyst activity and stereospecificity is likely to exist, even for catalysts prepared under the best conditions. Other factors, however, like the impurities arising from side reactions involving both $TiCl_4$, D_i, and the $MgCl_2$ precursor during the catalyst synthesis can be as much or even more important.

On the other hand, no unequivocal relationships have been reported for these catalysts as far as the effect of structural and physical parameters, such as the $MgCl_2$ disorder and crystallite size, and the catalyst porosity, pore size distribution, and surface area, are concerned. A contribution from these factors, however, seems to be highly probable as well.

2.3.2   Homogeneous Catalysts

2.3.2.1   Introduction

Although homogeneous catalysts were used in the past to synthesize, with low activity, partially stereoregular isotactic and syndiotactic PP, only in the last ten years, as a consequence of the discovery of metallocene catalysts, has the interest in this field become more and more deep both in the academic and industrial world.

Among all polymerization catalysts, metallocenes are the only catalysts which enable control over both the molecular weight and the microstructure (tacticity, regioregularity, comonomer distribution) of polyolefins over a very wide range, making possible the synthesis of improved and new polyolefin materials. The most important achievements in the field are the synthesis of a large number of novel polyolefin structures and the understanding of the catalyst structure–polymer structure relationship. Some industrial processes based on this new catalyst technology have already been announced. Much of the research has been conducted in industrial laboratories, and most results have only been reported in the patent literature (over 600 patent applications have been filed from 1976–1994).

This section is dedicated to the polymerization of propylene with metallocene catalysts and special emphasis is dedicated to isotactic PP. The references reported herein are by no means inclusive nor intended to establish priorities but only suggestion for further reading. Some reviews are already available [188 - 190].

2.3.2.2   Development and History

The first example of stereospecific polymerization of α-olefins by homogeneous catalysts is the polymerization of propylene with the catalyst obtained by reaction of vanadium compounds (VCl_4, $VOCl_3$, $ClVO(OEt)_2$) with R_2AlCl at low temperature ($-78\,°C$) in hydrocarbon solvents [191]. The syndiotactic polymer obtained, with low yield, via this catalyst is poorly stereoregular and presents some regioirregularities (4% to 5%). The living nature of this polymerization was proved by Doi et al. [192].

Isotactic polymers of propylene and 4-methyl-1-pentene have been obtained, with low yield, by means of Ti and Zr benzyl [193] and allyl [194] derivatives, in hydrocarbon solution.

2.3.2.3   Metallocene Catalysts

2.3.2.3.1   Structure   Metallocene catalysts result from the reaction of metallocenes and a cocatalyst, which is generally an organoaluminum compound. Not all biscyclopentadienyl transition metal complexes (metallocene) are, or can be turned into, olefin polymerization catalysts. The exact definition of the class of soluble organometallic complexes usually referred to as "metallocene catalysts" is group 4 (titanium, zirconium or hafnium) bent metallocenes.

Titanocene derivatives in combination with aluminumalkyls have been studied since the early days of Ziegler–Natta catalysis as soluble, chemically more defined surrogates of inorganic Ti compounds. Early metallocene catalysts of the type Cp_2TiCl_2/AlR_xCl_{3-x}, however, show poor activity towards ethylene and do not polymerize propylene, although they do copolymerize ethylene with higher α-olefins [195, 196]. Analogous research with zirconocene dichloride in combination with AlR_3 was started by Breslow [197] but met limited success, until the serendipitous discovery of the activating effect of small amounts of water on the system $Cp_2MX_2/AlMe_3$, and the subsequent synthesis of methylaluminoxane (MAO) by the group of Sinn and Kaminsky has provided organometallic and polymer chemists with a potent cocatalyst able to activate group 4 metallocenes toward the polymerization of α-olefins [198]. Of the three metals, Zr is the most active, followed by Hf and Ti; the latter also suffers from deactivation at higher temperatures, possibly because of reduction to Ti^{3+}. However, the activity of Cp_2TiR_2 and Cp_2ZrR_2 (R=Cl or alkyl group), although impressive towards the homo- and copolymerization of ethylene, was moderate with propylene and, more important, did not produce stereoregular polymers. Very low molecular weight atactic polymers were obtained in all cases.

In 1984, Ewen correlated catalyst symmetry with polymer structure and reaction mechanism [21, 199]. Since then, thanks to the combined efforts of both industrial and academic research groups worldwide, an impressive leap forward on the knowledge of, and control over, the mechanistic details of olefin insertion, chain growth, and chain transfer processes at the molecular level has been made.

Group 4 metallocenes are d^0, pseudotetrahedral organometallic compounds in which the transition metal atom bears two η^5-cyclopentadienyl ligands which remain attached to the metal during polymerization (and actually define the catalyst stereoselectivity and activity) and two σ ligands which are removed when the active catalyst is formed. Due to their aromaticity, cyclopentadienyl anions are six-electron donors, very robust ligands. A good reference book on the synthesis and characterization of these compounds prior to 1986 is available [200].

The most commonly encountered Cp-type ligands are cyclopentadienyl itself ($C_5H_5^-$, or Cp), alkylated cyclopentadienyls such as pentamethyl-cyclopentadienyl ($C_5Me_5^-$, or Cp*), indenyl ($C_9H_7^-$), and fluorenyl ($C_{13}H_9^-$, or Fl).

The general structure of a group 4 bent metallocene is shown in Fig. 2.27. The carbon atoms of the Cp ligands can bear hydrogen or other groups such as alkyl, aryl, or silane: up to ten different substituents are possible on a metallocene, and this structural diversity is the reason for the high steric and electronic versatility of the Cp ligands. Note that different substituents change not only the size and shape of the Cp ligand but also the Cp-M distance (*d*) and the Cp-M-Cp angle (α).

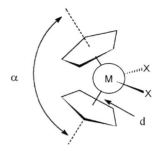

Figure 2.27 General structure of a group 4 metallocene   M = Ti, Zr, Hf. X = 2 e⁻ σ-ligand. α = 125-140 °

Metallocenes are fluxional molecules; therefore, the presence of substituents on the η^5-rings is not sufficient to impart a structural rigidity to the catalytic complex such as to ensure a constant steric environment at the coordination positions occupied by the two σ ligands. The presence of bulky substituents can only reduce the rate of ligand rotation [201]. The problem has been solved by Brintzinger and co-workers [202, 203] by linking the two η^5-rings through a bridge formed by one or more carbon or silicon atoms. Maximum rigidity is assured by a one-atom bridge; the number of atoms forming the bridge also influence the Cp-M-Cp angle.

Metallocenes used in olefin polymerization have been classified on the basis of their symmetry [204] (Fig. 2.28). In class I, the two η^5-ligands (represented by shaded rectangles) can be bridged or not; in the other classes they are bridged. In classes I and II, the two sites

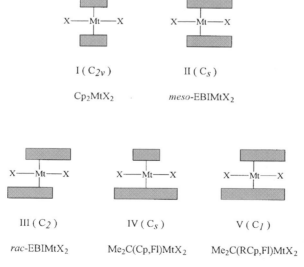

Figure 2.28 Classification of metallocene catalysts according to their symmetry. Reproduced with permission from Ref. [204], Hüthig & Wepf Verlag

occupied by the η^5-ligands are bisected by a horizontal mirror plane and consequently are achirotopic and identical in class I and different in class II. In the other classes, the two above sites are chirotopic; they are related by a two-fold rotation axis in class III and are homotopic (equal). In class IV, the two sites are related by a vertical mirror plane and are enantiotopic (mirror image to each other). No symmetry elements are present in class V, and the two sites are diastereotopic (different). A review of stereorigid and chiral cyclopentadienyl ligands and metallocenes covers this topic up to 1991 [205].

2.3.2.3.2   Cocatalyst   Methylaluminoxane (MAO) is the most widely used cocatalyst, since it is able to activate the largest number of metallocenes and other soluble transition metal complexes. It is obtained by controlled hydrolysis of $AlMe_3$ and consists of oligomers of approximate composition $(MeAlO)_n$, but its true composition is far from being known. Cryoscopic, GPC, and NMR studies have shown that MAO is a mixture of several different compounds, including residual (coordinated) $AlMe_3$ and possibly AlO_3 units, in dynamic equilibrium [205-209]. The true nature of the activating species in MAO has not been elucidated yet. A detailed study carried out by Barron et al. [210, 211] on the hydrolysis products of $Al(t\text{-}Bu)_3$ might give some important insight on the structure of oligomeric methylalumoxane; in the light of their results, dynamic cage structures are more likely than linear and cyclic ones. Tetracoordinated Al sites seem to prevail in MAO solutions [212]; however, the presence of three-coordinated Al sites also has been revealed by ^{27}Al NMR spectroscopy [213], and the Lewis acidity of these species is likely enhanced by the adjacent oxygen atoms.

The main drawbacks of MAO as cocatalyst are its high cost, due to the expensive $AlMe_3$ parent compound; the large amount needed (typically $Al/Zr = 10^3$ to 10^4 molar are used, although in supported systems Al/Zr ratios as low as 100 have proven sufficient); and, as a consequence, the high content of alumina residues in the final product. To solve the above problems, MAO surrogates have been investigated. Reports in the patent literature include the use of $MAO/Al(i\text{-}Bu)_3$ mixtures [214] or of the hydrolysis product of $Al(i\text{-}Bu)_3$ [215, 216] obtained at $Al(i\text{-}Bu)_3/H_2O = 2$. The latter cocatalyst, although highly effective in ethylene copolymerization, gives active propylene catalyst only when prepared under extremely controlled conditions and used immediately; on standing, a disproportionation process takes place producing $Al(i\text{-}Bu)_3$ and higher Al-O-Al products which are no longer active.

A major improvement towards simpler and cheaper metallocene-based systems has been the use of boron compounds, such as $B(C_6F_5)_3$, $NR_3H^+B(C_6F_5)_4^-$ and $Ph_3C^+B(C_6F_5)_4^-$, in combination with metallocene dialkyls [217-221]. As these systems are not able to scavenge impurities, and a large part of the activated catalyst has to be sacrificed for that purpose, much better results have been achieved by adding small amounts of AlR_3 (such as $Al(i\text{-}Bu)_3$ and $AlEt_3$) to the reaction system, with a double advantage: AlR_3 scavenges impurities and alkylates the metallocene so that the simpler metallocene dichloride can be used [222, 223].

2.3.2.3.3   Catalyst Activation   By mixing hydrocarbon solutions of Cp_2MCl_2 and MAO, a fast ligand exchange reaction generates Cp_2MClMe and also Cp_2MMe_2 [224, 225]; in the presence of excess MAO, the system becomes catalytically active. Spectroscopic evidence [213, 226] is consistent with the assumption that Lewis acidic centers present in MAO are able to accept CH_3^- (or Cl^-) anions from the alkylated metallocene, thus generating a metallocene alkyl cation, the active polymerization species [227, 228], and a poorly coordinating counteranion (Fig. 2.29).

The active metallocene alkyl cation can be generated also by means of one of the following methods [217 - 221, 228]:

$$Cp_2MMe_2 + [NHMe_2Ph]^+[B(C_6F_5)_4]^- \rightarrow Cp_2M^+Me[B(C_6F_5)_4]^- + Me_2NPh + CH_4$$

$$Cp_2MMe_2 + Ph_3C^+[B(C_6F_5)_4]^- \rightarrow Cp_2M^+Me[B(C_6F_5)_4]^- + Ph_3CMe$$

$$Cp_2MMe_2 + B(C_6F_5)_3 \rightarrow Cp_2M^+Me[B(C_6F_5)_3Me]^-$$

The coordination capability of the anion must be weak enough so as not to compete with the coordination of the monomer to the highly Lewis acidic metal center.

2.3.2.3.4 Isospecific Catalysts

Isotactic PP is obtained by using stereorigid racemic C_2-symmetric metallocenes (see Section 2.4.5.3), a class of compounds with the general formula shown in Fig. 2.30, and are usually referred to as chiral ansa-metallocenes.

Position 1 on the Cp is the connection to the bridge X, where X is usually $-CH_2CH_2-$, Me_2C, or Me_2Si; positions 3,4 (the front positions) bear the β substituents, while the 2,5 positions (the rear ones) bear the α substituents, where α and β indicate the distance from the bridge. The rear substituents are optional and have only a secondary effect on stereospecificity (but a major one on chain transfer rate), while the front one is the one imparting the required symmetry to the molecule.

By using one such compound, ethylenebis(1-indenyl)titanium dichloride, Ewen first proved the correlation between metallocene chirality and isotacticity [21], a textbook example of shape-selective catalysis: the racemic form yields isotactic PP, while the achiral, meso form produces low molecular weight atactic polymer. Soon after Ewen's disclosure, Kaminsky and Brintzinger reported that a similar C_2-symmetric zirconocene, racemic ethylenebis(tetrahydroindenyl)zirconiumdichloride (*rac*-EBTHIZrCl$_2$) provided much higher yields of isotactic PP [22, 229]. The prototypal and best studied example of this class of metallocenes is racemic-ethylenebis(indenyl)zirconium dichloride (*rac*-EBIZrCl$_2$), shown in Fig. 2.31 in comparison to the meso form.

The properties of the polymers obtained with the above catalysts were found to strongly depend on polymerization conditions. At temperatures usually adopted in industrial processes (50 °C to 70 °C), stereoregularity, regioregularity and molecular weight of the polymer decrease to values unacceptable for normal applications; therefore, in the following ten years

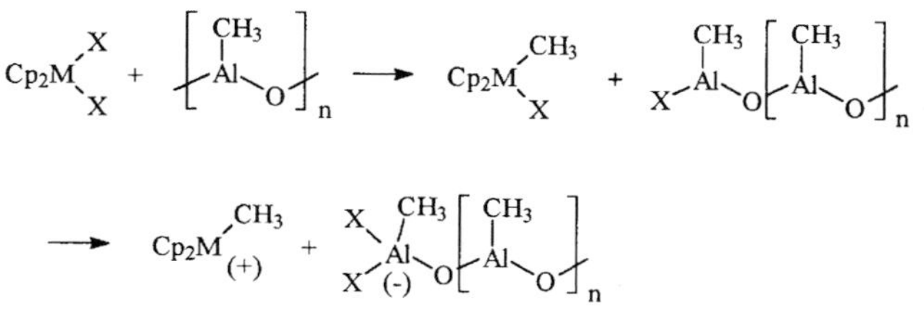

Figure 2.29 Formation of a metallocene alkyl cation (the active species) by reaction between a metallocene and methylalumoxane

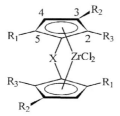

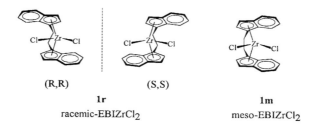

Figure 2.30 General formula for a chiral, racemic C_2-symmetric metallocene (one enantiomer only is shown)

(R,R)   (S,S)

1r   **1m**

racemic-EBIZrCl$_2$ meso-EBIZrCl$_2$

Figure 2.31 Racemic and meso Et(Ind)$_2$ZrCl$_2$

a large number of different ligand structures have been prepared to allow study of the substituent's effect on the above polymer properties and catalyst activity [230-232].

As far as stereospecificity is concerned, the nature of the substituent in the β-position shows a crucial effect (Table 2.4). A strong influence is given also by the stereorigidity of the metallocene that increases when a one-atom bridge is used and above all when a methyl group is in the α-position of the bridged cyclopentadienyl ligand (or in the 2-position of the indenyl ligand) [233].

When Me$_2$Si-bridged Cp ligands are used, stereospecificity increases with the bulkiness of the β-substituent: Me $< i$-Pr $< t$-Bu; the same trend is observed in the corresponding ethylene-bridged compounds [234]. Stereoselectivity of *rac-ansa*-indenyl metallocenes is improved when an annelated ring or protruding bulky groups are present in the 4-position, particularly when a methyl substituent is also present in the 2-position. In this case, stereospecificity remains high also at polymerization temperatures of 70 °C to 80 °C; at the same time, regiospecificity is also improved.

Generally, the stereospecificity of chiral *ansa*-metallocene catalysts increases when a short bridge between the η^5-rings is used (Table 2.5).

Stereospecificity is not influenced by metallocene and MAO concentration, but, at least with some metallocene catalysts (EBIZrCl$_2$, EBTHIZrCl$_2$), it decreases with lowering propylene concentration [235, 236]; therefore, one must be cautious in comparing stereospecificity of catalysts used at different monomer concentrations. Stereo and regioselectivity decreases by increasing polymerization temperature.

As far as activity is concerned, a different effect of ring substituents is observed for chiral *ansa*-indenyl and cyclopentadienyl catalysts. In the first case, activity substantially increases with the bulkiness of the substituent in 4-position; the reverse effect is observed for the latter when β-substituents are varied. However, kinetic measurements [237] show that, in this case, the same trend as for indenyl derivatives is noticed when the initial polymerization rate before

Table 2.4 Polymerization of Propylene with Isospecific *rac*-Metallocene-MAO Catalysts

Metallocene	[Al]/[Zr]	Temp. (°C)	Activity	*mmmm* (%)	M.pt. (°C)	M_W ($\times 10^{-3}$)	Reference
Me$_2$Si(3-MeCp)$_2$ZrCl$_2$	625	30	5.43[b]	92.5	147.8	13.7	[230]
Me$_2$Si(2,4-Me$_2$Cp)$_2$ZrCl$_2$	625	30	3.7[b]	97.1	160.4	86.5	[230]
Me$_2$Si(3-*t*-BuCp)$_2$ZrCl$_2$	625	30	0.10[b]	93.4	149.4	9.5	[230]
Me$_2$Si(3-*t*-BuCp)$_2$ZrCl$_2$	300	50	0.355[c]	77	128	1.98	[231]
Me$_2$Si(2-Me,4-*t*-BuCp)$_2$ZrCl$_2$	300	50	0.505[c]	94	149	9.19	[231]
Me$_2$Si(2-Me,4-*i*-PrCp)$_2$ZrCl$_2$	300	50	3[c]	73	107	4.96	[231]
Me$_2$Si(Ind)$_2$ZrCl$_2$	15,000	70	6.3[c]	81.7	137	36	[232]
Me$_2$Si(2-MeInd)$_2$ZrCl$_2$	15,000	70	3.33[d]	88.5	145	195	[232]
Me$_2$Si(Benz[e]Ind)$_2$ZrCl$_2$	15,000	70	9.2[d]	80.5	138	27	[232]
Me$_2$Si(2-MeBenz[e]Ind)$_2$ZrCl$_2$	15,000	70	13.56[d]	88.7	146	330	[232]
Me$_2$Si(4-PhInd)$_2$ZrCl$_2$	15,000	70	1.6[d]	86.5	148	42	[232]
Me$_2$Si(2-Me,4-PhInd)$_2$ZrCl$_2$	15,000	70	25.4[d]	95.2	157	729	[232]
Me$_2$Si(2-Me,4-NaphInd)$_2$ZrCl$_2^e$	15,000	70	29.5[d]	99.1	161	920	[232]

[a] kg PP/mmol Zr·atm
[b] Pressure 3 atm
[c] Pressure 2 atm
[d] Bulk polymerization
[e] Dimethylsilanediylbis[2-methyl,4-(1-naphthyl)-indenyl]zirconium dichloride

Table 2.5 Influence of the Nature of Bridge on Propylene Polymerization with *rac*-Metallocenes and MAO

Metallocene	Temp. (°C)	Activity[a]	*mmmm* (%)	M.pt. (°C)	Reference
Me$_4$C$_2$(3-*t*-BuCp)$_2$ZrCl$_2$	50	0.085[b]	62	103	[231]
Me$_2$Si(3-*t*-BuCp)$_2$ZrCl$_2$	50	0.355[b]	77	128	[231]
EBIZrCl$_2$	70	6.3[c]	78.5	132	[232]
Me$_2$Si(Ind)$_2$ZrCl$_2$	70	6.3[c]	81.7	137	[232]
(Me$_2$Si)$_2$(Ind)$_2$ZrCl$_2$	70	0.2[c]		amorphous	[243]

[a] kg PP/mmol M·h·bar
[b] 3 bar propylene
[c] Bulk polymerization

decay is considered. A short bridge between the C$_5$ rings reduces the α angle Cp-M-Cp (Fig. 2.27) and induces a higher activity; when the bridge is formed by three or four atoms, the catalyst becomes practically inactive in propylene polymerization but still polymerizes ethylene [237, 238]. MAO concentration strongly affects the activity of metallocene catalysts; the Al/Zr molar ratio required for activation, for reaching maximum activity (see section 2.5.3, Table 2.9), and in some cases for inhibition, varies for the different metallocenes [239 - 241].

Also, the molecular weight of the polymer is highly dependent on ligand structure, as the ligand substitution pattern generates different non-bonded interactions in the activation state leading to chain transfer, and such non-bonded interactions determine the type and the rate of transfer reactions. The greatest increase in molecular weight results from the presence of a methyl substituent at the C_5 ring in α-position to the bridge (Table 2.4). Higher molecular weights are obtained with hafnocenes in comparison with zirconocenes, although at the same time the catalytic activity decreases [242]. A detrimental effect of polymerization temperature on the molecular weight of PP is generally reported. One of the most important features of isotactic PP from metallocenes is the narrowness of the molecular weight distribution (Mw/Mn ≈ 2), which is the signature of a Schulz–Flory distribution for a single-center catalyst.

2.3.2.3.5 Syndiospecific Catalysts   Highly stereoregular syndiotactic polypropylene (sPP) has been obtained by Ewen [23] with $Me_2C(Cp,Fl)ZrCl_2$ (Fig. 2.32), a stereorigid metallocene with C_s molecular symmetry, in the presence of MAO.

Activity and stereoselectivity are strongly decreased by replacing the fluorenyl moiety with tetramethylcyclopentadienyl or 4,5-methylenephenanthryl groups [244]. The only important improvement of Ewen's catalyst has been that of modifying the bridge to obtain higher molecular weights by using a Ph_2C rather than Me_2C bridge [245, 246]. As observed for isospecific catalysts, when Zr is replaced by Hf, the molecular weight of the polymer increases, but stereoregularity decreases (Table 2.6).

Activity reaches a maximum value at a polymerization temperature of about 30 °C with the metallocene $Me_2C(Cp,Fl)ZrCl_2$, while it increases at least up to 60 °C by using the metallocene t-BuCH(Cp,Fl)ZrCl$_2$ [249]; the polymer produced with the latter compound has much broader molecular weight distribution (Mw/Mn ∼ 4). As already observed for isospecific catalysts, the stereospecificity is influenced by the polymerization temperature; % *rrrr* pentads of the polymer decreases from over 95% to 76% by changing the polymerization temperature from 0 °C to 70 °C.

A number of studies on the thermal behavior, crystal structure, and morphology of sPP have appeared in the literature [250 - 256]. A T_m around 220 °C and a ΔH_u around 7 kJ/mol for fully syndiotactic PP has been extrapolated [250]. If confirmed, the T_m of sPP would be notably higher than that of isotactic PP (iPP), although in practice, sPP always has a lower melting point than iPP of comparable stereoregularity and molecular weight.

Applications of sPP are still under investigation; improvement of mechanical properties has been reported for sPP/iPP blends [257].

2.3.2.3.6 Aspecific Catalysts   Highly amorphous PP can be obtained from heterogeneous catalysts, but a low molecular weight, broad molecular weight distribution product, containing some residual crystallinity, is produced. The importance of high molecular weight, truly atactic polypropylene (aPP) can be easily recognized. Atactic PP is produced by two types of metallocenes: achiral, C_{2v}-symmetric unbridged (e.g., Cp_2ZrCl_2) and by extension any alkyl-substituted metallocene lacking stereorigidity (e.g., $(MeCp)_2ZrCl_2$,

Figure 2.32 C_s-symmetric metallocene $Me_2C(Cp,Fl)ZrCl_2$

Table 2.6 Polymerization of Propylene with Syndiospecific Metallocene-MAO Catalysts

Metallocene	Temp. (°C)	Time (min.)	Activity[a]	rrrr (%)	M.pt. (°C)	M_W ($\times 10^{-3}$)	Reference
Me₂C(Cp,Fl)ZrCl₂	50	25	116	82	140	133	[247]
Me₂C(Cp,Fl)ZrCl₂	60	60	160	82	137	129	[248]
Me₂C(Cp,Fl)ZrCl₂	70	60	85.6	76	134	–	[244]
Ph₂C(Cp,Fl)ZrCl₂	50	60	29.4	97[b]	139	560	[246]
Me₂C(Cp,Fl)HfCl₂	50	30	1.4	74	–	777	[23]

[a] kg PP/mmol M
[b] Dyads

Ind₂ZrCl₂) as well as bridged, stereorigid C_{2v}-symmetric metallocenes (e.g., Me₂Si(Cp)₂ZrCl₂ or Me₂Si(Me₄Cp)₂ZrCl₂) [258, 259], and the achiral, meso isomers of *ansa*-metallocenes such as *meso*-EBIZrCl₂, *meso*-EBTHIZrCl₂, etc. [234, 260]. Most of the above-cited metallocenes produce only low molecular weight polymer.

Recently, some modified, bridged C_{2v}-symmetric metallocenes have been developed which produce high molecular weight atactic PP. One of the catalysts suitable for this purpose is Me₂Si(9-Fl)₂ZrCl₂; by changing the polymerization conditions (e.g., temperature, Al/Zr molar ratio and monomer concentration), atactic PP is obtained with average viscosimetric molecular weights in the range 10^5 to 10^6.

This material, which shows elastomeric properties (tension set 14% to 18% at 100% elongation), is completely amorphous ($T_g \approx 2\,°C$ by DSC), fully soluble in hydrocarbons and highly transparent (Haze ≈ 15 to 20%). Foreseen applications are in blends with other types of PP, to improve clarity and flexibility [261 - 264].

2.3.2.3.7 Catalysts for Elastomeric Polypropylene   Thermoplastic elastomers or elasto-plasts (TPEs) owe their elastomeric properties to physical network cross-links (formation of "hard" domains in a "soft" matrix).

Elastomeric PP (TPE-PP) has been obtained with several different heterogeneous catalysts [265 - 267] and is a material of commercial interest, as reported by DuPont [268]. According to DuPont, commercial production is to be started shortly and involves a solution process and a catalyst prepared by supporting a ZrR₄ alkyl on alumina. Potential applications are for car bumpers, medical contacts, grafting stock, and in general as EPR/iPP compatibilizer and aPP substitute.

DuPont's TPE-PP owes its properties of resilience and tensile strength to the presence of short, crystallizable isotactic blocks in high molecular weight, atactic and regioirregular chains. It can be defined as a propylene-block-homopolymer; this material is not homogeneous, as it can be separated by solvent extraction into fractions having different properties.

TPE-PP has been prepared by Chien et al. [269] with the bridged titanocene rac-MeCH(Me₄Cp,Fl)TiCl₂ activated with MAO. The polymer with T_m of 67 °C to 71 °C and narrow molecular weight distribution (1.7 to 1.9) is completely soluble in diethyl ether, and its molecular structure is described as a sequence of multiple blocks of stereoregular, crystal-lizable and stereoirregular, noncrystallizable segments, formed by 20 to 100 monomer units.

A new strategy for the production of TPE-PP has been used by Waymouth et al. [201]. The catalyst system (2-Ph-Ind)$_2$ZrCl$_2$-MAO produces TPE-PP, containing isotactic-block-atactic PP chains which differ from one another in length of the blocks and in their relative proportion. There is a continuous distribution of block lengths, which is attributed to catalyst isomerization during chain growth: the anti-syn isomerization rate must be lower than monomer insertion, but comparable to chain growth (Fig. 2.33).

2.3.2.3.8   Other Homogeneous Catalysts

Very few metallocene polymerization catalysts with transition metals other than group 4 have been reported. Watson's (Cp*$_2$LuMe)$_2$ oligomerizes propylene [270], while Bercaw's chiral metallocene, [*rac*-Me$_2$Si(2-SiMe$_3$-4-CMe$_3$-Cp)$_2$Y(μ-H)]$_2$, polymerizes propylene, butene, and higher α-olefins to highly isotactic polymers, although both activity and molecular weights are quite low [271]. Neither catalyst requires the presence of a cocatalyst. Vanadocene, niobiocenes, and tungstenocenes show very limited activities.

In addition to metallocenes, some other compounds of group 4 transition metals are able to polymerize propylene when activated by MAO. Titanium and zirconium tetrabenzyl and titanium tetraalkoxides polymerize propylene, with moderate yield, to high molecular weight, partially isotactic polymer [272]. High molecular weight, amorphous, regioirregular PP is obtained, with high yield, by using 2,2'-methylene-bis(6-*t*-butyl-4-methylphenoxy)titanium diisopropoxide or dichloride [273].

2.3.2.3.9   Supported Metallocene Catalysts

One of the most serious drawbacks that has hindered the industrial use of metallocene catalysts is the difficulty in controlling the polymer morphology. Although retrofitting of existing plants has been reported for solution processes, support of the catalyst on a carrier of narrow size distribution remains a key issue. Several scientific papers and patents report the use of SiO$_2$, Al$_2$O$_3$, MgCl$_2$, zeolites and polymers as carriers [274 - 289]. Almost invariably the catalyst activity is depressed.

In Table 2.7, the most important metallocene-based supported catalysts are reported. In most cases, the transition metal compound, MAO, and the carrier are reacted in different combinations, and AlR$_3$ is used as scavenger. Soga et al. have demonstrated that, when the metallocene is immobilized on a chemically modified silica, activation can be achieved by

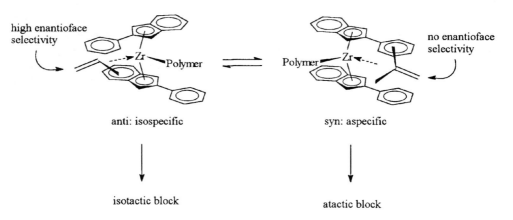

Figure 2.33 Syn and anti conformers of the propagating species from (2-Ph-Ind)$_2$ZrCl$_2$

Table 2.7 Selected Examples of Supported Metallocene Catalysts for Polypropylene

Catalyst	Cocatalyst	Polymer	Reference
SiO$_2$/MAO/Me$_2$C(Cp,Fl)ZrCl$_2$	TIBA	sPP	[274]
SiO$_2$/MAO/*rac*-Me$_2$Si(Me$_2$Cp)$_2$ZrCl$_2$	TIBA	iPP	[275]
SiO$_2$/AlMe$_3$/H$_2$O/*rac*-Me$_2$Si(4,6-*i*-Pr-2-Me-Ind)$_2$ZrCl$_2$	TIBA	iPP	[276]
SiO$_2$/EBTHIZrCl$_2$	MAO	iPP	[277]
SiO$_2$/CpTiCl$_3$	MAO	aPP	[278]
Al$_2$O$_3$/CpTiCl$_3$	MAO	aPP	[279]
Al$_2$O$_3$/AlMe$_3$/metallocene	TEA	iPP/sPP	[280]
PP/*rac*-Me$_2$Si(Ind)$_2$ZrCl$_2$/MAO	MAO	iPP	[281]
PP/*rac*-Me$_2$Si(2-Me-Ind)$_2$ZrCl$_2$/MAO	–	iPP	[282]
PP/AlMe$_3$/TIBA/H$_2$O/metallocene	–	iPP	[283]
PS/MAO/metallocene	TIBA	iPP/sPP/aPP	[284]
PP/MAO/metallocene	TIBA	iPP/sPP/aPP	[285]
MgCl$_2$/TEA/metallocene/Ph$_3$CB(PhF$_5$)$_4$	–	iPP/sPP	[286]
MgCl$_2$/ROH/CpTiCl$_3$/Et$_2$AlCl	MAO	aPP	[287]
SiO$_2$/*rac*-Me$_2$Si(Ind)$_2$HfMe$_2$/PhNMe$_2$HB(PhF$_5$)$_4$	–	iPP	[288]
SiO$_2$/EAO/Me$_2$C(Cp,Fl)ZrMe$_2$	SiO$_2$/Ph$_3$CB(C$_6$F$_5$)$_4$	sPP	[289]

EAO: ethylaluminoxane; PS: polystyrene

simple AlR$_3$ to obtain iPP without the need of any MAO [275, 278, 280]. In particular, a silica functionalized with =SiCl$_2$ groups is further reacted with a Li salt of a Cp-type ligand to give, after the subsequent reaction with the metal halide, a silica-anchored stereorigid metallocene linked through its bridge.

2.4   Mechanism of Propylene Polymerization

The remarkable advances in increasing activity and stereospecificity of heterogeneous catalysts have not been accompanied by equal progress in the knowledge of the structure of the active sites and of some steps of the polymerization reaction. However, recent advances in the knowledge of the true nature of the active centers in homogeneous metallocene-based catalysis has allowed the successful application to these sites of the same mechanism of enantioselectivity previously suggested for hypothetical sites in heterogeneous catalysis, thus explaining many experimental results. In this section, we will discuss the different steps of the growing reaction, such as the active metal-carbon bond, the regioselectivity, the nature of the active sites, the mechanism of enantioselectivity, and the role of the Lewis bases in MgCl$_2$-supported catalysts.

2.4.1   The Active Metal–Carbon Bond

Whereas different opinions are reported in the literature about the nature of the polymerization centers, it is unanimously assumed that polymerization of olefins with Ziegler–Natta
catalysts involves a stepwise insertion of the monomer into a transition metal-carbon bond as
follows:

$$Mt\text{–}R + nC{=}C \rightarrow Mt\text{–}(C\text{–}C)_n\text{–}R$$

The coordination of the monomer to the transition metal before the insertion step is generally
assumed.

The above mechanism is supported by the following experimental evidence:

1. C_6H_5 chain end groups were found in PP obtained by $TiCl_4$-$Al(C_6H_5)_3$ catalyst [290].
2. ^{13}C NMR analysis of iPP, prepared in the presence of δ-$TiCl_3$ or $MgCl_2$-supported
    catalysts [291, 292] and ^{13}C-enriched $Al(CH_3)_3$, shows the presence of isobutyl chain-
    end groups formed in the first step of the polyinsertion reaction according to the scheme:

$$Mt\text{–}^{13}CH_3 + C_3H_6 \rightarrow Mt\text{–}CH_2\text{–}CH(CH_3)\text{–}^{13}CH_3$$

The same end group was also observed in sPP and iPP prepared with the homogeneous
catalytic systems $Me_2C(Cp,Fl)$ $ZrCl_2$ and rac-$EBIZrCl_2$/MAO in the presence of ^{13}C-
enriched $Al(CH_3)_3$ [293].

3. The presence of radioactivity in the polymer obtained by quenching with ^{14}CO the
    polymerization of olefins with heterogeneous [294] and homogeneous [295] catalysts
    suggests that a transition metal–carbon bond is active in polymerization, since CO does
    not react with Al–C bonds.
4. The insertion of ethylene into a Ti–C bond has been proven for the catalytic system
    $Cp_2TiRCl/R'_{3-x}AlCl_x$ by ^{13}C NMR spectroscopy [296].
5. Many catalysts are active in olefin polymerization even in the absence of a main-group
    metal alkyl [297, 298].

Therefore, there is no doubt that polymerization occurs by insertion of the olefinic double
bond into a transition metal–carbon bond.

2.4.2   Insertion Mode and Regioselectivity

The insertion of an α-olefin in the metal-carbon bond may take place in two different ways:

$$Mt\text{–}CH_2\text{–}CH(CH_3)\text{–}P \quad (1,2 \text{ or primary insertion})$$

$$Mt\text{–}P + CH_2{=}CH\text{–}CH_3$$

$$Mt\text{–}CH(CH_3)\text{–}CH_2\text{–}P \quad (2,1 \text{ or secondary insertion})$$

It is unambiguously proved, by chain-end groups analysis, that the 1,2 insertion mode is working in isospecific polymerization of olefins, and also of styrene [299], with both heterogeneous [290 - 292] and metallocene-based [21, 300] catalysts and in syndiospecific polymerization of propylene with the homogeneous $Me_2C(Cp,Fl)$ $ZrCl_2$/MAO catalyst system [23]. On the contrary, the 2,1 insertion mode prevails in syndiospecific propylene polymerization with VCl_4/Et_2AlCl catalyst at low temperature and in syndiospecific styrene polymerization [301].

Regioregularity is extremely high in isotactic polymers obtained by heterogeneous catalysts [302]; head-to-head and tail-to-tail enchainments are sufficiently few as to be undetectable by IR and NMR spectroscopy. However, n-butyl end groups have been detected in propylene oligomers obtained with δ-$TiCl_3$-Et_2AlCl catalyst at high hydrogen concentration and in oligomers [303] and high molecular weight PP [155] prepared, in the presence of hydrogen, with the $MgCl_2$/$TiCl_4$/dialkylphthalate-$AlEt_3$-alkoxysilane catalyst system. The proportion of isotactic polymer chains terminated by chain transfer with hydrogen after a 2,1 insertion, leading to a n-Bu rather than to a i-Pr end group, according to the following scheme,

$$Ti-CH(CH_3)-CH_2-CH_2-CH(CH_3)-P + H_2 \longrightarrow Ti-H + CH_3(CH_2)_3-CH(CH_3)-P$$

$$Ti-CH_2-CH(CH_3)-CH_2-CH(CH_3)-P + H_2 \longrightarrow$$
$$Ti-H + CH_3-CH(CH_3)-CH_2-CH(CH_3)-P$$

is 12% to 28%, depending on the kind of alkoxy silane used. The Xylene soluble (XS) fractions contain also around 1% head-to-head regioirregularities in the polymer chains, about the same level found in XS fractions of PP obtained with $TiCl_3$/Et_2AlCl catalyst [302]. We can conclude, therefore, that an occasional 2,1 insertion is possible at isospecific centers in heterogeneous catalysts but this irregular placement precludes any further monomer insertion.

Isotactic PP obtained with chiral C_2-symmetric group 4 metallocenes includes a small number (about 1%) of isolated regioirregular structural units (Table 2.8) resulting from 2,1 and 1,3 insertion of the monomer as follows:

$$-CH_2-CH(CH_3)-CH(CH_3)-CH_2-CH_2-CH(CH_3)-\qquad \text{(2,1 insertion)}$$

$$-CH_2-CH(CH_3)-CH_2-CH_2-CH_2-CH_2-CH(CH_3)-\qquad \text{(1,3 insertion)}$$

revealed by the presence of $(CH_2)_2$ and $(CH_2)_4$ groups, respectively [304 - 306].

The content of the two regioirregularities and their relative proportion depends on the π-ligands, polymerization temperature, and monomer concentration [309]. In general regioirregularities are mainly of 2,1 type when the activity of the catalyst is very high [232, 306]. Zambelli et al. [305] suggest that 1,3 units are formed via isomerization of secondary Zr-alkyl units, resulting from 2,1 monomer insertion, to primary Zr-alkyl units prior to the next olefin insertion; two possible mechanisms have been proposed [236, 310]. The presence of only 2,1 regioirregularities in the polymer prepared with Me_2Si(benz-[e]-indenyl)$_2ZrCl_2$-MAO implies that a secondary Zr-alkyl unit inserts the monomer faster than it rearranges to a terminal primary Zr-alkyl unit [306]. The lower melting point of these polymers, in comparison with

Table 2.8 Regioirregularities in Polypropylene Prepared with *rac*-Metallocenes-MAO Catalysts Systems

Metallocene	Temp. (°C)	Pressure (kg/cm^2)	Misinsertions %		*mmmm* (%)	Reference
			2,1	1,3		
EBIZrCl$_2$	50	8.5	0.75	0.07	85.2	[236]
EBIZrCl$_2$	50	< 1	–	0.58	55	[236]
EBIHfCl$_2$	50	–	0.7	0.2	92.3*	[311]
EBIHfCl$_2$	−30	–	0.4	–	94.2*	[311]
EBTHIZrCl$_2$	50	2	–	1.5	49	[231]
EBTHIZrCl$_2$	−15	1.3	0.59	–	97.9	[308]
Me$_2$EBTHIZrCl$_2$	–	–	–	23.6	–	[307]
Me$_2$Si(4-*t*BuCp)$_2$ZrCl$_2$	50	2	–	1.5	77	[231]
Me$_2$Si(2-Me,4-*t*BuCp)$_2$ZrCl$_2$	50	2	–	0.4	94	[231]
Me$_2$Si(Ind)$_2$ZrCl$_2$	50	2	0.4	–	89	[306]
Me$_2$Si(2-MeInd)$_2$ZrCl$_2$	50	2	0.2	–	90	[306]
Me$_2$Si(Benz[e]Ind)$_2$ZrCl$_2$	50	2	0.8	–	88	[306]
Me$_2$Si(2-MeBenz[e]Ind)$_2$ZrCl$_2$	50	2	0.4	–	92	[306]

* Meso triads

Me$_2$EBTHIZrCl$_2$: Ethylen-bis(4,7-dimethyl-tegrahydroindenyl)zirconium-dichloride; 2,1 and 1,3 correspond to % of regiorregular 2,1 and respectively 1,3 inserted units

those of polymers prepared with heterogeneous catalysts having the same meso pentads content, has been attributed to the presence of the above regiodefects in the polymer chains [311].

A high content (4% to 5%) of head to head, tail to tail regioirregularities was found in sPP obtained by low temperature polymerization with VCl$_4$-Et$_2$AlCl catalyst [312]. A still higher content of regiodefects (> 30%) is present in aPP obtained with the homogeneous 2,2'-thiobis(6-*tert*-butyl-4-methylphenoxy)titanium dichloride-MAO catalyst system [273].

2.4.3.   Stereochemistry of the Insertion Reaction

The knowledge of the way the metal atom of the active site, bearing the growing chain, and the last carbon atom of the chain add synchronously to the double bond of the incoming monomer is essential to investigate the mechanism of stereospecific polymerization. In all the cases investigated, isospecific polymerization with heterogeneous [313] and homogeneous catalysts [21] and syndiospecific polymerization with VCl$_4$-based catalysts [314], the stereochemistry of the insertion has been shown to be of the cis type. In fact, the isospecific polymerization of *cis*-1-deutero propylene gives an *erythro*-diisotactic polymer, whereas a *threo*-diisotactic polymer is obtained from *trans*-1-deutero propylene (Fig. 2.34).

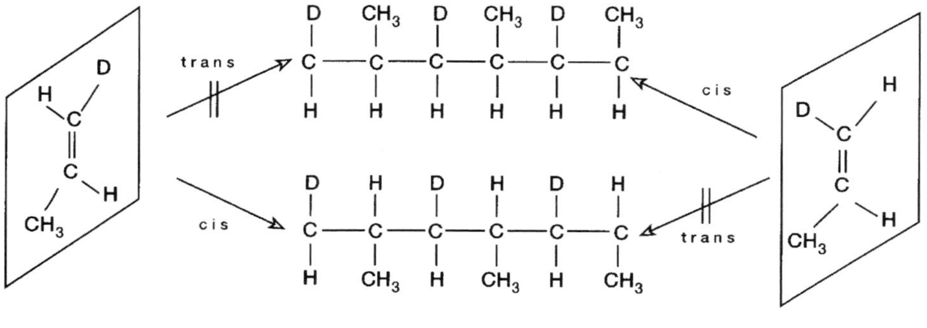

Figure 2.34 Stereochemistry of metal-carbon addition to the olefinic double bond

2.4.4   Steric Control of Monomeric Unit Insertion

Considering that α-olefins are prochiral, that is, they have two different sides (the two R,S enantiofaces are shown in Fig. 2.35), the absolute configuration of the tertiary carbon atoms of the main chain (R) or (S) is dictated by the enantioface undergoing the insertion, the insertion mode, and the stereochemistry (*cis* or *trans*) of the insertion [315]. If regioselectivity is high and insertion occurs only with cis stereochemistry, multiple insertions of the same enantioface produce a polymer chain with chiral centers of the same configuration (i.e., an isotactic polymer); multiple insertions of alternating enantiofaces produce a polymer chain with chiral centers of alternating configuration (i.e., a syndiotactic polymer); and random enantioface insertion produces a polymer chain with no configurational regularity (i.e., an atactic polymer).

To discriminate between the two prochiral faces of the olefin, the catalytic system must possess at least one chirality center. A chiral carbon atom is present in the growing chain in beta or alpha position with respect to the metal atom, depending on the 1,2 or respectively 2,1 insertion mode. The mechanism of stereoselection determined by chiral induction by the last unit is referred to as *chain end control*. A second possible element of chirality is the asymmetry of the initiating site; in this case, the stereoselection mechanism is referred to as *enantiomorphic site control* (Fig. 2.36). Steric errors during the chain growth lead to different chain microstructures which are therefore diagnostic of the stereoselection mechanism (Fig. 2.37).

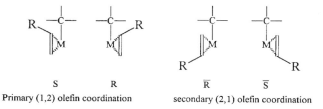

S   R   R̄   S̄
Primary (1,2) olefin coordination   secondary (2,1) olefin coordination

Figure 2.35 The different enantiofaces of the olefin and their possible coordination mode to the active center

Site control:
chiral induction from a
chiral coordination site

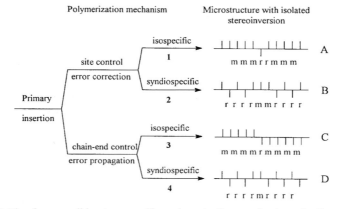

Chain end control:
chiral induction from the last
formed stereogenic carbon   Figure 2.36 The two possible sources of enantioface selectivity

Figure 2.37 The four possible stereospecific polymerization mechanisms leading to ordered polymer structures. A chain segment with the diagnostic isolated insertion mistake is shown in its modified Fisher projection for each case

The following experimental data are consistent with an enantiomorphic site control of the reaction in the isospecific polymerization of α-olefins.

- Stereoirregularities in isotactic polymers consist of pairs of syndiotactic racemic (*r*) dyads connecting stereosequences of isotactic meso (*m*) dyads of the type *mmmrrmmm*, corresponding to the idealized structure A of Fig. 2.37; that is, the formation of a configurational error does not affect the configuration of the following monomer unit [302, 316]. In the case of a stereochemical control by the configuration of the last asymmetric carbon atom of the growing chain, a steric error would be continuously repeated, giving rise to stereosequences of the type *mmmrmmm* corresponding to the idealized structure C of Fig. 2.37.
- The retention of the configuration in the growing chain is preserved after the insertion of an ethylene unit [317] and after an occasional 1,3 insertion [304, 318].
- Isospecific catalytic sites show stereoselectivity in racemic α-olefins polymerization [319] and also in their copolymerization with ethylene [320].
- Highly isotactic PP is obtained with the stereorigid chiral *rac*-Et(1-indenyl)₂titanium and zirconium dichlorides in the presence of MAO [21, 22], whereas atactic polymer results when using the corresponding achiral meso derivatives [21, 321].

- A straightforward evidence against chain-end stereochemical control in isospecific polymerization is given by end-groups ^{13}C NMR analysis of isotactic polybutene obtained with TiCl$_3$ and AlEt$_3$ enriched with ^{13}C at the methylene carbons. The end groups resulting from insertion of two monomer units into a Ti-[13]CH$_2$-CH$_3$ bond are stereoregular, despite the absence of asymmetry in the original ethyl group and in the alkyl group resulting after the first monomer insertion [291, 322].

Stereochemical control by the organometallic moiety of the catalyst has been also proved in syndiospecific polymerization of propylene with the Me$_2$C(Cp,Fl)ZrCl$_2$-MAO catalyst system on the basis of the stereochemical sequence of the configurations of the monomer units, consisting of blocks of syndiotactic dyads connected by pairs of isotactic dyads of the type *rrrmmrrr*, corresponding to structure B of Fig. 2.37 [23]. The stereoirregularities observed in the scarcely stereoregular iPP obtained, at low temperature, with MAO and Cp$_2$TiCl$_2$, a metallocene having C$_{2v}$ symmetry, are in accord with the structure C of Fig. 2.37 and therefore diagnostic of a chain-end stereochemical control [300]. Both chain-end and enantiomorphic site control are believed to be operating in propylene polymerization with non-bridged metallocene *rac-(η^5C$_5$H$_4$CHMePh)$_2$ZrCl$_2$-MAO* [323]. The stereochemical sequence of the configurations of the monomer units of the type *rrrmrrr*, present in scarcely stereoregular sPP obtained, at low temperature, with homogeneous vanadium catalyst [324, 325], is in accord with a chain-end stereochemical control.

2.4.5   Catalytic Site Models

2.4.5.1   TiCl$_3$ Catalysts

A great number of models for catalytic centers have been proposed to interpret the isospecific polymerization of olefins with TiCl$_3$-based catalysts [315, 326]. Natta [327], for the first time, proposed that the steric control is due to the structure of the active site located on the borders of crystal layers of TiCl$_3$. Electron microscopy observations [328] of the polymer growth on well-formed α-TiCl$_3$ crystals led to the conclusion that the active sites are not present on basal (001) surfaces. Arlman and Cossee [329] proposed that the active centers are located on lateral crystal surfaces which, in α-TiCl$_3$, corresponds to (110) planes.

Titanium atoms present on the above defined fracture surface have a vacant octahedral site and are bonded to five chlorine atoms (Fig. 2.38). One chloride ligand protrudes from the surface, the other four are bridged to further Ti atoms and are more strongly bound; neighboring Ti atoms have opposite chirality [330, 331].

By reaction with the cocatalyst, the single-bonded Cl atom should be easily substituted by an alkyl group, giving the active Ti-C bond. The so-called monometallic Cossee mechanism consists of two main steps: coordination of the monomer at the vacant octahedral coordination site with the double bond parallel to the Ti-C bond, and chain migratory insertion of the coordinated monomer with migration of the growing chain to the position previously occupied by the coordinated monomer; the transition state is assumed to be a four-membered ring of Ti, the last carbon atom of the growing chain and the two carbon atoms forming the double bond of the monomer. Stereoselectivity is assumed only if, before a further insertion, the chain skips back to the position occupied before the insertion (Fig. 2.39).

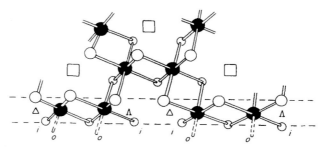

Figure 2.38 Schematic drawing of a lateral cut of a $TiCl_3$ layer. The chirality of two titanium atoms is indicated. Reproduced with permission from Ref. [331], Pergamon Press

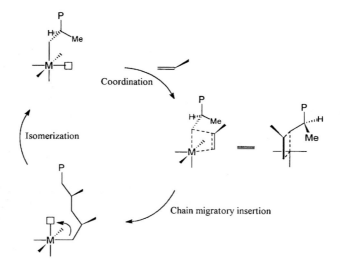

Figure 2.39 The Cossee polymerization mechanism

The surface model proposed by Allegra [332] obviates the necessity of the back skip step to assure the stereoselectivity because a C_2 symmetry axis locally relates the atoms relevant to the non-bonded interactions with the monomer and the growing chain. Therefore, the two situations resulting by exchanging, in the coordination step, the relative positions of the growing chain and of the incoming monomer are identical (Fig. 2.40). It is interesting to observe that similar symmetry properties are also present in isospecific racemic metallocene cations.

Corradini et al. [331], on the basis of some evaluations of the non-bonded interactions for the Cossee and Allegra models, suggest that the chiral environment of the metal atom imposes a chiral orientation of the first C—C bond of the chain, and this orientation has been identified as a crucial factor in determining the stereospecificity. As a matter of fact, the non-bonded interactions between the methyl group of the propylene molecule and the C-atom of the growing chain in β-position to the metal induce a preferential coordination of the

2. stereocontrol by dialkylaluminumalkoxides resulting from the reaction of AlR_3 with the ester group of the base [348], and
3. lowering, through coordination or reaction with the D_e, the concentration of free AlR_3 [349].

Accordingly, we will consider the following mechanisms based only on the coordinating power of the Lewis bases.

A. Selective Sites Poisoning and/or Modification

This mechanism [350] assumes the existence of many equilibria between the Lewis base (LB), the Al-alkyl, and the different active centers, present on the surface of $MgCl_2$, that differ in Lewis acid strength, steric hindrance, number of vacancies in the octahedral coordination shell of Ti, activity, and stereospecificity.

$$LB + AlR_3 \Longleftrightarrow AlR_3 \bullet LB$$

$$C_S + AlR_3 \bullet LB \Longleftrightarrow C_S \bullet LB + AlR_3$$

$$C_A + AlR_3 \bullet LB \Longleftrightarrow C_A \bullet LB + AlR_3$$

$$C_{TV} + AlR_3 \bullet LB \Longleftrightarrow C_{TV} \bullet LB + AlR_3$$

$$C_{TV} \bullet LB + AlR_3 \bullet LB \Longleftrightarrow C_{TV} \bullet 2LB + AlR_3$$

where C_S = stereospecific center, C_A = aspecific center, C_{TV} = aspecific center with two coordination vacancies, $C_{TV} \cdot LB$ = stereospecific center, and $C_S \cdot LB$, $C_A \cdot LB$, and $C_{TV} \cdot 2LB$ are deactivated centers.

A number of experiments [106, 120, 140] have shown the existence of equilibria between the LB present on the surface of the catalyst and LB complexed in solution with Al-alkyl (see section 2.3). The aspecific sites (C_A) would be deactivated preferentially with respect to the isospecific ones, owing to their stronger Lewis acidity. The enhanced productivity of stereoregular polymer, observed when the polymerization is carried out in the presence of LB [140, 151], has been explained by assuming that aspecific sites having two coordination vacancies (C_{TV}) are converted to single vacancy isospecific sites ($C_{TV} \cdot LB$) by complexation of one LB molecule. According to this hypothesis, a model of an isospecific active site, proposed by Soga [142], assumes the coordination of one of the carbonyl groups of a chelating LB (dialkylphthalate) both to a tetracoordinated titanium atom and to a penta-coordinated Mg atom of the support giving a highly isospecific site (Fig. 2.44).

In the model suggested by Guyot et al. [351], the active Ti is bound through chlorine bridges to the support $MgCl_2$, and it is alkyl bridged with Al-alkyl; the two alkoxy groups of the Lewis base $R_2Si(OMe)_2$ are complexed, one with the Al atom of the alkyl bridged Al-alkyl and the second with the Ti atom of the active site. One of the bulky R alkyl groups bound to Si covers one of the two vacancies of the Ti octahedron, and such tight geometry imposes the choice of the proper enantioface of the monomer.

Unfortunately, complexes of the LB with the transition metal have never been unambiguously recognized on the catalyst surface; IR [92] and NMR [95, 106] investigations

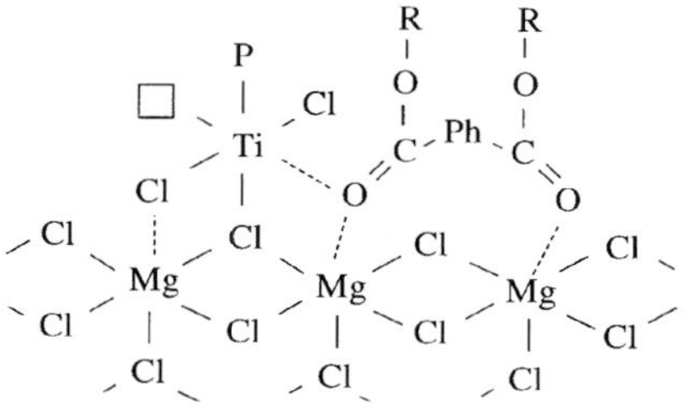

Figure 2.44 Proposed structure of isospecific active sites present in $MgCl_2$-supported catalysts. Reproduced with permission from Ref. [142], Hüthig & Wepf Verlag

have generally shown that the LB is complexed with $MgCl_2$; however, the concentration of the above complexes could be too low to be detected. Only in a few cases, an interaction between Ti and the LB has been suggested [105, 116], but one must be cautious to interpret these data because complexes between $TiCl_4$ and the LB are surely formed in solution during the synthesis of the catalyst, and their detection on the catalyst surface could be due to an inadequate washing of the catalyst [80]. On the other hand, if the electrophilicity of the transition metal is important for monomer coordination [352], it would be remarkably decreased by coordination with strong LBs.

B. Selective Coordination of Lewis Base and TiCl₄ on MgCl₂ Surface

The mechanism proposed by Corradini et al. [110] does not require the selective poisoning of aspecific centers, but it is based on the ability of the LB to compete with $TiCl_4$ for selective coordination on the different lateral faces of $MgCl_2$ crystals. On the basis of this simplified model, in catalysts prepared in the presence of LB, binuclear Ti_2Cl_6 stereospecific species should be located on the (100) faces, whereas the LB should preferentially saturate the vacancies of tetracoordinated Mg ions present on the (110) faces of $MgCl_2$ crystals, thus avoiding the formation on these planes of catalytic sites that, according to the previous studies [345], would be nonstereospecific (Fig. 2.14).

Some theoretical calculations appear to be in accord with this model. Barino et al. [353] have carried out a molecular mechanics study of the interaction between LBs and the two $MgCl_2$ crystal lateral surfaces. Taking into consideration as electron donors 1,3-dimethoxypropane derivatives, having different substituents on the central carbon atom, it has been found that those compounds which show a high stereochemical control in polymerization present a stronger attractive interaction with (110) than with (100) crystal faces; the opposite was observed for nonstereoregulating diethers.

Some structural features of chelating LB (dialkoxy silanes, dialkyl phthalates and 1,3 diethers) have been correlated with their stereoregulating power: oxygen–oxygen distance (about 3 Å) and methoxy conformation (i.e., methyl position aside from coordination directions between oxygen atoms and $MgCl_2$ surface) [106, 134, 354]. A distance of around 3 Å between the coordinating atoms seems to be especially suitable to form chelating complexes with tetracoordinated Mg ions present on (110) faces of $MgCl_2$ crystallites [106, 140], and these complexes should be particularly stable when the LB, as in alkoxy silanes and in 1,3 diethers, does not contain groups reactive toward Al-alkyls. The model suggested by Corradini appears, however, to be oversimplified because it seems inadequate to justify the following experimental data:

1. The enhanced productivity of stereoregular polymer in the presence of LBs [140, 151], and
2. the influence of the nature of the LB on MW and MWD of the resulting polymers and on the stereochemistry of the first insertion step [128, 292].

To justify the above experimental findings, the following hypotheses have been suggested which do not involve a direct coordination of the LB to the transition metal of the active center:

1. When the LB is coordinated to Mg ions located on the (100) face, it could be able to shift the equilibrium between monomeric (aspecific) and dimeric (isospecific) titanium species on (100) faces toward the dimeric ones [110].
2. The LB coordinated to Mg ions adjacent to titanium aspecific sites could sterically establish the right environment for isospecific polymerization.

A number of models related to sites of this type have been formulated by Barino et al. [353]. The presence on the surface of the catalyst of ethyl benzoate coordinated to Mg ions adjacent to titanium species has been suggested also by Rytter et al. [91] to explain the results of IR analysis. The coordination of the LB to Mg ions adjacent to Ti could also affect, by electronic or steric effects, the kinetic behavior of the active site, thus justifying the influence of the nature of the LB on the molecular properties of the polymer [80].

2.4.5.3   Homogeneous Catalysts

The presence in metallocenes-based catalysts of only one or a few types of active sites and the possibility to study these systems with NMR and X-ray techniques has allowed the formation of sound conclusions about the structure of the active sites and the enantioselectivity mechanism. The synthesis and structural characterization [217, 227, 228, 355-358] of complexes of the type $[L_2MR]^+[X]^-$ ($L = \eta^5$ ligand, X^- = non-coordinating anion), highly active in olefin polymerization, has led to the conclusion that the true catalyst site is a pseudotetrahedral metal cation bearing the η^5 ligands, the growing polymer chain as a σ ligand, and a coordination vacancy which allows the coordination of the incoming monomer.

The formation of cationic species also in metallocene-MAO catalyst systems was evidenced by Marks et al. [226] on the basis of solid state CPMAS ^{13}C NMR study of the reaction between $Cp^*_2Zr(^{13}CH_3)_2$ and MAO (see Section 2.3.2.3, Fig. 2.29).

As far as the insertion mechanism is concerned, a chain migratory mechanism is operating, but in this case the growing chain does not go back to its former position strictly following pathway B in Fig. 2.45 (chain back-skip at every insertion) as suggested for isospecific sites on the TiCl$_3$ surface. For metallocenes, pathway A is the rule, while B is an occasionally skipped insertion, or it can be the preferred pathway only for some highly asymmetric ligands, for example, in the aspecific meso-EBIZrCl$_2$ and in the isospecific Me$_2$Si(3-t-Bu-Cp,Fl)ZrCl$_2$ [356].

2.4.5.3.1   Metallocene Symmetry and Polymer Stereochemistry

The relationship between metallocene site symmetry and polymer stereochemistry is fully understood. We can visualize the general mechanism for enantioface selectivity in the chain migratory insertion with site switching operating with metallocene catalysts (enantiomorphic site control) using the key-in-the-lock formalism: every active metal atom has two available coordination sites (the two

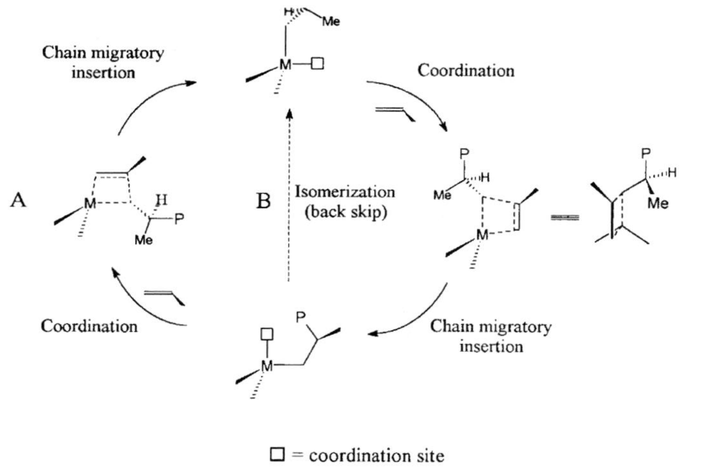

Chain migratory
insertion

Coordination

A

B   Isomerization
(back skip)

Coordination

Chain migratory
insertion

☐ = coordination site

Figure 2.45 The chain migratory with site switching mechanism operating with metallocene catalysts

locks), which can both insert the olefin, and that can be different in both shape and chirality. Because of site switching, the monomer (the key) has to be inserted alternatively on each site. As a consequence, iso, syndio, and hemiisotactic polymers are obtained (Figs. 2.46 and 2.47).

2.4.5.3.2   Aspecific Catalysts   In catalysts obtained from metallocenes with C_{2v} molecular symmetry such as Cp_2MX_2 (Fig. 2.48) and from achiral, meso isomers of ansa metallocenes such as *meso*-Et(Ind)$_2$MX$_2$, the positions of the coordinated olefin and of the alkyl ligand are not chirotopic and, therefore, the catalyst control is completely lacking. Stereospecific non-bonded interactions can only occur between the incoming monomer and the substituted carbon atom of the last unit of the growing chain end [23].

2.4.5.3.3   Isospecific Catalysts   In catalytic centers obtained from stereorigid racemic metallocenes with C_2 molecular symmetry such as *rac*-Et(Ind)$_2$MCl$_2$, the two coordination positions available for the incoming monomer and the growing chain are homotopic and, therefore, the configuration of the central metal atom does not change after the shift of the

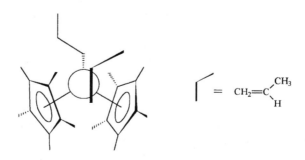

Figure 2.46 The key in the lock in the site switching mechanism

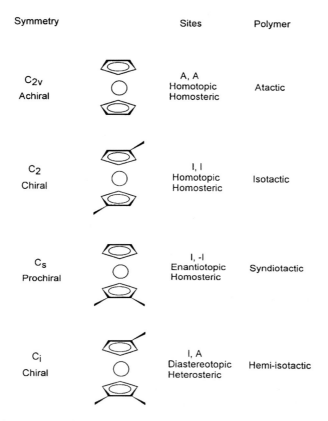

Symmetry		Sites	Polymer

C_{2v}
Achiral

A, A
Homotopic
Homosteric

Atactic

C_2
Chiral

I, I
Homotopic
Homosteric

Isotactic

C_s
Prochiral

I, -I
Enantiotopic
Homosteric

Syndiotactic

C_i
Chiral

I, A
Diastereotopic
Heterosteric

Hemi-isotactic

Figure 2.47 Steric control as a function of metallocene symmetry

growing chain to the position previously occupied by the coordinated monomer. As a consequence, if the constant approach of the same enantioface of the olefin is favored, the resulting polymer is isotactic (Fig. 2.49).

According to Corradini et al. [330], who have carried out a conformational analysis based on non-bonded interactions, the mechanism of enantioselectivity is similar to that proposed for heterogeneous catalytic models (i.e., the chiral environment of the metal atom forces the growing chain to always choose the same chiral orientation, corresponding to the placement of the αC-βC bond in the less encumbered sector of the metallocene π-ligand framework). Stereospecific non-bonded interactions occur between the β-carbon of the growing chain and the methyl group of the monomer.

A similar conclusion was reached by Morokuma et al. [359] on the basis of *ab-initio* Hartree–Fock calculations on the transition state model. These authors state also that the direct steric effect of the Cp substituents on the stereochemistry of olefin insertion is very small and not enough to control the stereochemistry.

The proposed model is in accordance with the relationship found by Pino [360] between the absolute configuration of the Zr cation and that of saturated propylene trimers obtained by

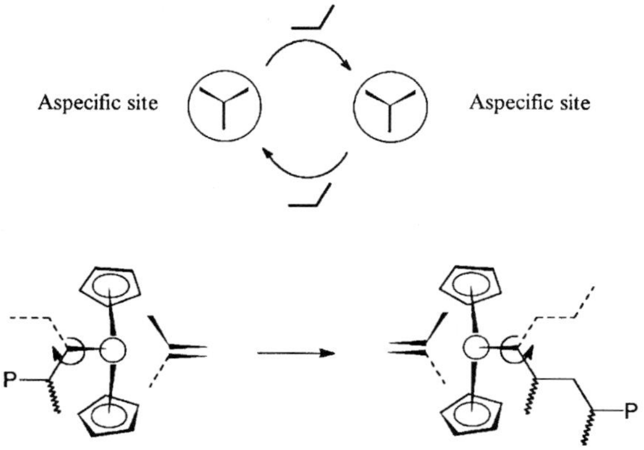

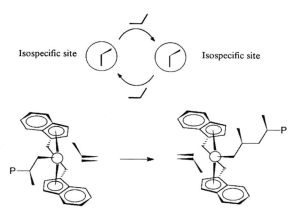

Figure 2.48 Propylene polymerization with metallocene aspecific catalyst

Figure 2.49 Propylene polymerization with C_2-symmetric metallocene isospecifc catalyst

hydrooligomerization. It also explains the dependence of the stereochemistry of the first insertion step from the nature of the alkyl group linked to the metal [361].

The influence on chain orientation of α-agostic interactions between the transition metal of the active site and the αC-H bond of the growing chain has been stressed by Brintzinger [362].

The temperature dependence of the stereospecificity of ethylene-bridged indenyl metallocenes has been attributed to the temperature influence on the equilibrium between λ (indenyl-backward) and δ (indenyl-forward) chelate ring conformers [363, 364], which may have different stereoregulating ability in propylene polymerization [310, 365]. In fact, the effect of temperature on polymer stereoregularity is much less pronounced when the rigidity of the ligand framework is enhanced by using mono-atom bridges and by introducing methyl groups in 2,2′ positions [232].

The strong decrease of the stereoregularity of PP, obtained from the chiral isospecific *rac*-EBIZrCl$_2$ and *rac*-EBTHIZrCl$_2$, at monomer concentration lower than 1 mol/L [236, 309] has been explained by assuming a slow rate of epimerization of the last inserted unit competing with chain propagation [235].

Isotactic PP also has been obtained with metallocenes which lack the C_2 symmetry, such as Me_2C- (or Me_2Si)-(3-t-butyl-cyclopentadienyl, fluorenyl)$ZrCl_2$ [366]. In this case, the diastereotopicity of the coordination positions excludes the formation of isotactic polymer via a chain migratory insertion mechanism. According to Razawi et al. [367], the bulky tertiary butyl group, residing on one of the cyclopentadienyls distal positions, interacts strongly with the growing polymer chain and hinders its migration to the coordination position underneath the β-substituent, which is available only for propylene coordination. The formation of isotactic polymer can be explained only by assuming the back-skip of the growing chain to the initial, less-hindered position after every monomer insertion (pathway B in Fig. 2.45).

2.4.5.3.4 Syndiospecific Catalysts   In catalytic centers resulting from stereorigid $Me_2C(Cp,Fl)ZrCl_2$, with C_s symmetry, a local symmetry plane relates the two enantiotopic coordination positions available for the growing chain and the monomer [23]. If a *cis*-chain migratory insertion is operating, the configuration of the complex cation is inverted at each insertion step and, therefore, if enantioselectivity exists, the approach of the incoming monomer to the reactive metal-carbon bond will occur, presenting alternatively the two enantiofaces (Fig. 2.50).

The loss of stereospecificity observed when the polymerization is performed in polar solvents [368] seems to be caused by the inversion of the configuration of the solvent-separated zirconocene cation via migration of the growing polymer chain to the initial position before a new monomer molecule insertion (pathway B in Fig. 2.45). A tight contact between the zirconium complex cation and the counter ion in apolar solvents should prevent the above migration. The isomerization, in the absence of coordinated monomer, of the pseudo-tricoordinated zirconocene cation has been suggested to explain the loss of stereospecificity observed at low monomer concentration [369].

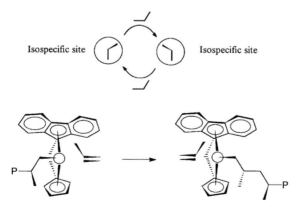

Figure 2.50 Propylene polymerization with C_s-symmetric metallocene syndiospecific catalyst

2.5   Polymerization Kinetics

Kinetic investigations of propylene polymerization with heterogeneous Ziegler–Natta catalysts are very useful in the industrial development of the reaction but have given a limited contribution to the understanding of the mechanism of polymerization. The heterogeneous nature of the catalyst, the presence on its surface of different types of active centers [71, 370 - 373], the activity decay during the polymerization, the chemical modification of the components of the catalyst during the time, and the influence of the procedure of contact of catalyst components on the rate and stereospecificity of the polymerization make it difficult to study the kinetics of polymerization with these catalysts.

For detailed discussions on polymerization kinetics, the reader is referred to many reviews published [38, 68, 73, 374 - 377]. This section will deal with the proposed kinetic models and the process variables which affect the polymerization kinetics: catalyst, cocatalyst, monomer and hydrogen concentration, temperature, time, and polymerization medium.

2.5.1   Kinetic Models

Many authors have used adsorption isotherm theories to describe the kinetics of polymerization with heterogeneous catalysts. Tait et al. [378] consider a competitive reversible adsorption reaction of monomers and Al-alkyls with the active sites; this adsorption is regarded as a complexation reaction and is described by Langmuir-Hinshelwood isotherms. Overall rate of polymerization (R_p) is given as:

$$R_p = K_p C^* K_M[M]/(1 + K_M[M] + K_A[A]) \tag{2.2}$$

where K_p represents the propagation rate constant, C^* is the concentration of active sites, [M] and [A] are the bulk liquid equilibrium concentrations of monomer and Al-alkyl, K_M and K_A are the equilibrium adsorption constants for the respective adsorption equilibria.

The kinetic model proposed by Böhm [379], which also includes the Cossee model, describes the catalytic process by the Rideal mechanism, and the complexation of the active transition metal center by the monomer represents the most important step. R_p can be given as

$$R_p = \frac{K_a K_p[M]}{K_p + K_d} \times \frac{C^*}{1 + (b/a) + (c/a)} \tag{2.3}$$

with the rate constants K_a and K_d for the formation and dissociation of the active center–monomer complex, the rate constant K_p for the insertion of the complexed monomer into the transition metal–carbon bond, and the term $1/1 + (b/a) + (c/a)$ for the influence of Al-alkyl adsorption and monomer coordination on active centers.

Zakharov et al. [339] describe the overall rate of polymerization by the equation:

$$R_p = K_p C_p[M] \tag{2.4}$$

where C_p is the number of propagating active centers correlated to the total number of active centers (C_o) by the expression

$$C_o = C_p + C_A \qquad (2.5)$$

where C_A is the number of centers complexed by Al-alkyl and temporarily inactive.

2.5.2   Catalyst Concentration

When heterogeneous catalysts are used, the polymerization rate is directly proportional to catalyst concentration [68, 380, 381]. Also, with the homogeneous catalyst systems $Me_2C(Cp,Fl)ZrCl_2/MAO$ and $Me_2Si(Ind)_2ZrCl_2/MAO$, a linear dependence of the polymerization rate on Zr concentration was noticed in the range 1 to 7×10^{-5} mol/L [241], while in some cases specific activities are observed to increase at low metallocene concentration [382].

2.5.3   Cocatalyst Concentration

The polymerization rate is not influenced by cocatalyst concentration with $TiCl_3$ catalysts [8, 383] unless extremely high (> 0.3 mol/L) aluminum trialkyl concentration is used [384]; in this case, the reversible effect of Al-alkyl concentration on polymerization rate has been explained by assuming a temporary deactivation of propagating centers by reversible adsorption of AlR_3. The corresponding species C_A have been correlated with AlR_3 concentration by the following equation:

$$C_A = \frac{C_O K_A K_D^{1/2}[Al_2Et_6]^{1/2}}{1 + (K_A K_D^{1/2}[Al_2Et_6]^{1/2})} \qquad (2.6)$$

where C_o is the total number of active centers, K_A is the equilibrium constant of $AlEt_3$ adsorption on active centers, and K_D is the equilibrium constant for Al_2Et_6 dissociation.

AlR_3 concentration has been reported, by many authors, to influence both maximum polymerization rate and decay rate in the case of $MgCl_2$-supported catalysts. This effect has been observed for $MgCl_2/TiCl_4$-$AlEt_3$ [68], $MgCl_2/TiCl_4$-$Al(i$-$Bu)_3$ [385], and $MgCl_2/TiCl_4/EB$-$AlEt_3$ [68, 157] catalyst systems. Reaction rate increases progressively with AlR_3 concentration, but, beyond a specific limit, a marked increase of the decay rate is observed. The increase of the reaction rate with Al-alkyl concentration has been explained [157, 386] by the need to have a minimum of Al-alkyl in solution to stabilize the active sites or to avoid contamination by poisons accidentally present in the system; the second hypothesis is supported by the fact that, in continuous industrial processes, a high polymerization rate is reached even at very low Al-alkyl concentrations (>0.5 mmol/L).

No influence of $AlEt_3$ concentration, in the range 0.2 to 2.5 mmol/L, on the polymerization rate was found in propylene polymerization with the catalyst system $MgCl_2/TiCl_4/2,2$-diisopropyl-1,3-dimethoxypropane-$AlEt_3$ [140].

A remarkable effect of Al/Mt ratio on reaction rate was evidenced in propylene polymerization with metallocenes-MAO catalysts. The plot of polymerization activity

Table 2.9 [Al]/[Zr] Molar Ratio Corresponding to Maximum Activity in Propylene Polymerization with Zirconocenes-MAO Catalyst Systems

Metallocene	Temp. (°C)	[Al]/[Zr]	Reference
rac-Me$_2$Si(Ind)$_2$ZrCl$_2$	25	10,900	[241]
Me$_2$C[Cp,Fl]ZrCl$_2$	25	1,300	[241]
rac-EBTHIZrCl$_2$	30	3,500	[239]
rac-EBIZrCl$_2$	30	$> 10^5$	[239]
Me$_2$C(3-MeCp,Fl)ZrCl$_2$	25	400	[240]

versus log [Al]/[Zr] has a bell shape; the maximum is reached at different [Al]/[Zr] ratios for the various metallocenes (Table 2.9) and does not change by changing monomer concentration [241]. It has been suggested that the high MAO concentration is required to increase the generation of cationic metallocene active sites and to prevent the formation of inactive metallocene dimers [382].

2.5.4   Monomer Concentration

A number of studies have proven the first-order dependence of polymerization rate on propylene concentration, over a broad concentration range, by using TiCl$_3$ and MgCl$_2$-supported heterogeneous catalysts [8, 71, 157, 387, 388]. Only at low monomer concentration, in some cases, a deviation from first order was found [387].

Reaction rate orders higher than one have been reported for olefin polymerizations catalyzed by metallocenes [213, 240, 241]; however, in some cases a first-order dependence from monomer concentration of the initial polymerization rate, before catalyst deactivation, was found [389]. The higher specific productivity, observed at high monomer concentration, could be explained, according to Brintzinger [306], by local temperature enhancements occurring when the system becomes heterogeneous upon precipitation of the polymer, rather than by a higher order dependence of R_p on monomer concentration.

2.5.5   Hydrogen Concentration

The dependence of catalyst productivity on the concentration of hydrogen, the most used molecular weight modifier in industrial practice, varies with the nature of the catalyst and of the monomer. The activity of TiCl$_3$ [390], MgCl$_2$-supported [80], and metallocene [391] catalysts in ethylene polymerization decreases considerably in the presence of hydrogen. The activity in propylene polymerization of catalysts based on α-TiCl$_3$ and Al-alkyls is reported to be lowered by hydrogen [392], whereas, on the contrary, the activity of Solvay TiCl$_3$ increases up to 50% at high hydrogen level [393].

A remarkable activating effect of hydrogen was observed in propylene polymerization with MgCl$_2$/TiCl$_4$-AlEt$_3$ [394], MgCl$_2$/TiCl$_4$/dialkyl phthalates-AlR$_3$/alkoxysilanes [155, 395, 396], MgCl$_2$/TiCl$_4$/1,3-diethers-AlR$_3$ [140], and EBIZrCl$_2$-MAO [397] catalyst systems. Catalyst productivity, compared with polymerization in the absence of hydrogen, increases up to three times and then remains constant or slightly decreases by further increasing hydrogen partial pressure. The hydrogen level needed to reach maximum productivity is dependent on the nature of the catalyst. Productivity enhancement is mainly due to the increase of initial polymerization rate; catalyst decay with time is either not affected or slightly retarded by the presence of hydrogen [394].

On the other hand, there is a strong enhancement of the decay rate of $MgCl_2$-supported catalyst systems containing esters of aromatic acids as external donor when hydrogen is present (Fig. 2.51). A reaction between Ti-H bonds and the carbonyl group of the ester has been suggested [80] as a possible cause.

The reversibility of the activating effect of hydrogen has been proven [395, 398, 399]. The mechanism involved in the activation process by hydrogen is still not completely clear. One of the most plausible explanations for such an effect is that propylene insertion is prevented or retarded after a regioirregular 2,1 insertion of the monomer in the growing chain, and chain transfer with hydrogen should reactivate these "dormant" centers. The presence of n-butyl chain end groups in polymers prepared in the presence of hydrogen strongly supports the above hypothesis [155, 303, 397]. A second hypothesis is based on the reactivation of Ti^{2+} sites, believed to be inactive in propylene polymerization, by hydrogen oxidative addition [400]; this explanation is supported by the fact that the concentration of active sites is significantly increased in the presence of hydrogen [401, 402]. A further activation mechanism is based on the reaction of hydrogen with "dormant" Ti-π-allyl centers, leading to active Ti-propyl sites [398]. The inactivation of the cation $[Cp_2^*MR]^+$ (M = Zr, Hf) during propylene polymerization by allylic C-H activation of the methyl group of the monomer was suggested by Teuben et al. [403]. The above mechanisms are not conflicting, and likely more than one activation process is operating.

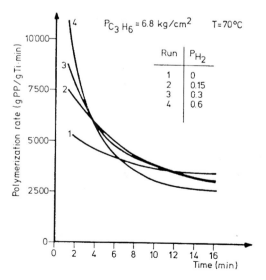

Figure 2.51 Propylene polymerization with the $MgCl_2/TiCl_4$/EB-AlEt$_3$/MPT catalyst, in the presence of hydrogen. Reproduced with permission from Ref. [80], Hüthig & Wepf Verlag

2.5.6   Temperature

A different dependence of polymerization rate on temperature was noticed for the various catalytic systems. For δ-TiCl$_3$-Et$_2$AlCl or AlEt$_3$ catalysts, the reaction rate increases in the temperature range 30 °C to 70 °C [8], and the active sites are stable in this range because, in experiments where the temperature was changed several times during the same run, the activities corresponding to the same temperatures remain constant [404]. An increase in both the value of the propagation rate constant (K_p) and of the number of propagating sites with increasing temperature was found. The effective activation energy (E_{eff}), determined from temperature dependence of the steady state R_p, is 46 kJ/mol. The activation energy E_p calculated from temperature dependence of K_p is 23 kJ/mol, and the coefficient of the number of active sites $E_{Cp} = E_{eff} - E_p$ is 23 kJ/mol. The reversible adsorption of Al-alkyl on the active centers has been suggested to be the reason for the reversible dependence of steady state R_p on temperature.

For MgCl$_2$-supported catalysts, R_p shows a maximum in the range 60 °C to 70 °C and then decreases with further increasing temperature [89, 140, 157]. The irreversibility of the process indicates an irreversible deactivation of active sites that could be due to overreduction of titanium and to reactions of Ti-C bonds with the LB. The values of apparent activation energy calculated at temperatures below deactivation lie between 40 and 50 kJ/mol [157].

The Arrhenius plot of activity is linear over the range -50 °C to 70 °C for homogeneous isospecific *rac*-EBIZrCl$_2$ and *rac*-EBTHIZrCl$_2$-MAO catalyst systems [239]; the overall activation energy for polymerization is 44 kJ/mol. An overall activation energy of 34.7 kJ/mol was found for propylene polymerization with syndiospecific *t*-BuCH(Cp,Fl)ZrCl$_2$-MAO catalyst [249].

The decrease of activity of the Cp$_2$Ti(Ph)$_2$-MAO catalyst at temperatures above -45 °C, has been ascribed to catalyst deactivation owing to the reduction of titanium to Ti^{3+} [21].

2.5.7   Polymerization Time

Catalyst systems based on α-TiCl$_3$ [8] and first generation δ-TiCl$_3 \cdot 0.3$AlCl$_3$ [404] show a polymerization rate that is constant for a long period of time after an initial acceleration stage which can last from a few minutes to some hours.

By using high activity Solvay TiCl$_3$, MgCl$_2$-supported, and metallocene catalysts, R_p decreases with increasing residence time; the induction period was absent or very short. The rate of catalyst decay depends on the type of catalyst system and polymerization temperature (Table 2.10). At higher temperatures an increased rate of decay has usually been observed.

Many studies demonstrate that, in propylene polymerization with MgCl$_2$-supported catalysts, monomer diffusion limitation through the polymer shell surrounding the catalyst is not the cause of rate decay [86, 157, 370]; therefore, rate decay should be ascribed to deactivation of propagating centers. The reduction of active Ti^{3+} to Ti^{2+} species, believed inactive in propylene polymerization [137, 406, 407], has been suggested as one of the possible causes of deactivation [111, 157]. Chien et al. [112] propose a non-reductive process which involves the simultaneous deactivation of two adjacent active sites. Caunt [408] suggests the poisoning of the active centers by EtAlCl$_2$ resulting from the reaction of Et$_2$AlCl with AlCl$_3$ present in TiCl$_3$ AA.

Table 2.10 Dependence of Propylene Polymerization Rate on Time

Catalyst	Temp. ($°C$)	$P_{C_3H_6}$ (kg/cm^2)	P_{H_2} (kg/cm^2)	[Al] ($mmol/dm^3$)	$t_{1/2}$ (min.)[a]	Reference
MgCl$_2$/TiCl$_4$-AlEt$_3$	70	3	–	5	8	[394]
MgCl$_2$/TiCl$_4$-AlEt$_3$	70	3	0.3	5	12	[394]
MgCl$_2$TiCl$_4$/EB-AlEt$_3$	41	1	–	10	20	[157]
MgCl$_2$/TiCl$_4$/EB-AlEt$_3$	65	1	–	10	12	[157]
MgCl$_2$/TiCl$_4$/EB-AlEt$_3$/MPT	60	6.8	0.6	5	6	[80]
MgCl$_2$/TiCl$_4$/EB-AlEt$_3$/MPT	60	4	–	5	30	(b)
MgCl$_2$/TiCl$_4$/DIBP-AlEt$_3$/CMMS	70	8.5	0.1	5	85	(b)
MgCl$_2$/TiCl$_4$/DIBDMP-AlEt$_3$	70	8.5	0.1	5	60	(b)
Cp$_2$ZrCl$_2$-MAO	40	2	–	51	5	[405]
Cp$_2$ZrCl$_2$-MAO	20	2	–	51	23	[405]
Cp$_2$ZrCl$_2$-MAO	0	2	–	51	> 400	[405]
rac-Me$_2$Si(Ind)$_2$ZrCl$_2$-MAO	40	2	–	20	60	[306]
rac-Me$_2$Si(Benz[e]Ind)$_2$ZrCl$_2$-MAO	40	2	–	20	180	[306]
rac-MeCH(1-η^5C$_5$Me$_4$)(1-η^5Ind)TiCl$_2$-MAO	25	1.7	–	54	3	[269]

[a] $t_{1/2}$ = time required to reduce to a half the maximum polymerization rate
[b] Montell results

DIBP: diisobutylphthalate; CMMS: cyclohexyl,methyl-dimethoxysilane; DIBDMP: 2,2-diisobutyl-1,3-dimethoxypropane

For MgCl$_2$-supported catalysts, the deactivation of the propagating sites also has been ascribed to their complexation by the electron donors present in solution in equilibrium with their complexes with Al-alkyls, and to irreversible chemical reactions of the Ti-C and Ti-H bonds with the functional groups of the electron donors [80, 89, 182, 409].

Deactivation of metallocene-based catalysts appears to proceed by an intermediate formation of binuclear metallocene cations of the type [Cp$_2$ZrMe(μ-CH$_3$)MeZrCp$_2$]$^+$ [221, 226, 382, 410] or of binuclear complexes with a methylene or alkylidene bridge between Zr and Al [411, 412] and by the reduction of the transition metal to the trivalent state [21]. The slow rate of deactivation of Me$_2$Si(benz[e]indenyl)$_2$ZrCl$_2$-MAO catalyst system should result from a steric hindrance to the mutual approach of the Zr centers by their large ligand framework [306].

Different conclusions have been reached by the various researchers concerning the decay kinetics with heterogeneous catalysts. A first-order deactivation of surface active sites was found for the decay rate from the maximum rate to the stationary rate with the TiCl$_3$-AlEt$_3$ catalyst [413]. Galli et al. [86] suggest first-order decay kinetics also with MgCl$_2$-supported catalysts and propose the following equation:

$$(R_t - R_\infty) = (R_o - R_\infty)e^{-k_d t} \qquad (2.7)$$

where R_t, R_o, and R_∞ are the instantaneous, initial, and stationary polymerization rates, respectively; k_d represents the decay rate constant; and t is the polymerization time. A second-order decay was found to be applicable through most of the polymerization time by some

Table 2.11 Number of Active Centers and Values of Propagation Rate Constant for Propylene Polymerizatin with Different Catalyst Systems

Catalyst	Temp. (°C)	No. of active centers (× 100)			Propagation rate constants			Method	Reference
		C_{tot} mol/ molTi	C_{iso} mol/ molTi	C_{ata} mol/ molTi	Kp_{tot} L/mol·s	Kp_{iso} L/mol·s	Kp_{ata} L/mol·s		
δ-TiCl₃.0.3AlCl₃-Et₂AlCl	70		0.17[a]			90		¹⁴CO Quench	[339]
δ-TiCl₃.0.3AlCl₃-AlEt₃	70		0.58[a]			100		¹⁴CO Quench	[339]
δ-TiCl₃.0.3AlCl₃-AliBu₃	70		0.8			90		¹⁴CO Quench	[339]
MgCl₂/TiCl₄-AlEt₃	70		4.2[a]			800		¹⁴CO Quench	[425]
MgCl₂/TiCl₄/EB-AlEt₃	70		2.8[a]			1,000		¹⁴CO Quench	[425]
MgCl₂/TiCl₄-AlEt₃	70	1.49	0.86	0.63		810	730	¹⁴CO Quench	[426]
MgCl₂/TiCl₄/EB-AlEt₃	70	1.2	0.68	0.52		1,250	340	¹⁴CO Quench	[426]
MgCl₂/TiCl₄/EB-AlEt₃	38	1.6			320			CO Poison	[157]
MgCl₂/TiCl₄/EB-AlEt₃/EB	65		8–10			500		¹⁴CO Quench	[71]
MgCl₂/TiCl₄/EB-AlEt₃/EB	70	5.5			310			CO Poison	[348]
MgCl₂/TiCl₄/EB-AlEt₃/EB	60	2.8			2,700			Kinetic	[428]
MgCl₂/TiCl₄/DIBP-AlEt₃/DPMS	60	7.6						¹⁴CO Quench	[428]
rac-EBTHIZrCl₂-MAO	30	66			970	1400–1800	18–130	CH₃O³H	[239]
rac-EBIZrCl₂-MAO	20	52						CH₃O³H	[429]
rac-EBIZrCl₂-Ph₃C⁺[B(C₆F₅)₄]⁻-AlEt₃	20	100			580			CH₃O³H	[429, 430]
rac-MeCH(CpMe₄)(Ind)TiCl₂-MAO	25	3.7			211			CH₃O³H	[269]

[a] Corresponding to maximum polymerization rate

polymerization rate of different para-substituted styrenes, in the presence of isospecific catalysts, increases concomitantly with the electron donor power of the substituents and suggested that the rate depends on the formation of a transition metal-olefin π-complex favored by the increased electron density on the double bond. However, the para-substituent also influences the polarization of the double bond, and the observed reactivity trend also could be explained according to the one-step propagation mechanism, discussed in Boor's review [432], where the driving force of the reaction is assumed to be the polarization of the Ti-C and olefinic double bonds.

The failure to observe π-complexes can be explained, taking into account the low number of active sites and assuming the formation of such complexes to be the kinetically determining step. Which part of the two-step mechanism is the rate determining stage has been widely debated [38, 338, 339].

The first-order kinetics with respect to monomer concentration, observed for the propagation reaction, suggests that monomer coordination is the slower step because a lower reaction order is predicted if monomer insertion is the rate determining step. Böhm [433] suggests that entropy change during complexation of the active site by the monomer is the rate-determining factor for the catalytic process.

The knowledge of the value of the activation energies for the coordination and insertion reactions could help to solve this problem. Quantum mechanical calculations, carried out in the past on non-realistic models of active sites for heterogeneous catalysis [434, 435], indicate that the activation energy for monomer coordination is very low, while it is significant for monomer insertion into the metal–alkyl bond.

The advances in the knowledge of the structure of the active species in homogeneous metallocene-based catalysts has induced many research groups to apply *ab initio* calculations on the reaction of the monomer with realistic models of active centers. Geometries and energetics during the monomer insertion process into the metal-methyl bond of metallocenes methyl cations have been calculated.

Morokuma et al. [359] have studied the reaction between ethylene and $H_2Si(Cp)_2Zr^+Me$ with *ab initio* Hartree–Fock method and have found a 6 kcal/mol activation energy at the level of transition state, while no energy barrier for π-complex formation was found. Ahlrichs et al. [436] applied the MP2 (Møller-Plesset second-order perturbation method), and the local density functional method to the reaction of ethylene with Cp_2Ti^+Me. They found neither a π-complex nor a transition state and concluded that ethylene insertion is a spontaneous process, rationalized by reference to a $2 + 2$ addition, which is symmetry allowed through the availability of d orbitals; therefore, the activation energy experimentally determined for ethylene polymerization is not related to coordination or insertion steps and must be ascribed to another stage in the overall polymerization scheme. The same conclusions about the absence of energy barrier, at least for the insertion in the metal–methyl bond, have been reached by Meier et al. [437] on the basis of the results obtained from *ab initio* molecular dynamics simulations of the same reaction studied by Morokuma; it was, moreover, found that the insertion reaction of ethylene occurs in an extremely short time (about 10^{-13} s).

The above reported studies do not take into consideration the influence of the solvent, counterion, and other species possibly present in the polymerization system, which may counteract the approach of the monomer to the metal of the active site; however, at least for the homogeneous catalyst systems studied, it seems that insertion is not the rate determining step.

2.5.11   Active Site Heterogeneity

The presence in heterogeneous Ziegler–Natta catalysts of at least two types of active sites associated with the isotactic and atactic polymeric fractions is well known; however, this simple picture is inadequate to explain the following experimental data:

1. The broad distribution of tacticity and MW even for the polymer fraction insoluble in xylene, and
2. the compositional heterogeneity of propylene copolymers both with ethylene and higher α-olefins (see Section 2.6.2.2).

The presence of at least two types of isospecific sites, differing in stereospecificity, in $TiCl_3$ and $MgCl_2$-supported catalysts was suggested by Kakugo et al. [172], to explain the isotacticity distribution in PP fractions eluted by temperature rising elution fractionation (TREF) above 100 °C. The relative proportion of the two active centers varies with the nature of the catalyst; the fraction of the highly isospecific centers increases with the isotactic index of the polymer [438]. The above model also accounts for the decreasing stereospecificity of AA-$TiCl_3$/Et_2AlCl catalyst with polymerization time, assuming that higher isospecific active centers would decay more quickly [172].

The MWD of PP produced with Ziegler–Natta catalysts is broad and falls in the ranges of 6 to 10 and 3 to 8 for polymers obtained with $TiCl_3$ [439] and $MgCl_2$-supported [440] catalysts, respectively. Monomer diffusion limitation through the polymer layer as a cause of MWD broadening has been discounted [157]. The presence on the surface of the catalyst of various types of active centers having different values of the apparent chain propagation constant [71, 157, 414, 441, 442] has been suggested as a source of MWD broadening [164]. Floyd et al. [443] state that the smooth unimodal MWD curves usually observed for PP obtained with heterogeneous catalysts can be simulated only by assuming the presence of at least three or four types of active sites, each following Flory's most probable distribution. Kashiwa et al. [166], to explain the change of the shape of the GPC curve of the isotactic fraction of PP obtained with $MgCl_2$-supported catalyst from monomodal to bimodal upon addition of the electron donor, suggest the formation of a new type of active center modified by the donor and characterized by a higher reactivity.

The narrow MWD (M_w/M_n about two) of polymers prepared with metallocene catalysts and the compositional homogeneity of the copolymers allow one to state that probably just one or only a few kinds of active centers are present in these systems generally known as "single site catalysts"

2.5.12   Chain Termination

Polymer chain termination occurs mostly through the following reactions:

1. β-Hydride elimination:

$$Mt-CH_2-CH(CH_3)-P \xrightarrow{k_{t\beta-H}} Mt-H + CH_2=C(CH_3)-P$$

2. β-methyl elimination:

$$Mt-CH_2-CH(CH_3)-P \xrightarrow{K_{t\beta-Me}} Mt-CH_3 + CH_2{=}CH-P$$

3. transfer with monomer:

$$Mt-CH_2-CH(CH_3)-P + CH_2{=}CH-CH_3 \xrightarrow{k_{tM}} Mt-CH_2-CH_2-CH_3 + CH_2{=}C(CH_3)-P$$

4. transfer with cocatalyst:

$$Mt-CH_2-CH(CH_3)-P + AlR_3 \xrightarrow{k_{tMR}} Mt-R + R_2Al-CH_2-CH(CH_3)-P$$

5. transfer with hydrogen:

$$Mt-CH_2-CH(CH_3)-P + H_2 \xrightarrow{k_{tH2}} Mt-H + CH_3-CH(CH_3)-P$$

where Mt and P denote, respectively, the transition metal and polymer chain. Reactions 1 and 5 are followed by a rapid insertion of the olefin into the Mt-H bond. All the above reported reactions are well known in organometallic chemistry.

The relative importance of the different chain transfer reactions depends on the catalyst system used and on the process conditions. Chain transfer by β-hydride elimination is not considered important in propylene polymerization with traditional and MgCl$_2$-supported heterogeneous catalysts at normal polymerization temperature [339, 444, 445]. This reaction becomes a significant chain termination process in most metallocene-based catalyst systems [269, 306, 391, 446]. The β-hydride transfer requires that the first C−C and the βC−H bonds of the growing chain lay in the equatorial plane containing the metal LUMO (lowest unoccupied molecular orbital) in between the two Cp rings; this conformation is favored by the agostic interaction between the Lewis acidic metal center and the βC-H bond [447].

The β-CH$_3$ elimination, never observed in propylene polymerization with heterogeneous catalysts, becomes the most important chain termination mechanism in propylene oligomerization by Cp*$_2$MCl$_2$/MAO (M=Zr,Hf) catalyst systems [258, 358] and by neutral Cp*$_2$LuR [448] and Me$_2$Si(C$_5$Me$_4$)$_2$ScR [447] complexes. The preference of β−CH$_3$ versus β-H elimination when the above catalysts are used has been ascribed to steric interactions between the β-CH$_3$ and the methyl substituent of the Cp ring; this interaction favors the orientation of the β-CH$_3$, instead of β-H, in the equatorial plane of the Cp*$_2$M wedge [403].

In the absence of hydrogen and under normal polymerization conditions, transfer with monomer is the most important chain termination process in propylene polymerization with heterogeneous catalysts [339, 444, 449]; k_{tM} values are higher for MgCl$_2$-supported than for TiCl$_3$ catalysts.

Values of k_{tM} similar to or higher than those of $k_{t\beta-H}$ have been found for the few metallocene catalysts studied [306]. The transition state, suggested by some authors [306] for the β-H transfer to a coordinated monomer, is a six-membered ring of the metal, the α and β carbon atoms of the growing chain, and the two carbon atoms of the double bond. The remarkable increase of the molecular weight of the polymers, observed when the hydrogen atom in 2 position of bridged bis-indenyl zirconocenes is substituted by a methyl group, appears to be due to a strong suppression of the β-hydride transfer to the monomer. The above described transition state model requires a metallocene coordination gap with a wide "lateral extension" angle [450]; this angle is narrowed by the presence of methyl substituents in the 2 position.

In propylene polymerization with heterogeneous [385] and homogeneous [208, 391] catalysts, chain transfer with the cocatalyst plays a secondary role; only when ZnEt$_2$ is used as cocatalyst does it become the most important termination reaction [451]. The mechanism is believed to be the same proposed for the redistribution of alkyl groups in the mixture of boron and aluminum trialkyls [452] and requires the reaction of "monomeric" AlR$_3$ with the active site bearing the polymer chain through an intermediate binuclear complex [453]. Therefore, the high efficiency of ZnEt$_2$ as chain transfer agent is due essentially to the low association degree of this compound in hydrocarbon solution; the dissociation constant of dimeric AlEt$_3$ [454] is, on the contrary, very low (about 10^{-4}). Higher k_{tMR} values for isospecific (in comparison to aspecific) sites have been reported by Chien et al. [239, 455].

Transfer with hydrogen is, in all cases, the most efficient chain terminating process. A half-order dependence of chain transfer rate with respect to [H$_2$] has been generally found for TiCl$_3$ [339, 374] and MgCl$_2$-supported catalysts [164, 394]. Hydrogen does not influence the MWD of the polymer [164].

2.5.13   Replication and Polymer Morphology

The reasons why a full control of the polymer morphology is highly desirable in PP manufacturing can be easily understood in terms of process economics and viability. A regular polymer morphology (i.e., particles with high density, regular shape, and narrow particle size distribution (PSD) means both a high reactor throughput, good flowability and packing, and even, as a limiting case, no need of further pelletization. In addition, a proper porosity, though lowering bulk density, helps the retention of the rubbery phase in heterophasic copolymers. Finally, the absence of fines prevents reactor fouling and explosion hazards during handling, and the absence of coarse particles eliminates undesirable fluidization effects.

The possibility of controlling to some extent the polymer shape, size, and PSD through the catalyst has been known since the very early industrial PP manufacturing [7], and is based on the fact that the polymer usually tends to duplicate, on a larger scale, the physical characteristics (shape and texture) of the parent catalyst. This phenomenon, usually called "replication," is closely related to how the catalyst grain expands as the polymerization proceeds. Though the particle growth mechanism has not yet been completely understood in every detail, nonetheless a large body of experimental evidence [64, 65, 456-468] demonstrates that the following phenomena usually take place:

1. As soon as the polymerization starts, the catalyst grain begins to disrupt into a huge number of small fragments. According to recent findings [468], this process is very fast and proceeds to the crystallite dimensions or even smaller.
2. The catalyst fragments, though no longer in contact with each other, are kept together and uniformly dispersed in the polymer acting as a "cement."
3. The fragments are spread outward as the particle grows but still remain uniformly distributed across the particle cross section. This implies that the polymer growth occurs around each fragment.

A fast and extensive catalyst "fragmentation" and a uniform polymer growth rate across the particle seem, thus, to be the key features for a faithful replication [468]. However, as clearly demonstrated by Galli and co-workers [19, 86, 344, 460, 461], several requirements concerning both the catalyst structure and the reaction conditions must be fulfilled for a uniform catalyst fragmentation and polymer growth rate to occur.

As far as the catalyst is concerned, a proper balance between reactivity and mechanical properties appears necessary, and this is possible only if the following requirements are met:

- High surface area;
- high porosity with a large number of cracks evenly distributed throughout the mass of the granule;
- high enough mechanical resistance to withstand handling, but low enough to allow breakage into microscopic particles during the polymerization;
- homogeneous distribution of the active centers; and
- free access of the monomer up to the innermost zones.

On the other hand, the polymerization conditions must be such as to avoid mass transfer limitation phenomena, which could result in an uneven polymerization rate across the particle.

This picture of the particle growth, which, according to Goodall [469], can be called the "Expanding Universe Model," appears to be supported not only by experimental evidence but also by the results coming from mathematical modeling studies. Models of the particle growth were initially developed [470 - 472] to evaluate the effect of intraparticle heat and mass transfer phenomena on polymerization kinetics and on polymer properties (MWD), but they have recently proved able to predict the polymer morphological features as well.

The most popular among such models is perhaps the "Multigrain Model" (MGM) [443, 472 - 474], which, though necessarily more simplified, can be regarded as a quantitative version of the "Expanding Universe Model." It assumes that (Figs. 2.52 and 2.53):

- Catalyst fragmentation is already complete at time zero;
- catalyst fragments are of uniform size; and
- the polymer grows as a spherical globule (microparticle) around each catalyst fragment.

A simulation of propylene polymerization carried out by Hutchinson by means of this model [475] confirmed that, as long as the polymerization rate keeps uniform throughout the particle along all the growth process, a faithful replication can be predicted. Uneven intraparticle polymerization rate can arise either from diffusion limitations, which then result in monomer concentration gradients, or from a non-uniform distribution of the active sites in the catalyst grain.

In propylene polymerization, serious mass transfer limitations and, thus, concentration profiles across the particle are likely to occur only in the very early polymerization stage as a result of either a bad catalyst design, such as large size and low porosity, or a high polymerization temperature, which causes the polymerization rate to overcome the diffusion rate. Though limited to the very early particle growth stage, these phenomena are nonetheless sufficient, according to Hutchinson [475], to generate voids inside the particle and even its fracturing under extreme conditions. In addition, he demonstrated that, in accordance with the experimental findings, these drawbacks can be overcome or strongly decreased by pre-polymerization, which has the effect of decreasing the polymerization rate per unit particle

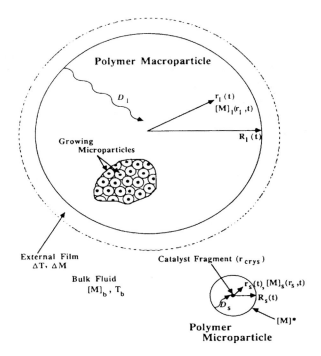

Figure 2.52 Schematic drawing of the multigrain model. Reproduced with permission from Ref. [475], John Wiley & Sons, Inc.

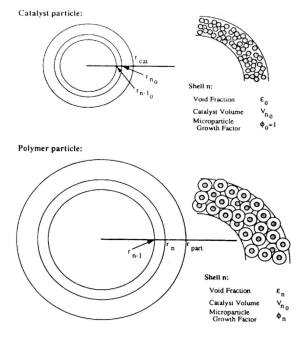

Figure 2.53 Schematic drawing of the polymer growth according to the multigrain model. Reproduced with permission from Ref. [475], John Wiley & Sons, Inc

volume and increasing at the same time the surface area available for the monomer diffusion. On the other hand, the Hutchinson's simulation demonstrated that an even more dramatic ("disastrous") effect on morphology can arise from an uneven distribution of the polymerization sites in the catalyst granule.

As shown by model simulations carried out, among others, by Laurence [476], Floyd [473] and Hutchinson [477], significant particle overheating can also occur in the early stage of the particle growth, especially with highly active large size catalysts and in gas-phase polymerizations, with a consequent particle agglomeration and sticking due to the polymer softening. This problem, too, can be prevented or at least strongly reduced by prepolymerization.

Both the experimental findings and modeling results confirm that a satisfactory control of polymer morphology through replication is possible, even with catalysts having very high activities, provided extreme care is taken during catalyst synthesis as well as in process design.

2.6   Copolymerization

2.6.1   Introduction

Isotactic PP is useful for many applications such as fibers, films, pipes, and injection molded items. Furthermore, the relatively high melting point allows one to exploit its interesting properties in a wide temperature range [478 - 481]. However, the glass transition temperature [482] of PP is around $0\,^{\circ}C$, which results in brittle behavior below that temperature. Also, for some applications the homopolymer is too rigid and the transparency is poor. So, to broaden the application field of this resin, a higher flexibility and clarity are desirable. Also, a lower melting point would be useful for a better weldability, whereas a better impact resistance at low temperature combined with a good stiffness would be an attractive combination of properties.

These objectives are accomplished through statistical (also called random or simultaneous) copolymerization and through sequential copolymerization [460, 483]. Statistical copolymerization of propylene with another olefin, usually ethylene or butene, results in a lower polymer melting point [484] and in higher flexibility [485]. As far as PP toughening is concerned, it is known [460, 484] that a material constituted of an elastomeric poly(propylene-*co*-ethylene) copolymer, well dispersed in a homopolymer matrix, shows an improved low temperature impact resistance together with an adequate stiffness. Thus, copolymerization is a means to change the polymer structure and morphology and, thus, its properties and, as a consequence, its applications. Although these approaches have been employed for decades, the high number of patents and papers appearing in the literature bear witness to the continuing interest in this topic [460, 486, 487 - 493].

This section deals with the statistical (random) and sequential copolymerization of propylene with various olefins, and with the effects of the different catalyst systems on the copolymer structure. A short comparison between heterogeneous and homogeneous catalysts is included, as well.

2.6.2   Statistical (Random) Copolymerization

2.6.2.1   Catalyst Activity

When propylene is copolymerized with small amounts of ethylene with either the TiCl$_3$/DEAC [494] or the MgCl$_2$/DIBP/TiCl$_4$-AlEt$_3$/PES [495] catalyst systems, its polymerization rate is increased. This behavior may be accounted for by assuming that propylene insertion in the Ti-carbon bond is easier when an ethylene unit is bonded to the transition metal, or that the ethylene insertion after a regioirregular (2,1) propylene insertion reactivates a "dormant" site. The copolymerization of propylene with 1-butene is also described in some papers [495 - 498]; however, no clear relationship between the catalyst activity and the comonomer content in the feed mixture is reported. Concerning the copolymerization with 1-hexene, a negative effect of the comonomer on activity is reported for a MgCl$_2$/TiCl$_3$-supported, aspecific catalyst, whereas a positive effect is observed when the isospecific TiCl$_3$/Cp$_2$Ti(CH$_3$)$_2$ system is used [499].

Copolymerization of propylene with 1-hexene also has been performed with MgCl$_2$/phthalate/TiCl$_4$ catalyst with PES and di-*t*-butyldimethoxysilane (DTBMS) as external donors [500]. Also, in this case, the comonomer increases the propylene reactivity when the most isospecific donor (DTBMS) is used. Propylene was also copolymerized with heavier 1-olefins [501] with the MgCl$_2$-TiCl$_4$/Al(*i*-Bu)$_3$ catalyst system. The activity is reported to increase over the whole range of comonomer concentrations for 1-octene, 1-decene, and 1-dodecene, whereas it increases up to a maximum and then decreases with 1-hexadecene and 1-tetradecene. Two hypotheses have been suggested to account for the activating effect of heavier comonomers: either they decrease the polymer crystallinity, so avoiding any diffusional barrier to the active sites, or they help create new active sites with a more favorable steric environment and, hence, a higher activity [501].

2.6.2.2   Reactivity Ratios and Copolymer Composition

An insight into the copolymer microstructure and the copolymerization mechanism can be realized from the reactivity ratios and their product. It is useful to recall that when $r_1*r_2 \approx 1$ the copolymer shows a random structure; when $r_1*r_2 > 1$ a blocky structure is evident and when $r_1*r_2 < 1$ the copolymer has an alternating structure. Some literature r_1 and r_2 values for propylene copolymers with other olefins [481] determined either by kinetic methods or by NMR analyses on the raw product are collected in Table 2.12.

From these data, and as already pointed out by Kissin [502], the comonomer reactivity (r_2) appears to decrease with increasing the steric hindrance around the double bond in the following order:

Ethylene > Propylene > 1-Butene > linear 1-olefins > branched 1-olefins

Furthermore, from the r_1*r_2 values, the poly(propylene-*co*-ethylene) and poly(propylene-*co*-1-butene) copolymers would appear to be blocky ($r_1*r_2 > 1$), whereas those with heavier 1-olefins seem nearly random ($r_1*r_2 \approx 1$). However, a more detailed investigation carried out by ^{13}C NMR analyses on carefully fractionated propylene-ethylene [503], propylene-1-butene [504], and propylene-1-hexene [500] copolymers obtained from MgCl$_2$-supported catalysts reveals that they consist of several fractions, all having an r_1*r_2 close to 1 but different sets of

Table 2.12 Reactivity Ratios for Olefins Copolymerization with Propylene

Catalyst	Comonomer	r_1 Propylene	r_2	r_1*r_2	Reference
TiCl$_3$/AlEt$_2$Cl	Ethylene	0.1	25	2.5	[481]
TiCl$_3$/AlEt$_2$Cl	Ethylene	0.4–0.7	4.2–9.3	–	[481]
TiCl$_3$/AlEt$_3$	Ethylene	0.15–0.18	13–14	–	[481]
Solvay-TiCl$_3$/Cp$_2$TiMe$_2$	Ethylene	0.22	10	2.2	[481]
TiCl$_4$/MgCl$_2$/PE/AlEt$_3$	Ethylene	0.09	6.1	0.5	[481]
TiCl$_4$/MgCl$_2$	Ethylene	n.d.	n.d.	4	[481]
Chromocene on silica	Ethylene	n.d.	72	n.d.	[481]
High yield Ti-catalyst[a]	Ethylene	n.d.	n.d.	2	[481]
TiCl$_4$/MgCl$_2$/EB	Ethylene	0.7–0.4	7.4–13.4	5	[481]
TiCl$_4$/MgCl$_2$/3ROH	Ethylene	0.02	6	0.13	[481]
SiO$_2$/TiCl$_3$/MgCl$_2$	Ethylene	0.14	7	1	[481]
SiO$_2$/TiCl$_4$/MgCl$_2$	Ethylene	0.34–0.18	5–10	1.9	[481]
TiCl$_3$/AlEt$_2$Cl/HMPTA/H$_2$	1-Butene	4.3	0.8	3.4	[481]
TiCl$_3$/AlEt$_2$Cl/HMPTA/no H$_2$	1-Butene	3.3	0.45	1.5	[481]
TiCl$_3$/AlCl$_3$/AlEt$_2$Cl	1-Butene	4.5	0.2	0.9	[481]
TiCl$_3$/AlEt$_2$Cl	1-Butene	4.7	0.51	2.4	[481]
TiCl$_3$/AlEt$_3$	1-Butene	2.4	0.5	1.2	[481]
TiCl$_3$(Stauffer AA)/AlEt$_2$Cl	4-Methyl-1-pentene	6.44	0.31	2	[481]
TiCl$_3$(Stauffer AA)/AlEt$_2$Cl	1-Hexene	4.18	0.16	0.67	[481]
TiCl$_3$/AlEt$_2$Cl	4-Methyl-1,4-hexadiene	25[b]	0.04[b]	1	[481]
TiCl$_4$/MgCl$_2$/Ali-Bu$_3$	1-Octene	6.5	0.2	1.3	[503]
TiCl$_4$/MgCl$_2$/Ali-Bu$_3$	1-Octene	7.7	0.15	1.1	[503]
TiCl$_4$/MgCl$_2$/Ali-Bu$_3$	1-Dodecene	9.9	0.13	1.3	[503]
TiCl$_4$/MgCl$_2$/Ali-Bu$_3$	1-Hexadecene	13.9	0.08	1.1	[503]
TiCl$_4$/MgCl$_2$/Ali-Bu$_3$	1-Tetradecene	12.7	0.1	1.3	[503]

[a] Probably MgCl$_2$/TiCl$_4$/aromatic ester and AlEt$_3$/aromatic ester as cocatalyst
[b] Activity ratio (i.e., molar ratio of comonomers in copolymer and feed)

individual r_1 and r_2 values. Accordingly, propylene copolymers can, in general, be considered as homogeneous and nearly Bernoullian as regards the intramolecular sequence distribution, but heterogeneous as far as the intermolecular composition distribution is concerned. As shown by model fitting procedures [505, 506], it is this last feature that gives rise to an apparent blockiness when unfractionated products are considered.

The broad composition distribution is generally accompanied by an equally broad stereoregularity and molecular weight distribution [497, 500, 503, 504, 507, 508], which seem more likely to have originated from the presence of catalyst sites having different isospecificity and reactivity toward the comonomer than by monomer diffusion limitations [506].

The reactivity of the active sites appears correlated, though only roughly, with their stereospecificity. However, it is usually observed that sites having the same high stereospecificity appear endowed with a rather broad spectrum of reactivities toward the comonomer [497, 503, 504, 508].

2.6.3   Sequential Copolymerization

As previously mentioned [403, 484], it is possible to obtain an impact resistant polyolefinic material through sequential polymerization. The products so obtained have often been named "block copolymers," however, according to the current literature [156, 481, 493, 509], this is an incorrect description. To synthesize a real ethylene-propylene block copolymer, at least the three following requirements should be met:

1.   Active sites able to polymerize both ethylene and propylene,
2.   active sites sufficiently stable along the polymerization time (living catalyst), and
3.   long average life of the growing macromolecules (living polymer).

The first condition is usually met, the second one only in part, and the third one is usually not satisfied. As a matter of fact, even in the absence of H_2 as chain transfer agent, the life of the growing polymer chains is only a few seconds [68, 449, 481, 510, 511]. As a consequence, true block copolymers can hardly be synthesized by Ziegler–Natta catalysis and a more suitable nomenclature, such as heterophasic or impact copolymers, should be used for these products.

2.6.3.1   *Kinetics and Catalyst Morphology*

Sequential polymerization is usually carried out in two steps. Usually, a propylene homopolymer or a slightly modified copolymer is synthesized in the first step. In the second step, a mixture of ethylene and propylene is copolymerized with the same catalyst system, so obtaining a heterophasic system consisting of a semicrystalline matrix with a nearly amorphous elastomeric component dispersed within it. The properties of such materials depend on the relative amount of the rubbery phase and on its molecular structure, such as the composition and molecular mass [481, 484, 493]. For example, Fig. 2.54 [486] shows how Izod resilience improves with the increase of the elastomeric portion, especially at low temperature.

To produce the polymer with the desired characteristics, a proper amount of rubber must be produced in the copolymerization step, and, consequently, a long-life catalyst showing a high residual activity after the homopolymerization step is required [509]. Furthermore, the rubber must be retained inside the granule and homogeneously dispersed in the homopolymer matrix to prevent undesired reactor fouling [156]; consequently, a proper catalyst architecture is required [460, 493]. This polymerization technique, in fact, behaves in such a way that the rubber grows around the homopolymer microglobules. The internal voids of homopolymer granule are occupied by the growing rubber, which, after the pores are filled, migrates to the particle surface [481, 493]. A high porosity is thus required to bear the desired amount of rubber inside the particle and prevent its migration to the surface with a consequent reactor fouling.

The high yield $MgCl_2$-supported catalysts meet both these requirements and, thus, copolymers with a high content of rubber homogeneously distributed in the polymer particle can easily be obtained (Figs. 2.55 and 2.56).

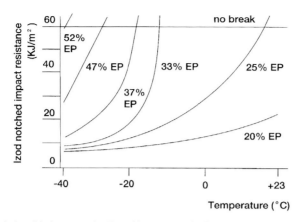

Figure 2.54 The relationship between the EP rubber content in the reactor blend and the Izod impact strength at different temperatures. Reproduced with permission from Ref. [486], John Wiley & Sons, Inc.

2.6.3.2   Rubber Molecular Structure

The structural parameters of the rubber may in principle be affected by the extent of the homopolymerization stage. As far as the molecular weight is concerned, some data obtained with TiCl$_3$ catalyst are collected in Table 2.13. It is worth noting that, as the homopolymer yield increases, the intrinsic viscosity of the copolymer increases, too. This finding has been explained [481] on the basis of the presence on the catalyst of two families of active centers having different kinetic behaviors and different K_p/K_{tr} ratios. The less stable sites, which

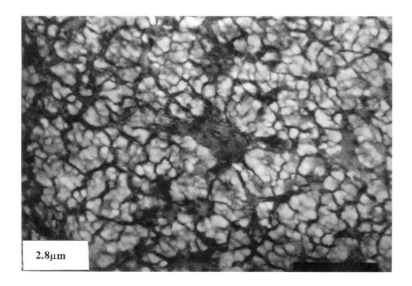

Figure 2.55 Impact polypropylene copolymers obtained by synthesis (8000 x)

2.6.4.1   Catalyst Activity

Similarly to the heterogeneous catalysts, ethylene is reported to increase the polymerization rate of propylene (Fig. 2.57) when homogeneous catalysts are used, the extent of the activating effect being dependent on the metallocene structure [516].

Few data are available for copolymerization with higher 1-olefins. In propylene-1-hexene copolymerization with the $Me_2C(Fl,Cp)ZrCl_2$-MAO catalyst system, an extremely small acceleration effect on polymerization rate has been observed only at a very low 1-hexene/propylene ratio (< 0.1); at higher ratios the rate decreases markedly [517].

2.6.4.2   Composition Distribution and Reactivity Ratios

Homogeneous catalysts are known to provide copolymers with narrow molecular mass distribution [518], and this implies that one active site is dominating [519]. A narrow composition distribution could be expected, as well, and actually has been observed on carefully fractionated copolymers [520]. Therefore, no uncertainties due to broad composition distribution could be forecast for the determination of the reactivity ratios. Some data regarding reactivity ratios and their product for ethylene/propylene copolymerization catalyzed by different metallocenes are collected in Table 2.14 [521].

It can be observed that the reactivity of ethylene varies greatly upon changing the catalyst symmetry (and thus stereospecificity) and that also r_1*r_2 depends on such a catalyst feature: random or alternating copolymers can thus be synthesized simply by changing the catalyst π-ligands.

Also, for heterogeneous catalysts, it has been proposed [503] that catalytic sites having different stereospecificity can show different reactivity toward the comonomer. In that case, however, the active centers are believed to provide all a nearly random, rather than alternating

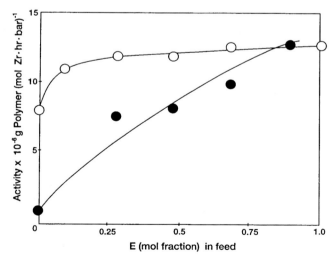

Figure 2.57 Variation of catalytic activity for copolymerization with ethylene content in the liquid phase: ○, $Et(Ind)_2ZrCl_2$/MAO; ●, $(Ind)_2ZrCl$/MAO. Reproduced with permission from Ref. [516], John Wiley & Sons, Inc.

Table 2.14 Reactivity Ratios r_1 and r_2 in Copolymerization of Ethylene (1) and Propylene (2) Performed in Presence of Different Metallocene/Methylaluminoxane (MAO) Catalytic Systems (From Ref. 521)

Metallocene[a]	Symmetry	Temperature (°C)	r_1	r_2	r_1*r_2
$(Me_5Cp)_2ZrCl_2$	C_{2v}	50	250	0	0.5
$(MeCp)_2ZrCl_2$	C_{2v}	50	60		
Cp_2ZrCl_2	C_{2v}	50	48	0.02	0.72
Cp_2ZrMe_2	C_{2v}	60	31.5	0.01	0.25
$Me_2Si(Cp)_2ZrCl_2$	C_{2v}	50	24	0.03	0.7
Cp_2TiPh_2	C_{2v}	50	19.5	0.02	0.29
Cp_2TiMe_2	C_{2v}	36	10.6	0	0.6
$EBIZrCl_2$	C_2	50	6.61	0.06	0.4
$EBIZrCl_2$	C_2	25	6.26	0.11	0.69
$EBIZrCl_2$	C_2	0	5.2	0.14	0.73
$Me_2C(Cp)(Fl)ZrCl_2$	C_s	25	1.3	0.2	0.26

[a] Me = methyl; Cp = cyclopentadienyl; Ph = phenyl; Fl = fluorenyl

sequences distribution. A different statistics of propagation (e.g., a first- or second-order Markovian [522, 523] instead of Bernoullian) has in fact been proposed to account for the differences between metallocenes and heterogeneous catalysts.

Table 2.15 [524] shows some values of reactivity ratios for propylene/1-hexene copolymerization with metallocenes having different stereospecificity. From these data, the comonomer reactivity seems to change according to the catalyst stereospecificity. A nearly random sequences distribution, however, is observed with all the metallocenes used. Thus, in this case, both homogeneous and heterogeneous catalysts appear to follow Bernoullian propagation statistics.

As a consequence of such catalyst behavior, it is possible to synthesize propylene random copolymers with new features with respect to those obtained with Ti-based catalysis. For example, poly(propylene-co-ethylene) and poly(propylene-co-1-butene) copolymers having very low xylene solubles can be achieved by using isospecific metallocenes [525]. Also, syndiospecific metallocenes have been used to synthesize poly(propylene-co-1-butene) copolymers having the same characteristics [526].

2.6.4.3   Sequential Copolymerization

No literature dealing with sequential copolymerization catalyzed by metallocenes is available at this time; however, some patent applications have been filed [527] in which sequential copolymers with a better low temperature impact resistance than those synthesized with heterogeneous catalysts are claimed. According to the inventors, this improvement can be related to the sharp peak in the glass transition temperature region shown by this product, which in turn would be a consequence of its narrower molecular mass and composition distribution. No mention, however, is made of other important properties, such as the stiffness and the heat distortion temperature (HDT).

Table 2.15 Monomer Sequence Distribution and Thermodynamic Parameters of Poly(Propylene-co-1-hexene) (From ref. [524]).

Run[d]	[PP]*	[PH]* [HP]*	[HH]*	r_P^a	r_H^a	$r_p r_H$	T_m^b (°C)	ΔH_f^b (J/g)	Crystallinity (%)[c]
1	100	0	0	–	–	–	n.d.	n.d.	n.d.
2	79.7	18.8	1.5	3.88	0.35	1.36	n.d.	n.d.	n.d.
3	64	31	5	3.77	0.35	1.32	n.d.	n.d.	n.d.
4	45	43.6	11.4	3.77	0.29	1.09	n.d.	n.d.	n.d.
5	31.3	45.2	23.5	3.79	0.38	1.44	n.d.	n.d.	n.d.
6	0	0	100	–	–	–	n.d.	n.d.	n.d.
7	100	0	0	–	–	–	110.8	46.9	22.5
8	89.3	10.7	0	2.54	–	–	67.9	4.1	2
9	71.2	26.3	2.5	2.47	0.42	1.04	n.d.	n.d.	n.d.
10	49.6	42.7	7.7	2.12	0.40	0.85	n.d.	n.d.	n.d.
11	0	0	100	–	–	–	n.d.	n.d.	n.d.
12	100	0	0	–	–	–	114.9	15.2	–
13	93.2	6.8	0	2.09	–	–	87.3	10.9	–
14	51.7	41	7.3	1.54	0.58	0.89	n.d.	n.d.	n.d.
15	0	0	100	–	–	–	n.d.	n.d.	n.d.

[a] r_p, r_H: reactivity ratios of propene and 1-hexene, respectively
[b] Obtained from premelted samples: T_m = melting temp.; H_f = heat of fusion
[c] Calculated on the basis of folded chain isotactic polypropene
[d] Runs 1–6 witn Cp₂ZrCl₂; runs 7–11 with EBTHIZrCl₂; runs 12–15 with Me₂C(Cp)(Fl)ZrCl₂
* [PP] = propylene-propylene; [PH] = propylene-hexene; [HP] = hexene-propylene; [HH] = hexene-hexene
"n.d." = Not determined

References

1. *Boor, J.Jr.:* Ziegler–Natta Catalysts and Polymerizations, Academic Press, New York, NY, 1979, p.21
2. German Patent 973 626 (1953) Ziegler, K., Breil, H., Martin, H., Holzkamp, E
3. a) Italian Patent 535 712 (1954) Montecatini
   b) Italian Patent 537 425 (1954) Montecatini
4. Italian Patent 526 101 (1954) Montecatini
5. *Galli, P.:* International Union of Pure and Applied Chemistry, Structural Order in Polymers, Ciardelli, F., Giusti, P., Eds., Pergamon Press, 1981, p.63
6. a) U.S. Patent 3 128 252 (1964) Esso Res. & Eng. Co
   b) U.S. Patent 3 032 510 (1962) Esso Res. & Eng. Co
   c) U.S. Patent 3 130 003 (1964) Esso Res. & Eng. Co
7. *Anderson Chem. Co., Division of Stauffer Chem Co.:* Technical Bulletin Titanium Trichloride Anhydrous, August 1959
8. *Natta, G., Pasquon, I.:* Adv. Catal. 11 (1959) 1
9. *Choi, KY.,* Ray, W.H.: J. Macromol. Sci., Rev. Macromol. Chem. Phys. C25(1) (1985) 57
10. a) German Patent 2 213 086 (1972) Solvay & CIE
    b) U.S. Patent 3 769 233 (1973) Solvay & CIE
11. *Bernard, A., Fiasse, B.:* Catalytic Olefin Polymerization, Keii, T., Soga, K., Eds., KodanshaElsevier, 1990, p.405
12. British Patent 1 286 867 (1968) Montedison

13. *Pasquon, I., Giannini, U.:* Catalysis Science and Technology, Anderson, J.R., Boudart, M., Eds., Springer Verlag, Berlin, 1984, Vol.6, Chapter 2
14. a) Belgian Patent 785 332 (1972) Montedison
    b) Belgian Patent 785 334 (1972) Montedison
15. German Patent 2 643 143 (1977) Montedison and Mitsui P.C
16. a) U.S. Patent 4 414 132 (1979) Shell Oil
    b) U.S. Patent 4 393 182 (1979) Shell Oil
17. *Goodall, B.L.:* Transition Metal Catalyzed Polyymerizations, Alkenes and Dienes, Quirk, R.P., Ed., Harwood Academic Publishers, New York, 1983, Part A, p.355
18. European Patent 45 977 (1982) Montedison
19. *Galli, P., Barbè, P.C., Noristi, L.:* Angew. Makromol. Chem. 120 (1984) 73
20. U.S. Patent 4 971 937 (1990) HIMONT Incorporated
21. *Ewen, J.A.:* J. Am. Chem. Soc. 106 (1984) 6355
22. *Kaminsky, W., Külper, K., Brintzinger, H.H., Wild, F.R.W.P.:* Angew. Chem. Int. Ed. Engl. 24 (1985) 507
23. *Ewen, J.A., Jones, R.L., Razavi, A., Ferrara, J.D.:* J. Am. Chem. Soc. 110 (1988) 6255
24. *Natta, G., Corradini, P., Allegra,G.:* J. Polym. Sci. 51 (1961) 399
25. *Natta, G.:* Chim. Ind. (Milano) 42(11) (1960) 1207
26. *Klemm, W., Krose, E.:* Z. Anorg. Chem. 253 (1947) 209
27. *Scumb, W.C., Sundstrom, J.:* J. Am. Chem. Soc. 55 (1933) 596
28. *Sherfey, J.M.:* J. Res. Natl. Bur. Stand. 46 (1951) 299
29. *Korotkov, A.A., TszunChan, L.:* Polym. Sci. USSR (Engl. Transl.) 3 (1962) 621
30. *Ruff, O., Neumann, F.:* Z. Anorg. Chem. 128 (1923) 81
31. *Bock, F., Moser, L.:* Monatsh. Chem. 34 (1913) 1825
32. *Beerman, C., Bestian, H.:* Angew. Chem. 71 (1959) 618
33. U.S. Patent 3 424 774 (1969) Esso Eng. & Chem. Co
34. a) British Patent 960 232 (1964) Hoechst
    b) U.S. Patent 3 108 973 (1963) Hercules
35. *Natta, G., Corradini, P., Allegra, G.:* Atti Accad. Naz. Lincei, Rend. Cl. Sci. Fis. Mat. Nat. [8]26 (1959) 155
36. *Natta, G., Pasquon, I., Giachetti, E.:* Angew. Chem. 69 (1957) 213
37. *Wilchinsky, Z.W., Looney, R.W., Tornqvist, E.G.M.:* J. Catal. 28 (1973) 351
38. *Kissin, Y.V.:* Isospecific Polymerization of Olefins, Springer Verlag Publishers, 1985, Chapt. 2
39. a) British Patent 960 232 (1964) Hoechst
    b) U.S. Patent 3 179 604 (1965) Union Carbide
    c) British Patent 1 390 355 (1971) Shell
40. *Goodall, B.L.:* Polypropylene and other Polyolefins, *Van der Ven, S.,* Ed., Elsevier, 1990, Chapter 1
41. *Natta, G., Pasquon, I., Zambelli, A., Gatti, G.:* J. Polym. Sci. 51 (1961) 387
42. *Natta, G., Zambelli, A., Pasquon, I., Giongo, G.M.:* Chim. Ind. (Milano) 48 (1966) 307
43. *Natta, G., Zambelli, A., Pasquon, I., Giongo, G.M.:* Chim. Ind. (Milano) 48 (1966) 1298
44. *Tornqvist, E.G.M.:* Ann. N.Y. Acad. Sci. 155 (1969) 447
45. *Yermakov,Y.I., Zakharov, V.A.:* Coordination Polymerization, Chien, J.W.C., Ed., Academic Press, NY, 1975, p.91
46. *Caunt, A.D., Tait, P.J.T., Davies, S.:* Transition Metal Catalyzed Polymerizations, Alkenes and Dienes, Quirk, R.P., Ed., Harwood Academic Publishers, New York, 1983, Part A, p. 149
47. British Patent 1 092 390 (1966) Mitsubishi P.C
48. German Patent 1 940 329 (1970) Hoechst
49. British Patent 943 206 (1963), French Patent 1 450 785 (1966) Eastman Kodak
50. *Tait, P.J.T.:* Comprehensive Polymer Science, Eastmond, G.C., Ledwith, A., Russo, S., Sigwalt, P., Eds., Pergamon Press, 1989, Vol. 4, p.1
51. German Patent 2 335 047 (1974) Solvay & CIE
52. a) European Patent Appl. 288 109 (1988) Solvay & CIE
    b) European Patent Appl. 569 078 (1993) Solvay & CIE
53. British Patent 2 124 240 (1982) Chisso
54. U.S. Patent 4 591 577 (1986) Chisso
55. a) U.S. Patent 4 195 069 (1980) Shell

b) British Patent 2 028 844 (1982) Shell

c) U.S. Patent 4 110 248 (1978) BP

d) U.S. Patent 4 199 474 (1980) BP

e) British Patent 1 557 329 (1979) Exxon

f) European Patent Appl. 021 478 (1981) Shell

56. *Nielsen, R.P.:* Transition Metal Catalyzed Polymerizations, Alkenes and Dienes, Quirk, R.P., Ed., Harwood Academic Publishers, New York, 1983, Part A, p. 47

57. a) British Patent 2 028 843 (1983) Chisso

b) U.S. Patent 4 347 158 (192) Da rt Industries

c) British Patent 2 018 783 (1979) Nippon Oil

d) French Patent 2 320 955 (1975) Stamicarbon

e) Belgian Patent 871 737 (1979) Toyo Stauffer

f) U.S. Patent 4 330 648 (1982) Phillips

g) U.S. Patent 4 382 019 (1983) Stauffer

58. a) *European Patent 007 094 (1982) BASF*

b) European Patent 017 895 (1982) BASF

c) British Patent 2 029 424 (1983) Chisso

d) German Patent 2 840 156 (1980) Hoechst

e) British Patent 2 049 709 (1983) Mitsubishi P.C

f) Belgian Patent 873 388 (1979) Mitsui T

g) European Patent 019 312 (1983) Shell

h) European Patent Appl. 044 445 (1982) Stauffer

i) Belgian Patent 886 892 (1981) Toho Titanium

j) French Patent 2 535 724 (1984) Nippon Oil

k) German Patent 3 434 739 (1985) Nippon Oil

l) U.S. Patent 4 581 426 (1986) Mitsui T

59. a) U.S. Patent 4 242 229 (1980) Mitsubishi P.C

b) European Patent 029 623 (1984) Shell

c) European Patent 004 791 (1983) Toa Nenryo Kogyo

d) European Patent Appl. 131 35 9 (1985) ICI

e) U.S. Patent 4 529 716 (1985) HIMONT Incorporated

60. a) U.S. Patent 4 469 648 (1984) Montedison

b) British Patent 2 029 840 (1983) Montedison

c) German Patent 2 605 922 (1976) Mitsui P.C

d) European Patent 022 675 (1984) Mitsui P.C

e) U.S. Patent 4 410 451 (1983) Phillips

f) U.S. Patent 4 948 770 (1990) Shell

g) WO Patent 92/21 705 (1992) Neste Oy

h) WO Patent 93/11 166 (1993) Neste Oy

61. a) British Patent 1 603 724 (1981) Montedison

b) U.S. Patent 4 277 372 (1981) Hercules

c) European Patent Appl. 049 467 (1982) Idemitsu

d) European Patent Appl. 113 937 (1984) Stauffer

e) European Patent 136 112 (1987) Toa Nenryo Kogyo

f) European Patent Appl. 096 770 (1983) Sumitomo

g) European Patent Appl. 322 798 (1989) Toho Titanium

h) European Patent Appl. 459 009 (1991) Toho Titanium

i) European Patent Appl. 426 139 (1991) Union Carbide Corp

j) British Patent 2 191 778 (989) ICI

62. a) U.S Patent 4 186 107 (1980) Hercules

b) Belgian Patent 857 811 (1978) Mitsubishi P.C

c) Belgian Patent 874 356 (1979) Sumitomo

d) European Patent 026 027 (1983) Ube Ind

e) European Patent 306 867 (1991) BASF

f) U.S. Patent 5 064 799 (1991) HIMONT Incorporated

g) U.S. Patent 5 244 854 (1993) HIMONT Incorporated
h) European Patent 173 472 (1990) Toa Nenryo Kogyo
i) European Patent Appl. 446 801 (1991) Sumitomo
j) European Patent Appl. 371 664 (1990) ICI
k) European Patent Appl. 336 545 (1989) BP
63. a) Belgian Patent 883 858 (1980) Mitsui P.C
   b) European Patent 086 288 (1986) Mitsui P.C
   c) U.S. Patent 4 728 705 (1988) Shell Oil
   d) U.S. Patent 4 968 653 (1990) Quantum Chem
   e) U.S. Patent 4 866 022 (1989) Amoco
   f) U.S. Patent 4 540 679 (1985) Amoco
   g) European Patent 258 485 (1992) Bejing Res. Inst. China
   h) U.S. Patent 4 703 026 (1987) Mitsubishi P.C
   i) U.S. Patent 4 551 439 (1985) Chisso
   j) European Patent Appl. 475 134 (1992) Tosoh
   k) European Patent Appl. 461 775 (1991) Shell Oil
   l) European Patent Appl. 461 268 (1991) Idemitsu
   m) European Patent Appl.s 436 801 (1991), 491 128 (1992) Hüls
   n) U.S. Patent 5 145 821 (1992) Quantum Chem. Corp
64. *Hock, C.W.:* J. Polym. Sci., Part A: Polym. Chem. 4 (1966) 3055
65. *Mackie, P., Berger, M.N., Grieveson, B.M., Lawson, D.:* J. Polym. Sci., Part B: Polym. Phys. 5 (1967) 493
66. *Arzoumanidis, G.G., Karayannis, N.M.:* Chem. Tech. (July 1993) 43
67. *Arzoumanidis, G.G., Karayannis, N.M.:* Appl. Catal. 76 (1991) 221
68. *Barbè, P.C., Cecchin, G., Noristi, L.:* Adv. Polym. Sci. 81 (1986) 1
69. *Spitz, R., Duranel, L., Guyot, A.:* Makromol. Chem. 189 (1988) 549
70. *Jeong, Y., Lee, D., Soga, K.:* Makromol. Chem. Rapid Commun. 12 (1991) 5
71. *Giannini, U.:* Makromol. Chem., Suppl. 5 (1981) 216
72. *Giunchi, G., Allegra, G.: J. Appl. Crystallogr. 17 (1984) 172*
73. *Dusseault, J.J., Hsu, C.C.:* J. Macromol. Sci., Rev. Macromol. Chem. Phys. *C33(2) (1993) 103*
74. *Bruni, G., Ferrari, A.:* Rend. Accad. Naz. Lincei 2 (1925) 457
75. *Bassi, I.W., Polato, F., Calcaterra, M., Bart, J.C.J.:* Z. Crystallogr. 159 (1982) 297
76. *Galli, P., Barbè, P.C., Guidetti, G., Zannetti, R., Martorana, A., Marigo, A., Bergozza, M., Fichera, A.:* Eur. Polym. J. 19 (1983) 1977
77. *Zannetti, R., Marega, C., Marigo, A., Martorana, A.:* J. Polym. Sci., Part B: Polym. Phys. 26 (1988) 2399
78. *Giannini, U., Giunchi, G., Albizzati, E., Barbè, P.C.:* Recent Advances in Mechanistic and Synthetic Aspects of Polymerization, NATO ASI Sect. 215, Fontanille, M., Guyot, A., Eds., D. Reidel Publishing Co., 1987, p. 473
79. *Albizzati, E.:* Chim. Ind. (Milano) 75 (1993) 107
80. *Albizzati, E., Galimberti, M., Giannini, U., Morini, G.:* Macromol. Chem., Makromol. Symp. 48/49 (1991) 223
81. *Zakharov, V.A., Paukshtis, E.A., Mikenas, T.B., Volodin, A.M., Vitus, E.N., Potapov, A.G.:* Macromol. Symp. 89 (1995) 55
82. *Yano, T., Inoue, T., Ikai, S., Shimizu, M., Kai, Y., Tamura, M.:* J. Polym. Sci., Part A: Polym. Chem. 26 (1988) 477
83. *Hu, Y., Chien, J.W.C.:* J. Polym. Sci., Part A: Polym. Chem. 26 (1988) 2003
84. *Gupta, V.K., Satish, S., Bhardwaj, I.S.:* J. Macromol. Sci., Pure Appl. Chem. A31(4) (1994) 451
85. *Yang, C.B., Hsu, C.C.:* Makromol. Chem. Rapid Commun. 14 (1993) 387
86. *Galli, P., Luciani, L., Cecchin, G.:* Angew. Makromol. Chem. 94 (1981) 63
87. *Wu, J.C., Kuo, C.I., Chien, J.C.W.:* Proc. of IUPAC 28 Macromolecular Symposium, Amherst, July 1216, 1982, p.241
88. *Chien, I.C.W., Wu, J.C., Kuo, C.I.:* J. Polym. Sci., Part A: Polym. Chem. 21 (1983) 725
89. *Spitz, R., Lacombe, J.L., Guyot, A.:* J. Polym. Sci., Part A: Polym. Chem. 22 (1984) 2641
90. *Chien, J.C.W., Wu, J.C., Kuo, C.I.:* J. Polym. Sci., Part A: Polym. Chem. 20 (1982) 2019
91. *Rytter, E., Nirisen, O., Kvisle, S., Ystenes, M., Oie, H.A.:* Transition Metal Catalyzed Polymerizations, ZieglerNatta and Metathesis Polymerizations, Quirk, R.P., Ed., Cambridge University Press, 1988, p. 292

92. *Terano, M., Kataoka, T., Keii, T.:* Makromol. Chem. 188 (1987) 1477
93. *Terano, M., Kataoka, T., Keii, T.:* J. Polym. Sci., Part A: Polym. Chem. 28 (1990) 2035
94. *Chien, J.C.W., Dickinson, C.L., Vizzini, J.:* J. Polym. Sci., Part A: Polym. Chem. 28 (1990) 2321
95. *Terano, M., Saito, M., Kataoka, T.:* Makromol. Chem. Rapid Commun. 13 (1992) 103
96. *Abis, L., Albizzati, E., Giannini, U., Giunchi, G., Santoro, E., Noristi, L.:* Makromol. Chem. 189 (1988) 1595
97. *Jones, P.J.V., Oldman, R.J.:* Transition Metals and Organometallics as Catalysts for Olefin Polymerization, Kaminsky, W., Sinn, H., Eds., SpringerIVerlag, Berlin, 1988, p.223
98. *Sergeev, S.A., Polubayarov, V.A., Zakharov, V.A., Anufrienko, U.F., Bukatov, G.D.:* Makromol. Chem. 186 (1985) 243
99. *Guyot, A., Spitz, R., Duranel, L., Lacombe, J.L.:* Catalytic Polymerization of Olefins, Keii, T., Soga, K., Eds., KodanshaElsevier, 1986, p.147
100. *Chien, J.C.W., Hu, Y.:* J. Polym. Sci., Part A: Polym. Chem. 27 (1989) 897
101. *Terano, M., Kataoka, T., Hosaka, M., Keii, T.:* Transition Metals and Organometallics as Catalysts for Olefin Polymerization, Kaminsky, W., Sinn, H., Eds., SpringerVerlag, Berlin, 1988, p.55
102. *Jeong, Y., Lee, D.:* Makromol. Chem. 191 (1990) 1487
103. *Jeong, Y., Lee, D., Shiono, T., Soga, K.:* Makromol. Chem. 192 (1991) 1727
104. *Yang, C.B., Hsu, C.C.:* Polym. Bull. 30 (1993) 529
105. *Yang, C.B., Hsu, C.C., Park, Y.S., Shurvell, H.F.:* Eur. Polym. J. 30(2) (1994) 205
106. *Albizzati, E., Giannini, U., Morini, G., Smith, C.A., Zeigler, R.:* Ziegler Catalysts, Fink, G., Mülhaupt, R., Brintzinger, H.H., Eds., SpringerVerlag, 1995, p. 413
107. *Sormunen, P., Hjertberg, T., Iiskola, E.:* Makromol. Chem. 191 (1990) 2663
108. *Iiskola, E.:* Intern. Symp. 40 Years Ziegler Catalysts, Freiburg, Sept. 13, 1993
109. *Clayden, N.J., Jones, P.J.V.:* New Frontiers in ZieglerNatta Catalyst Chemistry, ACS 44 Southwest Regional Meeting, Corpus Christi, Nov.30 Dec.2, 1988
110. *Busico, V., Corradini, P., DeMartino, L., Proto, A., Savino, V., Albizzati, E.:* Makromol. Chem. 186 (1985) 1279
111. *Busico, V., Corradini, Ferraro, A., Proto, A.:* Makromol. Chem. 187 (1986) 1125
112. *Chien, J.C.W., Weber, S., Hu, Y.:* J. Polym. Sci., Part A: Polym. Chem. 27 (1989) 1499
113. *Wang, H., Jiang, R., Fu, Z., Zhang, S., Qian, G., Zheng, Y., Gao, B.:* Transition Metal Catalyzed Polymerizations, ZieglerNatta and Metathesis Polymerizations, Quirk, R.P., Ed., Cambridge University Press, 1988, p.327
114. *Chien, J.C.W., Wu, J., Kuo, C.:* J. Polym. Sci., Part A: Polym. Chem. 21 (1983) 737
115. *Kang, K., Ok, M., Ihm, S.:* J. Appl. Polym. Sci. 40 (1990) 1303
116. *Ferreira, M.L., Damiani, D.E.:* J. Polym. Sci., Part A: Polym. Chem. 32 (1994) 1137
117. *Spitz, R., Lacombe, J.L., Primet, M.:* J. Polym. Sci., Part A: Polym. Chem. 22 (1984) 2611
118. *Chien, J.C.W., Wu, J.C.:* J. Polym. Sci., Part A: Polym. Chem. 20 (1982) 2445
119. *Tashiro, K., Yokoama, M., Sugano, T., Kato, K.:* Contemp. Topics Polym. Sci. 4 (1984) 647
120. *Spitz, R., Bobichon, C., LlauroDarricades, M.F., Guyot, A., Duranel, L.:* J. Mol. Catal. 56 (1989) 156
121. *Vähäsarja, E., Pakkanen, T.T., Pakkanen, T.A., Iiskola, E., Sormunen, P.:* J. Poly. Sci., Part A: Polym. Chem. 25 (1987) 3241
122. *Sormunen, P., Vähäsarja, E., Pakkanen, T.T., Pakkanen, T.A., Iiskola, E.:* J. Organomet. Chem. 319 (1987) 327
123. *Iiskola, E., Sormunen, P., Garoff, T., Vähäsarja, E., Pakkanen, T.T., Pakkanen, T.A.:* Transition Metals and Organometallics as Catalysts for Olefin Polymerization, Kaminsky, W., Sinn, H., Eds., SpringerVerlag, Berlin, 1988, p.113
124. *Solli, K., Bache, Ø., Ystenes, M.:* Int. Symp. on Advances in Olefin, Cycloolefin and Diolefin Polymerization, Lyon, Apr. 1217, 1992
125. *Busico, V., Corradini, P., DeMartino, L., Proto, A., Albizzati, E.:* Makromol. Chem. 187 (1986) 1115
126. *Kashiwa, N., Yoshitake, J., Toyota, A.:* Polym. Bull. 19 (1988) 333
127. *Sacchi, M.C., Tritto, I., Shan, C., Mendichi, R., Noristi, L.:* Macromolecules 24 (1991) 6823
128. *Sacchi, M.C., Forlini, F., Tritto, I., Mendichi, R., Zannoni, G., Noristi, L.:* Macromolecules 25 (1992) 5914
129. *Noristi, L., Barbè, P.C., Baruzzi, G.:* Makromol. Chem. 192 (1991) 1115

130. European Patent 086 288 (1986) Mitsui P.C
131. *Kezler, B., Bodor, G., Simon, A.:* Polymer 21 (1980) 1037
132. *Kezler, B., Grobler, A., Takacs, E., Simon, A.:* Polymer 22 (1981) 818
133. *Spitz, R., Bobichon, C., Guyot, A.:* Makromol. Chem. 190 (1989) 707
134. *Iiskola, E., Pelkonen, A., Kakkonen, H.J., Pursiainen, J., Pakkanen, T.A.:* Makromol. Chem. Rapid Commun. 14 (1993) 133
135. *Zambelli, A., Oliva, L., Ammendola, P.:* Gazz. Chim. It. 116 (1986) 259
136. *Proto, A., Oliva, L., Pellecchia, C., Sivak, A.J., Cullo, L.A.:* Macromolecules 23 (1990) 2904
137. *Kashiwa, N., Yoshitake, J.:* Makromol. Chem. 185 (1984) 1133
138. *Chien, J.C.W., Wu, J.C.:* J. Polym. Sci., Part A: Polym. Chem. 20 (1982) 2461
139. *Weber, S., Chien, J.C.W., Hu, Y.:* J. Polym. Sci., Part A: Polym. Chem. 27 (1989) 1499
140. *Albizzati, E., Giannini, U., Morini, G., Galimberti, M., Barino, L., Scordamaglia, R.:* Macromol. Symp. 89 (1995) 73
141. *Busico, V., Corradini, P., DeMartino, L., Graziano, F., Iadicicco, A.:* Makromol. Chem. 192 (1991) 49
142. *Soga, K., Shiono, T., Doi, Y.:* Makromol. Chem. 189 (1988) 1531
143. *Lee, D., Jeong, Y.:* Eur. Polym. J. 29(6) (1993) 883
144. *Barbè, P.C., Noristi, L., Baruzzi, G.:* Makromol. Chem. 193 (1992) 229
145. *Keii, T., Suzuki, E., Tamura, M., Doi, Y.:* Transition Metal Catalyzed Polymerizations, Alkenes and Dienes, Quirk, R.P., Ed. Harwood Academic Publishers, New York, 1983, Part A, p.97
146. *Seppälä, J.V., Härkönen, M.:* Makromol. Chem. 190 (1989) 2535
147. *Doi, Y., Suzuki, E., Keii, T.:* Makromol. Chem. Rapid Commun. 2 (1981) 293
148. *Kezler, B., Simon, A.:* Polymer 23 (1982) 916
149. *Sivak, A.J., Kissin, Y.V.:* J. Polym. Sci., Part A: Polym. Chem. 22 (1984) 3739
150. *Soga, K., Shiono, T., Doi, Y.:* Polym. Bull. 10 (1983) 168
151. *Kashiwa, N.:* Transition Metal Catalyzed Polyymerizations, Alkenes and Dienes, Quirk, R.P., Ed., Harwood Academic Publishers, New York, 1983, Part A, p.379
152. *Soga, K, Sano, T., Yamamoto, K., Shiono, T.:* Chem. Lett. (1982) 425
153. *Guyot, A., Bobichon, C., Spitz, R., Duranel, L., Lacombe, J.L.:* Transition Metals and Organometallics as Catalysts for Olefin Polymerization, *Kaminsky, W., Sinn, H.*, Eds., Springer Verlag, Berlin, 988, p.13
154. *Soga, K., Shiono, T.:* Transition Metal Catalyzed Polymerizations, ZieglerNatta and Metathesis Polymerizations, Quirk, R.P., Ed., Cambridge University Press, 1988, p.266
155. *Chadwick, J.C., Miedema, A., Sudmeijer, O.:* Makromol. Chem. 195 (1994) 167
156. *Simonazzi, T., Cecchin, G., Mazzullo, S.:* Progr. Polym. Sci. 16 (1991) 303
157. *Keii, T., Suzuki, E., Tamura, M., Doi, Y.:* Makromol. Chem. 183 (1982) 2285
158. *Brockmeyer, N., Rogan, J.B.:* IPEC Proc. Res. Dev. 24(2) (1985) 278
159. *Nirisen, Ø., Rytter, E., Lindstrøm, T.L.:* Makrom. Chem. Rapid Commun. 7 (1986) 103
160. *Dumas, C., Hsu, C.C.:* J. Appl. Polym. Sci. 37 (1989) 1625
161. *Tait, P.J.T., Wang, S.:* Br. Polym. J. 20 (1988) 499
162. *Chien, J.C.W., Hu, Y.:* J. Polym. Sci., Part A: Polym. Chem. 26 (1988) 2973
163. *Rincon-Rubio, L.M., Wilen, CE., Linfors, LE.:* Eur. Polym. J. 26(2) (1990) 171
164. *Keii, T., Doi, Y., Suzuki, E., Tamura, M., Murata, M., Soga, K.:* Makromol. Chem. 185 (1984) 1537
165. *Kashiwa, N., Kawasaki, M., Yoshitake, J.:* Catalytic Polymerization of Olefins, Keii, T., Soga, K., Eds., KodanshaElsevier, 1986, p.43
166. *Kashiwa, N., Yoshitake, J.:* Polym. Bull. 12 (1984) 99
167. *Seppälä, J.V., Härkönen, M., Luciani, L.:* Makromol. Chem. 190 (1989) 2535
168. *Galli, P., Simonazzi, T., Del Duca, D.:* Acta Polym. 39 (1988) 81
169. *Wu, Q., Yang, NL.:* Makromol. Chem. 191 (1990) 89
170. *Kashiwa, N., Yoshitake, J., Tsutsui, T.:* Polym. Bull. 19 (1988) 339
171. *Kakugo, M., Miyatake, T., Naito, Y., Mizunuma, K.:* Transition Metal Catalyzed Polymerizations, ZieglerNatta and Metathesis Polymerizations, Quirk, R.P., Ed., Cambridge University Press, 1988, p.624
172. *Kakugo, M., Miyatake, T., Naito, Y., Mizunuma, K.:* Macromolecules 21 (1988) 314
173. *Miyatake, T., Mizunuma, K., Kakugo, M.:* Catalytic Olefin Polymerization, Keii, T., Soga, K., Eds., KodanshaElsevier, 1990, p. 155
174. *Härkönen, M., Seppälä, J.V., Väänänen, T.:* Makromol. Chem. 192 (1991) 721
175. *Kashiwa, N., Kojoh, S.:* Macromol. Symp. 89 (1995) 27

176. *Härkönen, M., Seppälä, J.V.:* Makromol. Chem. 192 (1991) 2857
177. *Härkönen, M., Kuutti, L., Seppälä, J.V.:* Makromol. Chem. 193 (1992) 1413
178. a) European Patent Appl. 452 916 (1991) Idemitsu
     b) European Patent Appl. 419 249 (1991) Amoco
179. European Patent Appl. 350 170 (1990) Mitsui P.C
180. U.S. Patent 5 166 340 (1992) HIMONT Incorporated
181. *Okano, T., Chida, K., Furuhashi, H., Nakano, A., Ueki, S.:* Catalytic Olefin Polymerization, Keii, T., Soga, K., Eds., KodanshaElsevier, 1990, p. 177
182. *Spitz, R., Lacombe, J.L., Guyot, A.:* J. Polym. Sci., Part A: Polym. Chem. 22 (1984) 2625
183. U.S. Patent 4 315 836 (1980) Montedison
184. *Langer, A.W., Burkhardt, T.J., Steger, J.J.:* Polym. Sci. Technol. 19 (1983) 225
185. *Burkhardt, T.J., Langer, A.W., Barist, D., Funk, W.G., Gaydos, T.:* Transition Metal Catalyzed Polymerizations, ZieglerNatta and Metathesis Polymerizations, Quirk, R.P., Ed., Cambridge University Press, 1988, p.227
186. *Vermel, E.E., Zakharov, V.P., Bukatova, Z.K., Shkurina, G.P., Yechevskaya, L.G., Moroz, E.M., Sudakova, S.V.:* Vysokomol. Soedin 22(1) (1980) 22
187. *Chadwick, J.C., Miedea, A., Ruisch, B.J., Sudmeijer:* Makromol. Chem. 193 (1992) 1463
188. *Gupta, V.K., Satish, S., Bhardwaj, I.S.:* J. Macromol. Sci., Rev. Macromol. Chem. Phys., C34 (1994) 439
189. *Möhring, P.C, Coville, N.J.:* J. Organomet. Chem. 479 (1994) 1
190. *SRI International: Metallocenes: Catalysts for the New Polyolefin Generation, Multiclient Project 3536, May*July 1993, vol. 13
191. *Natta, G., Pasquon, I., Zambelli:* J. Am. Chem. Soc., 84 (1962) 1488
192. *Doi, Y., Ueki, S., Keii, T.:* Macromolecules 12 (1979) 814
193. *Giannini, U., Zucchini, U., Albizzati, E.:* J. Polym. Sci., Part B: Polym. Lett. 8 (1970) 405
194. *Ballard, D.G.H.:* Adv. Catal. 23 (1973) 263
195. *Breslow, D.S., Newburg, N.R.:* J. Am. Chem. Soc. 79 (1957) 5072
196. *Natta, G., Pino, P., Mazzanti, G., Giannini, U.:* J. Am. Chem. Soc. 79 (1957) 2975
197. U.S. Patent 2 924 593 (1960) Hercules
198. *Sinn, H., Kaminsky, W.:* Adv. Organomet. Chem. 18 (1980) 99
199. U.S. Patent 4 522 982 (1985) Exxon
200. *Cardin, D.J., Lappert, M.F., Raston, C.L.:* Chemistry of Organo Zirconium and Hafnium Compounds, Hellis Horwood, J. Wiley & Sons, Inc., 1986
201. *Coates, G.W., Waymouth, R.M.:* Science 267 (1995) 217
202. *Schnutenhaus, H., Brintzinger, H.H.:* Angew. Chem. Int. Ed. Engl. 18 (1979) 777
203. *Wild, F., Zsolnai, L., Huttner, G., Brintzinger, H.H.:* J. Organomet. Chem. 232 (1982) 233
204. *Farina, M., Di Silvestro, G., Terragni, A.:* Macromol. Chem. Phys. 196 (1995) 353
205. *Halterman, R.L.:* Chem. Rev. 92 (1992) 965
206. *Sinn, H., Bliemeister, J., Clausnitzer, D., Tikwe, L., Winter, H., Zarncke, O.:* Transition Metals and Organometallics as Catalysts for Olefin Polymerization, Kaminsky, W., Sinn, H., Eds., Springer Verlag, Berlin, 1988, p.257
207. *Cam, D., Albizzati, E., Giannini, U.:* Makromol Chem. 191 (1990) 1641
208. *Resconi, L., Bossi, S., Abis, L.:* Macromolecules 23 (1990) 4489
209. *Sugano, T., Matsubara, K., Fujita, T., Takahashi, T.:* J. Mol. Catal. 82 (1993) 93
210. *Mason, M.R., Smith, J.M., Bott, S.G., Barron, A.R.:* J. Am. Chem. Soc. 115 (1993) 4971
211. *Harlan, C.J., Mason, M.R., Barron, A.R.:* Organometallics 13 (1994) 2957
212. *Nekhaeva, L.A., Boudarenko, G.N., Rykov, S.V., Nekaev,A.I., Kreutsel, B.A., Marin, V.P.; Vyshinskaia, L.I., Khrapova, I.M., Polonskii, A.V., Korneev, N.N.:* J. Organomet. Chem. 406 (1991) 139
213. *Siedle, A.R., Lamanna, W.M., Newmark, R.A.:* Makromol. Chem. Macromol. Symp. 66 (1993) 215
214. European Patent Appl. 452 920 (1991) Mitsui P. C
215. U. S. Patent 5 126 303 (1992) HIMONT Incorporated
216. European Patent Appl. 575 875 (1993) Spherilene s.r.l
217. *Yang, X., Stern, C.L., Marks, T.J.:* J. Am. Chem. Soc. 113 (1991) 3623
218. *Yang, X., Stern, C.L., Marks, T.J.:* J. Am. Chem. Soc. 116 (1994) 10015
219. *Bochmann, M., Lancaster, S. J.:* Organometallics 12 (1993) 633
220. *Chien, J.C.W., Tsai, W., Rausch, M.D.:* J. Am. Chem. Soc. 113 (1991) 8570

221. *Herfert, N., Fink, G.:* Makromol. Chem. Rapid Commun. 14 (1993) 91
222. European Patent Appl. 513 380 (1992) Idemitsu
223. *Tsai, W., Rausch, M.D., Chien, J.C.W.:* Appl. Organomet. Chem. 7 (1993) 71
224. *Kaminsky, W., Bark, A., Steiger, R.:* J. Mol. Catal. 74 (1992) 109
225. *Tritto, I., Li, S., Sacchi, M. C., Zannoni, G.:* Macromolecules 26 (1993) 7111
226. *Shista, C., Hatorn, R.M., Marks, T.J.:* J. Am. Chem. Soc. 114 (1992) 1112
227. *Jordan, R.F., Bajgur, C.S., Willet, R., Scott, B.:* J. Am. Chem. Soc. 108 (1986) 7410
228. *Jordan, R.F.:* Adv. Organomet. Chem. 32 (1991) 325
229. U.S. Patent 4 769 510 (1988) Hoechst
230. *Mise, T., Miya, S., Yamazaki, H.:* Chem. Lett. (1989) 1853
231. *Röll, W., Brintzinger, H.H., Rieger, B., Zolk, R.:* Angew. Chem. Int. Ed. Engl. 29 (1990) 279
232. *Spaleck, W., Küber, F., Winter, A., Rohrmann, J., Bachmann, B., Antberg, M., Doll, V., Paulus, E. F.:* Organometallics 13 (1994) 954
233. *Burger, P., Diebold, J., Gutmann, S., Hund, H.U., Brintzinger, H.H.:* Organometallics 11 (1992) 1319
234. *Collins, S., Guthier, W.J., Holden, D.A., Kuntz, B.A., Taylor, N.J., Ward, D.G.:* Organometallics 10 (1991) 2061
235. *Busico, V., Cipullo, R.:* J. Am. Chem. Soc. 116 (1994) 9329
236. *Resconi, L., Fait, A., Piemontesi, F., Colonnesi, M., Rychlicki, H., Zeigler, R.:* Macromolecules (in press)
237. *Hermann, W.A., Rohrmann, J., Herdtweck, E., Spaleck, W., Winter, A.:* Ang. Chem. Int. Ed. Engl. 28 (1989) 1511
238. *Mengele, W., Diebold, J., Troll, C.; Röll, W., Brintzinger, H.H.:* Organometallics 12 (1993) 1931
239. *Chien, J.C.W., Sugimoto, R.:* J. Polym. Sci., Part A: Polym. Chem. 29 (1991) 459
240. *Herfert, N., Fink, K.:* Makromol. Chem. Macromol. Symp. 66 (1993) 157
241. *Herfert, N., Fink, G.:* Makromol. Chem. 193 (1992) 1359
242. *Ewen, J., Haspeslagh, L., Atwood, J., Zhang, H.:* J. Am. Chem. Soc. 109 (1987) 6544
243. *Spaleck, W., Aulbach, M., Bachmann, B., Küber, F., Winter, A.:* Macromol. Symp. 89 (1995) 237
244. *Ewen, J., Elder, M.J.:* Makromol. Chem. Macromol. Symp. 66 (1993) 179
245. Eur. Pat. Appl. 387 690 (1990) Hoechst
246. *Razawi, A., Atwood, J.L.:* J. Organomet. Chem. 459 (1993) 117
247. *Ewen, J.A., Elder, M.J., Jones, R.L., Haspeslagh, L., Atwood, J.L., Bott, S.G., Robinson, K.:* Makromol Chem., Macromol. Symp. 48/49 (1991) 253
248. *Ewen, J.A., Elder, M.J., Harlan, C.I., Jones, R.L., Atwood, J.L., Bott, S. G., Robinson, K.:* ACS Polymer Preprints 32 (1991) 469
249. *Fierro, R., Yu, Z., Rausch, M.D., Dong. S., Alvares, D., Chien, J.C.W.:* J. Polym Sci., Part A: Polym.Chem. 32 (1994) 661
250. *Balbontin, G., Dainelli, D., Galimberti, M., Paganetto, G.:* Makromol. Chem. 193 (1992) 693
251. *Galambos, A., Wolkowicz, M., Zeigler, R.:* ACS Symp. Ser. 496, Vandenberg, E.J, Salamone, J.C., Eds., (1992) p. 104
252. *Lovinger, A.J., Lotz, B., Davis, D.D., Padden, F.J.:* Macromolecules 26 (1993) 3494
253. *Sozzani, P., Simonutti, R., Galimberti, M.:* Macromolecules 26 (1993) 5782
254. *De Rosa, C., Corradini, P.:* Macromolecules 26 (1993) 5711
255. *Rodriguez*Arnold, J., Zhang, A., Cheng, S.D.Z., Lovinger, A., Hsieh, E.T., Chu, P., Johnson, T.W., Honnel, K.G., Geerts, R.G., Palckal, S.J., Hawley, G.R., Welch, M.P.: Polymer 35 (1994) 1884
256. *Lovinger, A.J., Lotz, B., Davis, D.D., Schumacher, M.:* Macromolecules 27 (1994) 6603
257. *Shimura, T., Kohno, M., Inoue, N., Akiyama, M., Asanuma, T., Sugimoto, R., Kimura, S., Abe, M.:* Stud. urf. Sci. Cat. 89 (1994) 327
258. *Resconi, L., Piemontesi,F., Franciscono, G., Abis, L., Fiorani, T.:* J. Am. Chem. Soc. 114 (1992) 1025
259. *Resconi, L., Abis, L., Franciscono, G.:* Macromolecules 25 (1992) 6814
260. European Patent Appl. 584 609 (1994) Hoechst
261. European Patent Appl. 604 908 (1994) Spherilene s.r.l
262. European Patent Appl. 604 917 (1994) Spherilene s.r.l
263. *Resconi, L., Jones, R.L., Albizzati, E., Camurati, I., Piemontesi, F., Guglielmi, F., Balbontin, G.:* ACS Polymer Preprints 35 (1994) 663
264. *Silvestri, R. Resconi, L., Pelliconi, A.:* Proc. Int. Congr. METALLOCENES 95, Brussels, April 2627, 1995, pp. 207–216

265. U.S. Patent 4 335 225 (1982) DuPont
266. *Collette, J.W., Ovenall, D.W., Buck, W.H., Feguson, R.C.:* Macromolecules 22 (1989) 3858
267. *European Patent Appl. 423 786 (1991) Himont Incorporated*
268. *Ittel, S.:* ACS Polymer Preprints 35 (1994) 665
269. *Llinas, G.H., Dong, S.H., Mallin, D.T., Rausch, M.D., Lin, Y.G., Winter, H.H., Chien, J.C.W.:* Macromolecules 25 (1992) 1242
270. *Watson. P.L.:* J. Am. Chem. Soc. 104 (1982) 337
271. *Coughlin, E.B., Bercaw, J.E.:* J. Am. Chem. Soc. 114 (1992) 7606
272. *Oliva, L., Longo, P., Pellecchia, C.:* Makromol. Chem. Rapid Commun. 9 (1988) 51
273. *Miyatake, T., Mizunuma, K., Kakugo, M.:* Makromol. Chem. Macromol Symp. 66 (1993) 203
274. Japan Patent 05 170 823 (1993) Mitsui Toatsu
275. *Soga, K., Kaminaka, M.:* Macromol. Rapid Commun. 15 (1994) 593
276. European Patent Appl. 567 952 (1994) Hoechst
277. European Patent Appl. 523 416 (1994) Hoechst
278. *Soga, K., Uozumi, T., Saito, M., Shiono, T.:* Macromol. Chem. Phys. 195 (1994) 1503
279. Japan Patent 05 239 139 Mitsubishi P.C
280. *Kaminaka, M., Soga, K.:* Makromol. Chem. 194 (1993) 1745
281. European Patent Appl. 518 092 (1994) BASF
282. European Patent Appl. 563 917 (1994) Hoechst
283. European Patent Appl. 598 543 (1994) Mitsubishi P.C
284. European Patent Appl. 633 272 (1994) Spherilene s.r.l
285. Italian Patent Appl. MI 94/A 002028 Spherilene s.r.l
286. European Patent Appl. 500 944 (1992) Mitsui Toatsu
287. Japan Patent Appl. 315 820 (1986) Showa Denko
288. WO 91/09882 (1991) Exxon
289. Japan Patent 05 155 926 (1993) Mitsui Toatsu
290. *Natta, G., Pino, P., Mantica, E., Danusso, F., Mazzanti, G., Peraldo, M.:* Chim. Ind. (Milan) 38 (1956) 124
291. *Zambelli, A., Locatelli, P., Sacchi, M. C., Tritto, I.:* Macromolecules 15 (1982) 831
292. *Sacchi, M.C., Tritto, I., Locatelli, P.:* Prog. Polym. Sci. 16 (1991) 331
293. *Longo, P., Proto, A., Grassi, A., Ammendola, P.:* Macromolecules 24 (1991) 4624
294. *Zakharov, V.A., Bukatov, G.D., Yermakov, Yu., Demin, E.A.:* Dokl. Akad. Nauk. SSSR 207 (1972) 857
295. *Chien, J.C.W., Wang, B.P.:* J. Polym. Sci., Part A: Polym. Chem. 27 (1989) 1539
296. *Fink, G., Rotler, R.:* Angew. Makromol. Chem. 94 (1981) 25
297. *Natta, G., Pino, P., Mazzanti, G., Lanzo, R.:* Chim. Ind. (Milan) 39 (1957) 1032
298. *Pino, P., Giannini, U., Porri, J.:* Encyclopedia of Polymer Science and Engineering, Second Edition, John iley & Sons, Inc., 1987, Vol. 8, pp. 147220
299. *Ammendola, P., Tancredi, T., Zambelli, A.:* Macromolecules 19 (1986) 307
300. *Zambelli, A., Ammendola, P., Grassi, A., Longo, P., Proto, A.:* Macromolecules 19 (1986) 2703
301. *Zambelli, A., Longo, P., Pellecchia, C., Grassi, A.:* Macromolecules 20 (1987) 2035
302. *Wolfsgruber, C., Zannoni, G., Rigamonti, E., Zambelli, A.:* Makromol. Chem. 176 (1975) 2765
303. *Busico, V., Cipullo, P., Corradini, P.:* Makromol. Chem. Rapid.Commun. 13 (1992) 15
304. *Soga, K., Shiono, T., Takemura, S., Kaminsky, W.:* Makromol. Chem. Rapid Commun. 8 (1987) 305
305. *Grassi, A., Zambelli, A., Resconi, L., Albizzati, E., Mazzocchi, R.:* Macromolecules 21 (1988) 617
306. *Stehling, U., Diebold, J., Kirsten, R., Röll, W., Brintzinger, H.H., Jüngling, S., Mülhaupt, R., Langhauser, F.:* Organometallics 13 (1994) 964
307. *Spaleck, W., Antberg, M., Aulbach, M., Bachmann, B., Dolle, V., Haftka, S., Kuber, F., Rohrmann, J., Winter, A. Fink, G., Mülhaupt, R., Brintzinger, H.H.:* Ziegler Catalysts, Springer–Verlag, 1995, p. 83
308. *Tsutsui, T., Mizuno, A., Kashiwa, N.:* Makromol. Chem. 190 (1989) 1177
309. *Busico, V., Cipullo, R., Chadwick, J.C., Modder, J.F., Sudmeijer, O.:* Macromolecules 27 (1994) 7538
310. *Rieger, B., Mu, X., Mallin, D., Rausch, M., Chien, J.C.W.:* Macromolecules 23 (1990) 3559
311. *Toyota, A., Tsutsui, T., Kashiwa, N.:* J. Mol. Catal. 56 (1989) 237
312. *Zambelli, A., Locatelli, P., Rigamonti, E.:* Macromolecules 12 (1979) 156
313. *Natta, G., Farina, M., Peraldo, M.:* Atti Accad. Naz. Lincei. Cl. Sci. Fis. Mat. Nat. Rend. 25 (1958) 424
314. *Zambelli, A., Giongo, M., Natta, G.:* Makromol. Chem. 112 (1968) 183

315. *Pino, P., Mülhaupt, R.:* Angew. Chem. Int. Ed. Engl. 19 (1980) 857
316. *Doi, Y., Asakuru, T.:* Makromol. Chem. 176 (1975) 507
317. *Crain, W.O. Jr., Zambelli, A., Roberts, J. D.:* Macromolecules 4 (1971) 330
318. *Cheng, H.N., Ewen, J.A.:* Makromol. Chem. 190 (1989) 1931
319. *Pino, P.* Adv. Polym. Sci. 4 (1965) 393
320. *Ciardelli, F., Locatelli, P., Marchetti, M., Zambelli, A.:* Makromol. Chem. 175 (1974) 923
321. *Ewen, J.A.:* Catalytic Polymerization of Olefins, Keii, T., Soga, K., Eds., Kodansha-Elsevier, 1986, p. 271
322. *Locatelli, P., Tritto, I., Sacchi, M.C.:* Makromol. Chem. Rapid Commun. 5 (1984) 495
323. *Erker, G., Nolte, R., Tsay, Y.H., Kruger, C.:* Angew. Chem. Int. Ed. Engl. 28 (1989) 628
324. *Zambelli, A., Locatelli, P., Provasoli, A., Ferro, D. R.:* Macromolecules 13 (1980) 267
325. *Bovey, F.A., Tiers, G.V.D.:* J. Polym. Sci. 44 (1960) 173
326. Ref. 1, pp. 236341
327. *Natta, G.:* J. Inorg. Nucl. Chem. 8 (1958) 589
328. *Hargitay, B., Rodriguez, L.A.M., Miotto, M.:* J. Polym. Sci. 35 (1959) 599
329. *Arlman, E.J., Cosse, P.:* J. Catal. 3 (1964) 99
330. *Corradini, P., Guerra, G.:* Prog. Polym. Sci. 16 (1991) 239
331. *Corradini, P., Busico, V., Guerra, G.:* Comprehensive Polymer Science, Eastmann, G. C., Ledwith, A., Russo, S., Sigwalt, P., Eds., Pergamon Press, 1989, Vol. 4, pp. 2950
332. *Allegra, G.:* Makromol. Chem. 145 (1971) 235
333. *Zambelli, A., Sacchi, M.C., Locatelli, P., Zannoni, G.:* Macromolecules 15 (1982) 211
334. *Brookhart, M., Green, M.L.H.:* J. Organomet. Chem. 250 (1983) 395
335. *Kissin, Y.V., Chirkov, N. M.:* Eur. Polym. J. 6 (1970) 525
336. *Fellman, J.D., Rupprecht, G. A., Schrock, R. R.:* J. Am. Chem. Soc. 101 (1979) 5099
337. *Mc Kinney R.S.:* J. Chem. Soc. Chem. Commun. (1980) 490
338. *Ystenes, M.:* J. Catal. 129 (1991) 383
339. *Zakharov, V.A., Bukatov, G.D., Yermakov, Y.I.:* Adv. Polym. Sci. 51 (1983) 61
340. *Armstrong, D.R., Perkins, P.G., Stewart, J.J.P.:* J. Chem. Soc. Dalton Trans. (1972) 1972
341. *Patat, P., Sinn, H.:* Angew. Chem. 70 (1958) 496
342. *Natta, G., Mazzanti, G.,* Tetrahedron 8 (1960) 86
343. *Rodriguez, L.A.M., van Looy, H.M.:* J. Polym. Sci. A1, 4 (1966) 1971
344. *Galli, P.:* Proc. of IUPAC 28th Macromol. Symp., Amherst, July 1216, 1982, p.248
345. *Corradini, P., Barone, U., Fusco, R., Guerra, G.:* Gazz. Chim. Ital. 113 (1983) 601
346. *Shiono, T., Uchino, H., Soga, K.:* Polym. Bull. 21 (1989) 19
347. *Doi, Y.:* Makromol. Chem. Rapid Commun. 3 (1982) 635
348. *Jacobson, F.I.:* Proc. of IUPAC 28 Macromol. Symp., Amherst, July 1216, 1982, p.246
349. Ref. 40, p. 101
350. *Pino, P., Rotzinger, B., von Achenbach, E.:* Catalytic Polymerization of Olefins, Keii, T., Soga, K., Eds., KodanshaElsevier, 1986, p. 461
351. *Guyot, A., Spitz, R., Journaud, G., Eisenstein, O. :* Macromol. Symp. 89 (1995) 39
352. *Farina, M., Puppi, C.:* J. Mol. Catal. 82 (1993) 3
353. *Barino, L., Scordamaglia, R.:* Macromol. Symp. 89 (1995) 101
354. *Scordamaglia, R., Barino, L.:* Int. Symp. 40 Years Ziegler Catalysts, Freiburg, Sept. 13, 1993
355. *Hlatky, G.G., Turner, H.W., Eckman, R.R.:* J. Am. Chem. Soc. 111 (1989) 2728
356. *Hlatky, G.G., Eckman, R.R., Turner, H.W.:* Organometallics 11 (1992) 1413
357. *Bochmann, M., Jaggar, A.J., Nicholls, J.C.:* Angew. Chem. Int. Ed. Engl. 29 (1990) 780
358. *Eshuis, J.J.W., Tan, Y.Y., Teuben, J.H.:* J. Mol. Catal. 62 (1990) 277
359. *KawamuraKuribayashi, H., Koga, N., Morokuma, K.:* J. Am. Chem. Soc. 114 (1992) 8687
360. *Pino, P., Cioni, P., Wei, J.:* J. Am. Chem. Soc. 108 (1986) 7410
361. *Longo, P., Grassi, A., Pellecchia, C., Zambelli, A.:* Macromolecules 20 (1987) 1015
362. *Leclerc, M., Brintzinger, H.H.:* Int. Symp. 40 Years Ziegler Catalysts, Freiburg, Sept. 13, 1993
363. *Smith, J., von Seyerl, J., Huttner, G., Brintzinger, H.H.:* J. Organomet. Chem. 173 (1979) 175
364. *Piemontesi, F., Camurati, I., Resconi, L., Balboni, D., Sironi, A., Moret, M., Zeigler, R., Piccolrovazzi, N.:* Organometallics 14 (1995) 1256
365. *Rieger, B.:* J. Organomet. Chem. 428 (1992) 633

366. European Patent Appl. 537 130 (199) Fina Technology Inc
367. *Razawi, A., Peters, L. Nafpliotis, L., Vereecke, D., Den Dauw, K., Atwood, J.L., Thewald, U.:* Macromol. Symp. 89 (1995) 345
368. *Herfert, N., Fink, G.:* Makromol. Chem. 193 (1992) 773
369. *Ewen, J.A., Elder, M., Curtis, S., Cheng, H.N.:* Catalytic Olefin Polymerization, Keii, T., Soga, K., Eds., KodanshaElsevier, 1990, p. 439
370. *Doi, Y., Suzuki, E., Keii, T.:* Ind. Eng. Chem., Prod. Res. Dev. 21 (1982) 580
371. *Böhm, L.L.:* Polymer 19 (1978) 562
372. *Rishina, L.A., Vizen, E.T.:* Eur. Polym. J. 16 (1980) 965
373. *Kuroda, N., Nishikitani, Y., Matssuura, K., Miyoshi, M.:* Makromol. Chem. 188 (1987) 1897
374. *Keii, T.:* Kinetics of ZieglerNatta Polymerization, Kodansha, 1972
375. *Tait, P.J.T.:* Coordination Polymerization, Academic Press, 1975, p. 155
376. *Zakharov, V.A., Yermakov, Yu. I.:* Catal. Rev. Sci. Eng. 19 (1979) 67
377. *Seppälä, J.K., Auer, M.:* Prog. Polym. Sci. 15 (1990) 147
378. *Burfield, D.R., Mc Kenzie, I.D., Tait, P.J.T.:* Polymer 13 (1972) 302
379. *Böhm, L.L.:* Polymer 19 (1978) 545, 553
380. *Mejzlik, J., Lesna, M., Kratochvila, J.:* Adv. Polym. Sci. 81 (1987) 83
381. *Burfield, D.R.:* Polymer 25 (1984) 1645
382. *Fischer, D., Jüngling, S., Mülhaupt, R.:* Makromol. Chem. Macromol. Symp. 66 (1993) 191
383. *Schneko, H., Dost, W., Kern, W.:* Makromol. Chem. 121 (1969) 159
384. *Zakharov, V.A., Bukatov, G.D., Chumaevskii, N.B., Yermakov, Yu. I.:* Makromol. Chem. 178 (1977) 967
385. *Pino, P., Rotzinger, B.:* Makromol. Chem. Suppl. 7 (1984) 41
386. *Zakharov, V.A., Makhtarulin, S.I., Yermakov, Yu. I.:* React. Kinet. Cat. Lett. 9 (1978) 137
387. Ref. 38, p. 1415
388. Ref. 40, p.105
389. *Fischer, D.:* Dissertation, Universitt Freiburg (1992)
390. Ref. 374, p. 145
391. *Chien, J.C.W., Wang, B. P.:* J. Polym. Sci., Part A: Polym. Chem. 28 (1990) 15
392. Ref. 374, p. 115
393. Ref. 40, p. 77
394. *Guastalla, G., Giannini, U.:* Makromol. Chem. Rapid Commun. 4 (1983) 519
395. *Spitz, R., Masson, P., Bobichon, C., Guyot, A.:* Makromol. Chem. 190 (1989) 717
396. *Chien, J.C.W., Nozaki, T.:* J. Polym. Sci., Part A: Polym. Chem. 29 (1991) 205
397. *Tsutsui, T., Kashiwa, N., Mizuno, A.:* Makromol. Chem. Rapid Commun. 11 (1990) 565
398. *Guyot, A., Spitz, R., Dassaud, J.P., Gomez, G.:* J. Mol. Catal. 82 (1993) 37
399. *Dudchenko, V.K., Zakharov, V.A., Bukatov, G.D.:* Plast. Massy (6) (1992) 20
400. *Chien, J.C.W., Nozaki, T.:* J. Polym. Sci., Part A: Polym. Chem. 29 (1991) 505
401. *Parson, J.W., AlTurki, T. M.:* Polym. Commun. 30 (1989) 72
402. *Bukatov, G.D., Goncharov, V.S., Zakharov, V.A., Dudchenko, V.K., Sergeev, S.A.:* Kinet. Katal. 35 (1994) 392
403. *Eshuis, J.J.W., Tan, Y.Y., Meetsma, A., Teuben, J.H.:* Organometallics 11 (1992) 362
404. *Zakharov, V.A., Chumaevskii, N.B., Bukatov, G.D., Yermakov, Yu.I.:* Makromol. Chem. 177 (1976) 763
405. *Fischer, D., Mülhaupt, R.:* J. Organomet. Chem. 417 (1991) C7
406. *Soga, K., Ohnishi, R., Sano, T.:* Polym. Bull. 7 (1982) 547
407. *Soga,K., Chen, S., Ohnishi, R.:* Polym. Bull. 8 (1982) 473
408. *Caunt, A.D.:* J. Polym. Sci., Part C: Polym. Symp. 4 (1963) 49
409. Ref. 40, p. 113
410. *Bochmann, M., Lancaster, S.J.:* Angew. Chem. Int. Ed. Engl. 33 (1994) 1634
411. *Kaminsky, W., Külper, K., Niedoba, S.:* Makromol. Chem. Macromol. Symp. 3 (1986) 377
412. *Kaminsky, W., Renner, F.:* Makromol. Chem. Rapid Commun. 14 (1993) 239
413. *Keii, T., Soga, K., Saiki, N.:* J. Polym. Sci., Part C: Polym. Symp. 16 (1967) 1507
414. *Chien, J.C.W., Kuo, C.:* J. Polym. Sci., Polym. Chem. Ed. 23 (1985) 761
415. *Tait, P.J.T.:* Macromol. Chem. (London), 1 (1980) 3
416. Ref. 40, p. 107

417. *Longo, P., Oliva, L., Grassi, A., Pellecchia, C.:* Makromol. Chem. 190 (1989) 2357
418. *Boucher, D.G., Parson, I.W., Haward, R.N.:* Makromol. Chem. 175 (1974) 3461
419. *Feldman, C.F., Perry, E.:* J. Polym. Sci. 46 (1960) 217
420. *Chien, J.C.W.:* J. Am. Chem. Soc. 81 (1959) 86
421. *Corradini, P., Busico, V., Cipullo, R.:* Makromol. Chem. Rapid Commun. 13 (1992) 21
422. *Burfield, D.R., Savariaz, C.M.:* Macromolecules 12 (1979) 243
423. *Tait, P.J.T.:* Development in Polymerization, Applied Science Publishers, 1979, Vol. 2, p. 81
424. *Cooper, W.:* Comprehensive Chemical Kinetics, Elsevier, 1976, Vol. 15, pp. 249257
425. *Zakharov, V.A., Bukatov, G.D., Yermakov, Yu.I.:* Coordination Polymerization,: Polymer Science and Technology, Plenum Press, 1982, Vol.19, p. 267
426. *Bukatov, G.D., Shepelev, S.H., Zakharov, V.A., Sergeev, S.A., Yermakov, Yu.I.:* Makromol. Chem. 183 (1982) 2657
427. *Kashiwa, N., Yoshitake, J.:* Makromol. Chem. Rapid Commun. 3 (1982) 211
428. *Tait, P.J.T.:* Int. Symp. 40 Years Ziegler Catalysts, Freiburg, Sept. 13, 1993
429. *Chien, J.C.W., Tsai, W.M.:* Makromol. Chem. Macromol. Symp. 66 (1993) 141
430. *Chien, J.C.W., Song, W., Rausch, M.D.:* J. Polym. Sci., Part A: Polym. Chem. 32 (1994) 2387
431. *Danusso, F., Sianesi, D.:* Chim. Ind. (Milan) 44 (1962) 474
432. *Boor, J.Jr.:* Macromol. Rev. 2 (1967) 115
433. *Böhm, L.L.:* J. Appl. Polym. Sci. 29 (1984) 279
434. *Novaro, O., Blaisten-Brojas, E., Clementi, E., Giunchi, G., RuizVizcaya, M.E.:* J. Chem. Phys. 68 (1978) 2337
435. *Cassoux, P., Crasmier, F., Labarre, J.F.:* J. Organomet. Chem. 165 (1979) 303
436. *Weiss, H., Ehrig, M., Ahlrichs, R.:* J. Am. Chem. Soc. 116 (1994) 4919
437. *Meier, R.J., van Doremaele, G.H.J., Iarlori, S., Buda, F.:* J. Am. Chem. Soc. 116 (1994) 7274
438. *Kioka, M., Makyo, H., Mizuno, A., Kashiwa, N.:* Polymer 35 (1994) 580
439. *Zucchini, U., Cecchin, G.:* Adv. Polym. Sci. 51 (1983) 101
440. *Suzuki, E., Tamura, M., Doi, Y., Keii, T.:* Makromol. Chem. 180 (1979) 2235
441. *Warzelhan, V., Burger, T.F., Stein, D.J.:* Makromol. Chem. 183 (1982) 489
442. *Rishina, L.A., Vizen, E.T.:* Eur. Polym. J. 16 (1980) 965
443. *Floyd, S., Heiskanen, T., Taylor, T.W.:* J. Appl. Polym. Sci. 33 (1987) 1021
444. *Pino, P., Rotzinger, B., von Achenbach, E.:* Makromol. Chem. Suppl. 25 (1985) 461
445. *Baulin, A.A., Radionov, A.G., Ivanchev, S.S., Domreva, N.N.:* Eur. Polym. Sci. 16 (1980) 937
446. *Kaminsky, W., Ahlers, A., Möller-Linderdorf, N.:* Angew. Chem. Int. Ed. Engl. 28 (1989) 1216
447. *Burger, B., Thompson, M., Cotter, D., Bercaw, J.:* J. Am. Chem. Soc. 112 (1990) 1566
448. *Watson, P.L., Parshall, G.W.:* Acc. Chem. Res. 18 (1985) 51
449. *Kashiwa, N., Yoshitake, J.:* Polym. Bull. 11 (1984) 479
450. *Burger, P., Hartmann, K., Brintzinger, H.H.:* Makromol. Chem. Macromol. Suppl. 66 (1993) 127
451. *Boor, J.Jr.:* J. Polym. Sci., Part C: Polym. Symp. 1 (1963) 237
452. *Köster, R., Bruno, G.:* Liebigs Ann. Chem. 629 (1960) 89
453. *Cossee, P.:* Trans. Farad. Soc. 58 (1962) 1926
454. Ref. 38, p.24
455. *Chien, J.C.W., Ang, T., Kuo, C.I.:* J. Polym. Sci., Part A: Polym. Chem. 23 (1985) 723
456. *Berger, M.N., Grieveson, B.M.:* Makromol. Chem. 83 (1965) 80
457. *Buls, W.H., Higgins, T.L.:* J. Polym. Sci., Part A: Polym. Chem. 8 (1970) 1025
458. *Buls, W.H., Higgins, T.L.:* J. Polym. Sci., Part A: Polym. Chem. 8 (1970) 1037
459. Ref.1, chapter 8
460. *Galli, P., Haylock, J.C.:* Prog. Polym. Sci. 16 (1991) 443
461. *Galli, P., Haylock, J.C.:* Makromol. Chem. Macromol. Symp. 63 (1992) 19
462. *Kakugo, M., Sadatoshi, H., Yokoama, M., Kojima, K.:* Macromolecules 22 (1989) 547
463. *Kakugo, M., Sadatoshi, H., Sakai, J., Yokoama, M.:* Macromolecules 22 (1989) 3172
464. *Kakugo, M., Sadatoshi, H., Sakai, J.:* Catalytic Olefin Polymerization, Keii, T., Soga, K., Eds., KodanshaElsevier, 1990, p. 345
465. *Conner, W.C., Webb, S.W., Spanne, P., Jones, K.W.:* Macromolecules 23 (1990) 4742
466. *Ferrero, M.A., Sommer, R., Spanne, P., Jones, K.W., Conner, W.C.:* J. Polym. Sci., Part A: Polym. Chem. 31 (1993) 2507

467. *Ferrero, M.A., Koffi, E., Sommer, R., Conner, W.C.:* J. Polym. Sci., Part A: Polym. Chem. 30 (1992) 2131
468. *Noristi, L., Marchetti, E., Baruzzi, G., Sgarzi, P.:* J. Polym. Sci., Part A: Polym. Chem. 32 (1994) 3047
469. Ref. 40, p.9
470. *Singh, D., Merrill, R.P.:* Macromolecules 4 (1971) 599
471. *Schmeal, W.R., Street, J.R.:* J. Polym. Sci., Part B: Polym. Phys. 10 (1972) 2173
472. *Nagel, E.J., Kirillov, V.A., Ray, W.H.:* Ind. Eng. Chem., Prod. Res. Dev. 19 (1980) 372
473. *Floyd, S., Choi, K.Y., Taylor, T.W., Ray, W.H.:* J. Appl. Polym. Sci. 32 (1986) 2231
474. *Floyd, S., Choi, K.Y., Taylor, T.W., Ray, W.H.:* J. Appl. Polym. Sci. 32 (1986) 2935
475. *Hutchinson, R.A., Chen, C.M., Ray, W.H.:* J. Appl. Polym. Sci. 44 (1992) 1389
476. *Laurence, R.L., Chiovetta, M.G.:* Polymer Reaction Engineering, Reichert, K.H., Geiseler, W., Eds., Hanser Publishers, 1983, p.74
477. *Hutchinson, R.A., Ray, W.H.:* J. Appl. Polym. Sci. 34 (1987) 657
478. *Natta G.:* Rend. Acc. Nazl. Lincei 4 (1955) 61
479. *Natta, G.:* J. Polym. Sci. 34 (1959) 531
480. *Natta, G., Pasquon, I., Zambelli, A., Gatti, G.:* Makromol. Chem. 70 (1964) 191
481. *Van der Ven, S:* Polypropylene and Other Polyolefins, Elsevier, 1990
482. *McCrum, N.G., Read, B.E., Williams, G.:* Anelastic and Dielectric Effects in Polymeric Solids, J. Wiley & Sons, Inc., 1967, p. 379
483. *Anonymous,* Modrn Plastics, April 1986, 14
484. *Galli, G., Simonazzi, T., Barbè, P.C.:* Proc. of 6 Italian Symposium on Macromolecular Science, Pisa, October 1014, 1983
485. *Ficker, H.K., Walker, D.A.:* Plastics and rubber processing and applications 14 (1990) 103
486. *Sasaki, T., Ebara, T., Johoji, H.:* Polymers for Advanced Technologies 4 (1993) 406
487. European Patent Appl. 400 333 (1990) HIMONT Incorporated
488. European Patent Appl. 373 660 (1989) HIMONT Incorporated
489. European Patent Appl. 416 379 (1990) HIMONT Incorporated
490. European Patent Appl. 411 627 (1990) HIMONT Incorporated
491. U. S. Patent 4 734 459 (1986) HIMONT Incorporated
492. European Patent Appl. 472 946 (1991) HIMONT Incorporated
493. *Cecchin, G.:* Macromol. Symp. 78 (1994) 213
494. *Wang, J.G., Chen, H., Huang, B.T.:* Makromol. Chem. 194 (1993) 1807
495. *Locatelli, P., Tritto, I., Sacchi, M.C., Zannoni, G.:* Makromol. Chem. Rapid Commun. 9 (1988) 575
496. *Locatelli, P., Tritto, I., Sacchi, M.C., Forlini, F.:* Makromol. Chem. Rapid Commun. 14 (1993) 231
497. *Locatelli, P., Fan, Z.Q., Tritto, I., Sacchi, M.C., Forlini, F.:* Makromol. Chem. 195 (1994) 2805
498. *Soga, K., Ohtake, M., Ohnishi, R., Doi, Y.:* Makromol. Chem. 186 (1985) 1129
499. *Soga, K., Ouzumi, T., Park, J.R.:* Makromol. Chem. 191 (1990) 2853
500. *Fan, Z.Q., Forlini, F., Tritto, I., Locatelli, P., Sacchi, M.C.:* Makromol. Chem. 195 (1994) 3889
501. *Xu, Z., Feng, L., Wang, D., Yang, S.:* Makromol. Chem. 192 (1991) 1835
502. *Kissin, Y.:* Transition Metal Catalyzed Polyymerizations, Alkenes and Dienes, Quirk, R.P., Ed., Harwood Academic Publishers, New York, 1983, Part A, p. 597
503. *Cheng, H.N., Kakugo, M.:* Macromolecules 24 (1991) 1724
504. *Collina, G., Noristi, L., Stewart, C.A.:* J. Mol. Catal. A: Chem. 99 (1995) 161
505. *Cozewith, C.:* Macromolecules 20 (1987) 1237
506. *Ross, J.F.:* J. Macromol. Sci., Chem. A21 (1984) 453
507. *Kakugo, M., Miyatake, T., Mizunuma, K., Kawai, Y.:* Macromolecules 21 (1988) 2309
508. *Locatelli, P., Sacchi, M.C., Tritto, I., Forlini, F.:* Macromolecules 23 (1990) 2406
509. *Cecchin, G.:* AIM Symposium on Copolymers, Gargnano, June 38, 1990
510. *Keii, T., Terano, T., Kimura, K., Ishii, K.:* Transition Metals and Organometallics as Catalysts for Olefin Polymerization, Kaminsky, W., Sinn, H., Eds., Springer Verlag, Berlin, 1988, p.3
511. *Collina, G., Cecchin, G.:* Int. Symp. Frontiers in Polymerization, Lige, Oct. 68, 1993
512. *Gilet, L., Grenier*Loustalot, M., Bounoure, J.: Polymer 33 (1992) 4605
513. *Kaminsky, W.:* Transition Metal Catalyzed Polyymerizations, Alkenes and Dienes, Quirk, R.P., Ed. Harwood Academic Publishers, New York, 1983, Part A, p. 225
514. *Brintzinger, H.H.:* Transition Metals and Organometallics as Catalysts for Olefin Polymerization, Kaminsky, W., Sinn, H., Eds., SpringerVerlag, Berlin, 1988, p.249

515. *Ewen, J.A., Haspeslagh, L., Elder, M.J., Atwood, J.L.:* Transition Metals and Organometallics as Catalysts for Olefin Polymerization, Kaminsky, W., Sinn, H., Eds., SpringerVerlag, Berlin, 1988, p.281
516. *Chien, J.C.W., He, D.:* J. Polym. Sci., Part A: Polym. Chem. 29 (1991) 1585
517. *Herfet, N., Montag, P., Fink, G.:* Makromol. Chem. 194 (1993) 3167
518. *Kaminsky, W., Miri, M.:* J. Polym. Sci., Polym. Chem. Ed. 23 (1985) 2151
519. *Baldwin, F.P., ver Strate, G.:* Rubber Chem. Technol. 45 (1972) 709
520. *Camurati, I., Ferrara, G., Franzese, R.:* unpublished results
521. *Zambelli A., Grassi A., Galimberti M., Mazzocchi R., Piemontesi F.:* Makromol. Chem. Rapid Commun. 12 (1991) 523
522. *Randall, J.C., Rucker, S.P.:* Macromolecules 27 (1994) 2120
523. *Herfert, N., Fink, G.:* Polym. Mater. Sci. Eng. 67 (1992) 31
524. *Uozumi, T., Soga, K.:* Makromol. Chem. 193 (1992) 823
525. European Patent Appl. 318 049 (1988) Ausimont S.r.l
526. European Patent Appl. 464 684 (1991) HIMONT Incorporated
527. U.S. Patent 5 280 074 (1992) Hoechst AG.

3   Structure and Morphology

Roger A. Phillips, Michael D. Wolkowicz

3.1   Introduction

Since the application on an industrial scale of Ziegler–Natta catalyst technology, the structure, morphology, and properties of isotactic polypropylene (PP) have been extensively examined. The properties of PP are intimately related to both the fabrication history of the material and its intrinsic polymer structure. The intrinsic polymer structure is related to the catalyst, polymerization, and compounding technologies. The wide range of end-use applications for which PP is currently produced is testimony to the variety of properties that can be achieved. Expansion of the property range, which makes such versatility possible, is expected in upcoming years with continued advancements in catalyst and polymerization technologies. These technologies are expected to bring further improvements in isotacticity and molecular weight control, unique stereospecific microstructures, an expanding base of reactor comonomer technologies, and new reactor-based grafting technologies, to name only a few. For each of these technological developments, an understanding of polymer morphology provides a critical bridge between polymer structure, processing, fabrication history, and end-use properties. This understanding is challenged not only by the advent of new PP-based structures but also by impressive advancements in such varied areas of polymer physics as crystalline structure, crystallization kinetics, polymer phase behavior, rheology, and polymer dynamics.

    While it is difficult to provide in-depth treatment for all areas related to the morphology of PP-based products, a general perspective of many of the more important morphological issues are drawn from the literature. It is hoped that this overview will give an appreciation for the rich variety of physical behaviors exhibited by PP.

3.1.1   Building Blocks of PP Morphology

Polypropylene homopolymer is semicrystalline in nature. As with any semicrystalline polymer, the morphology exhibits a hierarchy of characteristic scales as shown in Fig. 3.1. Macromorphology is seen on the visual scale (i.e., millimeters). This scale corresponds to such features as the gross reactor particle shape [1 - 4] and skin-core structures [5 - 9] for example. On a finer scale, the spherulite structure is revealed and is on the order of 1 micron to 50 microns [10 - 17]. This size scale can be readily accessed by techniques such as optical microscopy or small angle light scattering (SALS). The spherulite is composed of building blocks of lamellar-shaped crystals. The lamellar periodicity, or center-to-center distance between lamellae, is represented by the long spacing. The long spacing has values in the range of 100 Å to 300 Å [12, 14, 16, 18 - 23]. This scale is typically investigated by either small angle X-ray scattering (SAXS) or by higher resolution electron microscopy. On a finer scale, the lamellae are composed of crystallographically ordered regions. The individual chains contained within the crystalline regions are arranged with specific symmetry and unit cell dimension [24 - 28]. The unit cell dimensions (6 Å to 20 Å) are shown in Fig. 3.1 for the α-form of isotactic polypropylene. Structure on this scale is commonly probed by wide angle X-ray scattering (WAXS) and electron diffraction techniques. Polypropylene homopolymer exhibits a rich variety of morphological features across this entire hierarchy of scale.

3.1.2   Crystallinity and Stereoregularity

The crystallizability of the chain is a critical factor governing the resultant morphology. The degree of crystallinity of PP homopolymer is governed primarily by the tacticity of the chain. Isotactic chains result from the head-to-tail addition of propylene monomer units, where the

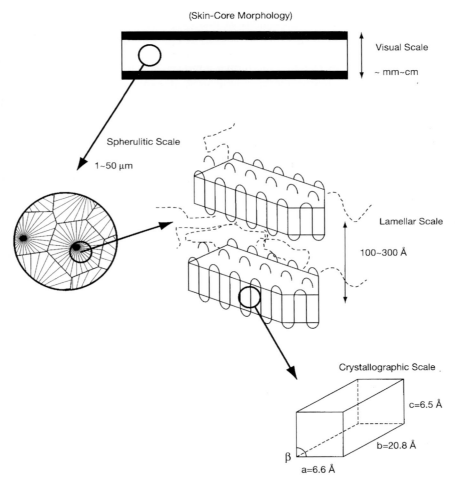

Figure 3.1   Characteristic hierarchy of morphological scales in PP. The skin-core morphology of an injection molding is used to illustrate morphology on the visual scale

methyl groups always have the same configuration with respect to the polymer backbone. Syndiotactic chains result from the same head-to-tail addition of monomer units, but the methyl groups have an alternating configuration with respect to the polymer backbone. The stereospecificity (isospecific or syndiospecific) refers to the consistency of the methyl group placement. Atactic chains do not have any consistent placement of the methyl groups. Figure 3.2 shows a schematic of isotactic, syndiotactic, and atactic PP chains.

The level of tacticity can be varied considerably in PP. Tacticities of 100% are ideal, but often are not reached in practice. Crystallization of either isotactic or syndiotactic PP chains can result in a relatively high degree of crystallinity, in the range of 40% to 70%. High crystallinity requires high tacticity, which implies the presence of long, uninterrupted, stereospecific sequences along the chain. As the tacticity along the polymer chain is reduced, the crystallinity decreases. In the extreme case, the crystallinity of atactic PP is zero. A major achievement of modern catalysts is better control over tacticity.

Figure 3.3 illustrates a simplistic view of stereoisomerism in PP homopolymer. This discussion focuses on chains of isotactic PP, although the same general concept also can be applied to syndiotactic PP. A chain of isotactic PP can be viewed as an unbroken string of isotactic sequences (continuous line) interrupted by an occasional defect (shaded square blocks). The defect refers to a disruption of the consistent placement of the methyl group during monomer addition to the growing polymer chain. The nature of these stereospecific defects have been discussed in great detail in the literature [29 - 40]. Thus, any change from the correct placement of the propylene molecule becomes a defect in stereoregularity and lowers the tacticity. The stereoregularity can be viewed in terms of the defect distribution along a single chain ("intra-chain" defect distribution) and the distribution among chains with various defect frequencies ("inter-chain" distribution). Early work by Natta [24] suggested that samples obtained under various conditions of solvent fractionation could be discriminated on the basis of tacticity. These differences are the result of the inter-chain distribution. Often the term "stereoblock" is used to refer to fractions of the inter-chain distribution of intermediate tacticity. The specific nature of the inter-chain distribution is sensitive to the catalyst and polymerization process.

The stereochemistry of the PP chain strongly influences the crystallinity. This is illustrated in Fig. 3.4, which shows wide angle X-ray patterns of isotactic, syndiotactic, and atactic PP. Figure 3.4 shows pronounced crystalline reflections when the PP chain

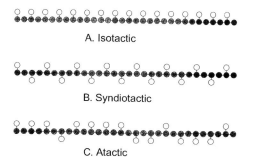

A. Isotactic

B. Syndiotactic

C. Atactic

Figure 3.2   Schematic illustration of the stereochemical configurations of PP: A) isotactic PP, B) syndiotactic PP, C) atactic PP

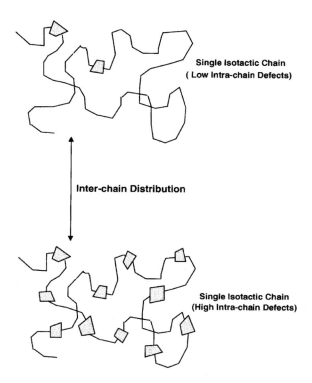

Figure 3.3   Conceptual illustration of tacticity distribution in iPP. The continuous lines represent uninterrupted isotactic sequences; the shaded blocks represent errors in tacticity (defects). The occurrence of defects vs. isotactic sequences along a given chain determines the intra-chain defect distribution. The difference in defect frequencies among chains determines the inter-chain defect distribution

contains either regular isotactic or syndiotactic sequences. Those patterns are related to the specific crystal unit cell symmetries for isotactic and syndiotactic PP. Atactic PP shows no strong reflections, exhibiting only a very broad and diffuse scattering from X-rays that is characteristic of a noncrystalline material.

3.1.3   Relationship of Morphology to Structure, Processing, and Properties

In addition to stereoregularity, there are many other determinants of PP morphology. Figure 3.5 shows that the polymer morphology provides a critical bridge among polymer structure, polymer processing, and end-use properties. In addition to the effect of tacticity discussed above, important structural properties of the PP chain include the molecular weight and polydispersity, composition in blends and copolymers, and details of the intra-chain architecture which include comonomer distribution in random, heterophasic, and graft copolymers. Important processing parameters can include the melt processing conditions, orientation, thermal history, the addition of nucleators and additives, and post-synthesis reactions relating to polymer degradation of molecular weight and polymer cross-linking.

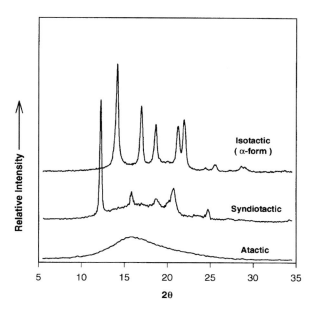

Figure 3.4   Wide angle X-ray scattering patterns of isotactic, syndiotactic, and atactic PP

Understanding the effects of these structural and processing variables on PP morphology is essential, because it is the morphology which provides the most direct link with polymer properties.

As indicated earlier, the bulk morphology consists of basic "building blocks" of vastly different scales: macroscopic, spherulitic, lamellar, and crystallographic. The specific components of this hierarchy can include:

1. Skin/core macrostructures and related spatial gradients of the morphology,
2. spherulitic and blend phase morphologies,
3. lamellar morphology, size, and organization, and
4. crystal structure.

Many of these specific components of the morphological hierarchy of PP are discussed in the following sections, beginning with the smallest scale, the crystallographic scale. Several forms of PP are discussed: α-form isotactic polypropylene (iPP); the polymorphic forms of iPP: β, γ, and mesomorphic (smectic); and syndiotactic polypropylene (sPP). Features of the different morphological size scales, melting behavior, and crystallization kinetics are reviewed for each of these cases. Lastly, the relationship between polymer structure, processing, and morphology in PP is highlighted through selected examples for PP homopolymer and the important area of rubber-modified PP.

These discussions attempt to summarize many of the important developments in the understanding of PP morphology, primarily from the perspective of PP homopolymer. The understanding of PP morphology is still evolving, and an attempt is made to provide a balanced representation of conflicting views and areas of uncertainty.

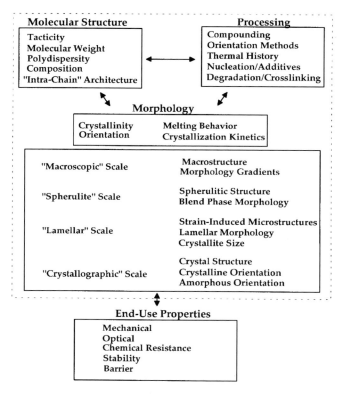

Figure 3.5   Relationships among polymer structure, processing, morphology, and end-use properties. The polymer morphology is composed of various building blocks over a hierarchy of scales

3.2   Morphology of α–Form Isotactic PP

In the crystalline state, it has long been recognized that iPP can exist in several different primary crystalline forms [25, 41]. These forms exhibit different crystallographic symmetries and/or ordering of the isotactic chains. The dominant form for iPP is the α-form.

3.2.1   Crystallographic Symmetry

The α-form was indexed in early work by Natta and Corradini [24]. Some authors have differentiated the α-form by two different space group symmetries, C2/c (α_1-form) and P2$_1$/c (α_2-form) [27, 42 - 45]. General discussions of space group symmetries and unit cell lattices are available in the literature [24 - 28, 46, 47] and in standard reference materials [48]. Figure 3.6 shows the corresponding crystal structure, which shows a helical conformation of the PP chain arranged on a monoclinic unit cell [24, 26]. The corresponding helical conformation in the crystalline state can be formed by either right- or left-handed rotation about the central

Table 3.1 Isotactic PP α-Form Monoclinic Room Temperature Unit Cell Parameters

Reference	Space group	a (Å)	b (Å)	c (Å)	Monoclinic angle, $\beta,°$	Sample preparation
[24]	C2/c	6.65	20.96	6.50	99.33	Oriented fiber pattern
[26]	P2₁/c	6.63	20.78	6.5	99.5	spun fiber, annealed 110 °C
[27]	C2/c	6.67	20.8	6.50	98.67	Oriented, annealed 140 °C
[27]	P2₁/c	6.65	20.73	6.50	98.67	Oriented, annealed 170 °C
[28]*	P2₁/c	6.63	20.98	6.52	98.5	Unoriented, annealed 160 °C
[28]*	P2₁/c	6.61	20.94	6.53	98.8	Unoriented, annealed 160 °C
[25]	P2₁/c	6.66	20.78	6.50	99.62	Slow cooled from 190 °C

* These two differ only in details of the refinement procedures used in structure determination

axis. The helix also has unique (non-identical) "up" and "down" directions independent of the handedness. Table 3.1 gives a summary of selected unit cell refinements from the literature [24 - 28].

The monoclinic unit cell was originally indexed by Natta and Corradini [24] in the C2/c space group (α_1-form). This structural assignment has subsequently been associated with crystallization at high undercooling [27, 42 - 45], and is characterized by statistical disorder of the up and down chain orientations [24, 26 - 28, 42 - 46]. The monoclinic unit cell has also been indexed in the P2₁/c space group (α_2-form) [25 - 28], which allows for specific ordering of the up and down chain orientations as indicated in Fig. 3.6. The P2₁/c space group has been associated with crystallization at low undercooling or high temperature annealing [27, 42 - 45]. This is consistent with packing energy considerations, which suggest that the P2₁/c space group is slightly preferred thermodynamically [45 - 47]. A transition between these two limiting symmetries of the α-form requires significant conformational rearrangement of chains. This suggests that some form of melting on heating is required to promote the transition from α_1 to α_2 symmetry [43 - 45].

An order parameter has been defined using wide angle X-ray scattering (WAXS) that correlates the relative tendency for formation of the α_1 and α_2 symmetries [27, 42 - 44]. This parameter shows increasing order (α_2-form) with increasing temperature during annealing in the solid-state, especially for temperatures greater than about 150 °C, and has a rough proportionality to the melting point [43]. The range of annealing temperature over which this continuous change occurs is sensitive to the sample melting point [43, 44] and, for oriented structures, the draw ratio [27]. The change of the ordering parameter with annealing is irreversible on cooling [27]. These observations are consistent with an increase in perfection of the crystalline regions during annealing.

3.2.2   Lamellar Morphology

Lamellar and spherulitic microstructures of α-form iPP have been extensively examined [10, 12, 16 - 19, 22, 23, 49 - 52]. The lamellar morphology of iPP has been used to explain the optical classification of α-form spherulites [16, 17, 21, 50, 52], indicating a strong link between lamellar and spherulitic morphologies. The crystal habit of semicrystalline

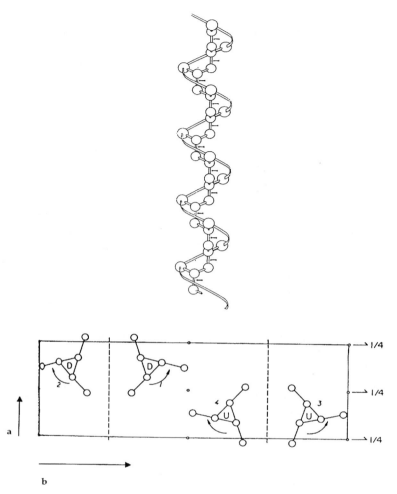

Figure 3.6   The 3_1-helical conformation of isotactic polypropylene in the crystalline state [24], and the corresponding unit cell structure (P2$_1$/c space group) seen in c-axis projection [26]. Left- and right-handed helices are indicated by the curved arrows. Up (U) and down (D) chain inclinations are discussed in the text. Upper portion reprinted from Ref. [1], by permission of John Wiley & Sons, Inc. Lower portion reprinted from Ref. [26], p. 101, by courtesy of Marcel Dekker, Inc

homopolymers quiescently crystallized from the melt is generally accepted to be that of the folded chain lamellae shown in Fig. 3.7. The magnitude of the lamellar thickness, 50 Å to 200 Å, is small with respect to the other two crystal dimensions.

Isotactic PP in the α-form exhibits a unique tendency for lamellae to organize into a "cross-hatched" pattern [12, 16 - 19, 21 - 23, 50 - 52]. This feature of the morphology is illustrated schematically in Fig. 3.8. Figure 3.9 shows a micrograph from a scanning electron microscope (SEM) of a bulk iPP sample exhibiting dense cross-hatching. The prominent features of cross-hatching, as summarized schematically in Fig. 3.8, have been determined

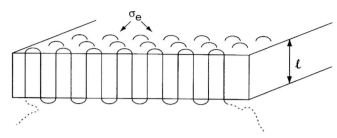

Figure 3.7   Folded chain lamellar morphology in semicrystalline polymers (l is the lamellar thickness, and σ_e is the fold surface interfacial energy)

from electron microscopy studies of solution-crystallized [12, 18] and melt-crystallized [16, 17, 19, 21, 23] α-form iPP. These studies indicate the coexistence of radial lathlike lamellae with "cross-hatched" tangential lamellae oriented nearly orthogonal to the radial direction. As indicated in Fig. 3.8, the preferred growth direction of the dominant radial (R, "parent") lamellae has been determined to be associated with the a^*-crystallographic direction, with the chain axis (c-axis) approximately perpendicular to the radial direction [16, 19, 21, 22, 50, 51]. It has been proposed that the near orthogonal branching angle corresponds to the matching of the a-and c-axis pair in the radial lamellae with the c-and a-axis of the tangential lamellae [16, 19, 21, 50, 51]. This relationship is due to the relatively modest mismatch between the c-and a-axis unit cell parameters shown in Table 3.1. Observations of lamellar branching angles appear to be consistent with the above-noted molecular epitaxy [16, 19, 21, 50, 51].

The radial lamellae nucleate orthogonal overgrowths, as evidenced by the larger thickness of radial lamellae at higher crystallization temperatures [16, 23]. The orthogonal overgrowths can exhibit reduced stability relative to the radial lamellae on heating [23, 53]. Although early speculation suggested the possible role of the γ-form in initiating cross-

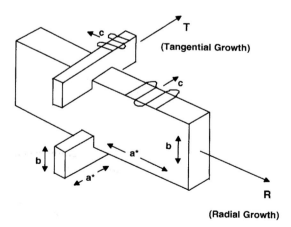

Figure 3.8   Schematic of cross-hatched lamellar morphology of iPP adapted from [21]. The radial (R) parent lamellae and tangential (T) daughter lamellae are shown, and approximate relative relationships of the chain axis in each

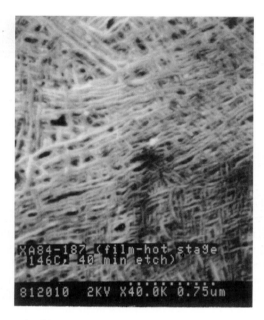

Figure 3.9   SEM micrograph of dense cross-hatching in iPP. The sample was electron beam irradiated and crystallized under isothermal conditions at 146 °C. Features of the cross-hatching were brought out by permanganic acid etching. 1 mm = 360 Å

hatching [21], more recent studies suggest a pure form of epitaxy (only α-form) [16, 51, 54] that most likely involves contact faces of helices with similar hand for the cross-hatched members [51, 54]. Lamellar cross-hatching increases as the isothermal crystallization temperature is reduced [12, 16, 23].

3.2.3   Spherulitic Morphology

The α-form spherulites have been classified into different forms with distinctly different optical characteristics in cross-polarized light. Norton and Keller have reviewed these classifications and summarized the forms as Type I, Type II, and mixed spherulites [16]. These classifications are similar to earlier work [10, 16, 17]. According to these classification schemes, spherulites with a well-defined Maltese cross appearance (in cross-polarized light) and positive optical birefringence were called Type I. Type II spherulites also exhibit a Maltese cross pattern, but exhibit negative birefringence. Mixed spherulites exhibit no well-defined Maltese cross pattern. Color Plates 3.1 and 3.2 show, respectively, Type I and Type II spherulites with crossed polarized light. Note the blue section is in different quadrants because of the different signs of the birefringence. The Norton and Keller classification suggested that Type II spherulites are formed at elevated temperature (> 138 °C), whereas the Type I spherulites form at lower temperature (< 136 °C) [16]. The actual temperature ranges observed in practice are dependent on the melt history and specific grade of iPP [10, 16, 55].

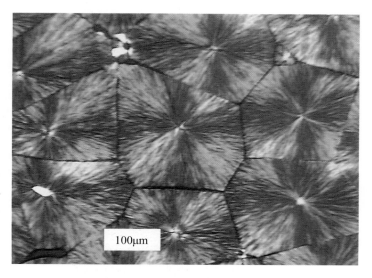

Color Plate 3.1. Morphology of Type I spherulites of iPP homopolymer viewed by an optical microscope with cross-polarized light and $1/4$ λ plate. Grown under isothermal conditions at $130\,^{\circ}$C

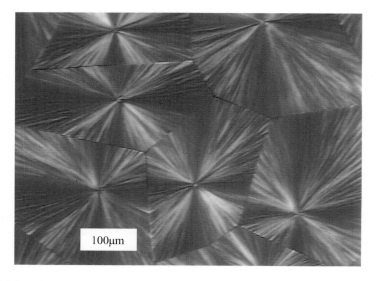

Color Plate 3.2. Morphology of Type II spherulites of iPP homopolymer viewed by an optical microscope with cross-polarized light and a $1/4$ λ plate. Type II spherulite grown under isothermal conditions at $140\,^{\circ}$C

The different optical characteristics of the spherulites have been linked to the lamellar morphology through the balance of cross-hatched radial and tangential lamellae. As shown schematically in Fig. 3.8, the lamellae are composed of chains nearly normal to the lamellar surfaces [16, 17, 21 - 23, 50]. In this way, the negatively birefringent Type II spherulites are dominated by the radial lamellae (chains perpendicular to spherulite radius), whereas the Type I positively birefringent spherulites contain increased quantities of the tangential lamellae (chains parallel to spherulite radius). During heating, a sign change of the birefringence for Type I spherulites is observed [10] due to the premelting of the orthogonal overgrowths. The transition between negative and positive birefringence of α-form spherulites occurs when approximately one-third of the lamellae are tangential [50]. At higher crystallization temperatures (155 °C), axialitic morphologies composed of sheaf-like structures have been observed, with little tendency for cross-hatching [23, 52, 56].

3.2.4   Melting Behavior

Like the crystallinity, the melting point of α-form iPP is strongly dependent on tacticity [57 - 63] and thermal history [53, 57, 58, 60, 64 - 77]. Thermal history effects are generally observed in semicrystalline polymers. The melting point and nature of the melting distribution are governed by the intra-and inter-chain defect distributions. Catalyst technologies are continuing to evolve toward increasingly perfect chains and polymers with tailored tacticity. Knowledge of the "perfect chain" characteristics, such as crystallinity and melting point, remain a significant area of interest for both iPP and sPP.

The observed melting point of a semicrystalline polymer will differ from the equilibrium value due to a variety of factors, including

1.   Polymer molecular weight [78 - 82],
2.   a distribution of noncrystallizable components along the chain [78, 79, 83],
3.   specific thermodynamic interactions in a polymer blend [79, 84],
4.   diluent effects [78, 79],
5.   orientation [70, 85 - 87], or
6.   various morphological effects.

Some of the morphological effects can include defect incorporation in the crystalline lattice [88], polymorphism (Section 3.3), finite size effects relating to the crystallization undercooling [89 - 91], and effects related to solid-state annealing/reorganization [92, 93].

3.2.4.1   Equilibrium Melting Point

A particular lamellar thickness, l, is kinetically favored at a given crystallization temperature, resulting in a folded conformation of chains within the lamellae (Fig. 3.7). It can readily be shown [89, 91] that a thin lamellar dimension results in a melting point depression as given by eq 3.1.

$$T_m = T_m^\circ \left\{ 1 - \left(\frac{2\sigma_e}{\Delta h_f l} \right) \right\} \qquad (3.1)$$

With reference to Fig. 3.7, σ_e is the fold surface interfacial energy, Δh_f is the heat of fusion per unit volume of crystal, l is the lamellar thickness, T_m is the observed melting point, and T_m° is the theoretical equilibrium melting point of a perfect and infinitely large crystal. Equation 3.1 relates the melting point to the lamellar thickness and predicts that thick crystals melt at high temperature and, conversely, thin crystals melt at lower temperature.

The nucleation theory of Hoffman et. al. [91] and the Hoffmann–Weeks extrapolation method [90] indicate that, for sufficiently high crystallization temperature (T_c), the melting point (related to crystal thickness by eq 3.1) also increases linearly with increasing crystallization temperature. These theories predict that T_m° can be estimated by the intersection of the melting point versus crystallization temperature line (T_m vs. T_c) with the line $T_m = T_c$ [90].

The value of T_m° is determined experimentally by extrapolation. These extrapolations can be based on the dependence of melting point, T_m, on diluent concentration [78, 79], molecular weight [78, 79], lamellar thickness [89, 91], or crystallization temperature [90]. For high molecular weight and highly isotactic samples of iPP, the equilibrium melting point (T_m°) for the α-form has been quoted to lie in a surprisingly wide range. The results vary between 180 °C and 220 °C. A representative summary of literature determinations is given in Table 3.2. The results from Table 3.2 suggest that values of T_m° in the range of 185 °C to 188 °C appear to have been duplicated by a number of different experimental techniques. However, a general concensus on a more precise value for the equilibrium melting point within the limits noted above has not been reached.

Table 3.2 Representative Literature Evaluations of iPP α-form T_m°

Reference	Method	T_m° (°C)	ΔH° (J/m)
[94]	Melting point depression: diluents	186	208
[74]	Hoffman-Weeks extrapolation	208	148
[70][a]	Hoffman-Weeks extrapolation	185, 220	
[67]	Hoffman-Weeks extrapolation	208	
[96]	Hoffman-Weeks extrapolation	203	
[77]	Hoffman-Weeks extrapolation	191	
[97]	Hoffman-Weeks extrapolation	186	
[71]	Hoffman-Weeks extrapolation	197	
[75][a]	Hoffman-Weeks extrapolation	185, 208	
[64]	Hoffman-Weeks extrapolation	220	
[73]	Hoffman-Weeks extrapolation	186	
[56]	Hoffman-Weeks extrapolation	185	197
[58]	Hoffman-Weeks extrapolation	185	
[60]	T_m vs. chain length	188	
[56]	T_m vs. lamellar thickness	185	
[53]	T_m vs. lamellar thickness	186	
[95]	T_m vs. long spacing	202	
[57][b]	Literature summary	187.5	164
[99]	Database		207
[100]	Handbook		209
[98]	Database		165

[a] Values evaluated from multiple endotherms
[b] Arguments relating to surface fold energies

Similarly large variations are observed for published values of the heat of fusion of 100% crystalline material, ΔH°. These values lie roughly in the range of 150 J/g to 210 J/g, with an average of about 165 J/g [74, 98]. A summary also appears in Table 3.2. Again, agreement on the precise value is not widely found. The density of iPP in the α-form varies between the limit of 100% amorphous ($\rho_a = 0.850$ g/cm^3 to 0.855 g/cm^3) [57, 100] and 100% crystalline ($\rho_c = 0.936$ g/cm^3 to 0.946 g/cm^3) [24, 57, 100].

Crystallinity is strongly correlated to tacticity [59, 61]. The melting point, T_m, and crystallization temperature, T_c, are also strongly correlated to the tacticity [57 - 63, 101]. This is due to the role of stereo defects in disrupting the length of the crystallizable, isotactic sequences. The influence of tacticity on T_m° has been determined by experiments utilizing Hoffmann–Weeks extrapolations of iPP with varying stereoregularity [58, 60, 101]. However, the value of T_m° for a perfectly regular chain is not expected to differ substantially from measurements using iPP with the high tacticities produced by existing commercial technology.

3.2.4.2   Multiple Endotherms

In addition to the influence of tacticity, variation in values of T_m° quoted in the literature result from extrapolations required by the various techniques, or the occurrence of multiple endotherms in DSC procedures used for measurement of T_m [70, 73, 75]. This behavior is prominent over a range of crystallization temperatures [57, 60 - 62, 64 - 66, 68 - 70, 72, 73, 75, 76, 101, 102]. Multiple endotherms are observed in a wide variety of semicrystalline polymers. Multiple melting behavior can arise from:

1. Melting of crystals of different polymorphic forms (in iPP, this implies $\alpha_{1,2}$, β, γ, and mesomorphic forms),
2. reorganization effects (melting, recrystallization, and remelting) during the course of heating,
3. melting of discrete morphological populations of the same crystallographic form but differing in size and perfection,
4. orientation effects, or
5. segregation effects (by tacticity, composition, and/or molecular weight).

In iPP most of these effects can occur. Because crystallization behavior, crystallinity, and melting behavior are closely related to the intrinsic polymer characteristics, they are important methods for studying the chain structure. Consequently, understanding the causes of, and mechanisms involved in, multiple melting behavior is an important, yet challenging, task. The influence of polymorphism is discussed in subsequent sections. While polymorphism is an important factor in iPP, it is not the sole cause of multiple endotherms. Table 3.3 lists a number of experimental observations regarding multiple melting behavior.

Early work on the multiple melting behavior of iPP, and the evolution of this behavior during isothermal crystallization, showed a reduced tendency for multiple endotherms with an increase in crystallization temperature and/or an increase in molecular weight [68, 69]. This observation is attributed to the diminished influence of melting-recrystallization-remelting (MRM) during the DSC scan. During a DSC scan of a semicrystalline polymer, if the heating rate is sufficiently slow, time is available for metastable crystallites to melt, recrystallize, and remelt (MRM) during the scanning. Figure 3.10 shows that the MRM

Table 3.3 Multiple Melting Behavior

Observation	References
Less reorganization at higher MW due to lower molecular mobility	[68, 69]
Recrystallization rate in semicrystalline polymers lower with higher MW	[166]
Higher MW or tacticity reduce multiple melting	[58, 60 - 62, 68, 69]
Multiple melting in low tacticity/low MW fractions	[62]
MRM source of multiple melting	[72, 72, 75]
Higher crystallization temperature reduces multiple melting	[68 - 70, 73, 75]
MRM & morphological heterogeneity causes multiple melting	[60, 76]
Morphological heterogeneity causes multiple melting	[75]
Both MRM & morphological heterogeneity give multiple melting	[60, 76]
Morphological heterogeneity or variation in crystallizabilities contribute to multiple melting	[60, 64, 70, 75, 76, 101, 102]
Morphological heterogeneity in other semicrystalline polymers	[103 - 105]
Multiple melting by segregation of multiple crystallizable species	[62]

mechanism gives rise to an apparent multiple endothermic response that is highly sensitive to the heating rate [92, 93]. The heating rate controls both the instantaneous undercooling and time available for recrystallization. Most studies investigating the melting behavior of iPP following isothermal crystallization agree that MRM can occur, but differ in detail on the extent of, and temperature ranges, where the interpretation is appropriate [60, 63, 64, 68, 69, 72, 73, 75, 76].

The upper molecular weight where multiple melting is no longer observed appears sensitive to the tacticity level, where fractions of higher isotacticity exhibit a reduced tendency for reorganization [62]. The observation that high molecular weight [62, 68, 69]

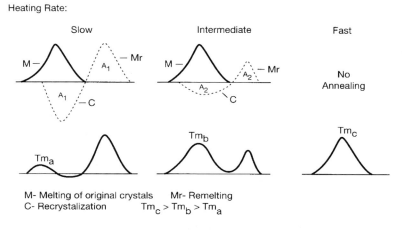

Figure 3.10 Relation of melting-recrystallization-remelting (MRM) mechanism to DSC scans at different heating rates. The top figures show the melting of original metastable crystals (M), recrystallization (C), and remelting (M_r). The bottom figures show the DSC scans that would actually be observed. Reprinted with permission from Ref. [93], Copyright 1984 American Chemical Society

and high crystallization temperature [68, 69, 73, 75] reduce the tendency for multiple melting is consistent with a decrease in recrystallization rate at higher molecular weight, and an increase in crystallite size or perfection, with associated increase in melting point, at higher crystallization temperatures. The tacticity dependence is closely related and results from the influence of chain regularity on the melting point and crystal perfection.

It has frequently been proposed that different crystallite populations and/or species of different crystallizability contribute to the multiple melting response of iPP under appropriate conditions [60, 64, 70, 75, 76, 102]. This behavior is consistent with that of other semicrystalline polymers [103 - 105]. Although conversion from the α_1 to α_2 form on annealing at elevated temperature seems established experimentally [42 - 45], as discussed earlier, multiple melting in semicrystalline polymers does not require a polymorphic transition. Direct experimental evidence is not currently available which quantifies the thermodynamic properties of the α_1-to-α_2 transition.

Crystallization time can also affect multiple melting behavior. Perfection of crystallites during isothermal crystallization has been observed [53, 68, 69]. These more perfect crystallites, with thicker lamellae, give higher melting points. Calculated values of T_m^o can vary due to a slope increase of the Hoffman–Weeks plots as crystallization progresses [53]. Opinions on the influence of tacticity on self-annealing behavior during heating vary [58, 60], and the connection to multiple melting is not as firmly established.

3.2.4.3   Summary

The following summarizes the melting behavior of α-form iPP. The melting point and crystallinity are strongly related to the tacticity of iPP. However, the interpretation of the thermal behavior is complicated by the presence of multiple melting endotherms and isothermal thickening during crystallization. The origins of the multiple endotherm behavior, in the absence of other polymorphic forms (β-, γ-, and mesomorphic forms) can be explained by a number of mechanisms common to semicrystalline polymers. These mechanisms can include:

1.   Tendency for melting-recyrstallization-remelting (MRM) during scanning in a DSC,
2.   self-annealing/perfection of crystallites during heating, and
3.   crystallites of varying stability.

The mechanism of MRM and/or solid-state reorganization is normally more appropriate to lower crystallization temperatures due to the metastability of the resultant crystallites. Generally, the influence of the MRM mechanism is diminished as the molecular weight increases and as the crystallization temperature approaches the equilibrium melting point. This general mechanism is applicable to a wide variety of solid-state forming operations, in addition to the interpretation of melting behavior. Morphological heterogeneity has been suggested to explain multiple endotherms, a mechanism consistent with observations in other polymers. The dominant (though likely not exclusive) mechanism for multiple melting at any given crystallization temperature is dependent on the chain molecular weight and tacticity. This is due to the role of molecular weight on chain mobility during recrystallization, and the influence of tacticity on overall crystallinity, crystallite stability, and melting point.

3.2.5   Crystallization Kinetics and Morphology Development

3.2.5.1   Isothermal Crystallization: Regime Analysis

The crystallization kinetics of i-PP has been extensively examined via an Avrami analysis [106]. The Avrami equation is given by eq 3.2:

$$(1 - \chi) = \exp(-Kt^n) \tag{3.2}$$

In eq 3.2, χ is the crystalline fraction (unitless), t is the time (min), K is a crystallization constant (min^{-n}), and n is a constant which can be related to the crystallization mechanism and dimensionality of growth. Volumes of literature have addressed this relationship, using primarily optical microscopy, DSC, and dilatometry. Several thorough reviews cover iPP [60, 107].

The kinetics of crystallization for the α-form of iPP has also been extensively examined in the context of secondary nucleation theory [56, 58, 74, 77, 96, 97, 108 - 115]. The theory of Hoffman and co-workers identifies different regime transitions related to the changes in nucleation and growth mechanisms with undercooling [91, 111, 116 - 120]. The proposed kinetic regimes are illustrated schematically in Fig. 3.11. These different kinetic regimes describe the growth rate (G) by the relative rates of surface nucleation (i) and crystalline layer growth (g) at the evolving growth front. Regime I is representative of the situation where the growth of a single crystalline layer of molecular stems is fully completed following the initial nucleation event. A "stem" is one pass of the chain through the crystal, at the growing surface. In regime II, multiple nucleation events can occur prior to completion of the growing layer from the initial nucleation site. In regime III, the nucleation density along the substrate approaches the width of a molecular cross section [111, 118, 120], and multiple layers of stems grow before the first layer is completed. The transition from regime I toward II and III is favored by increasingly higher undercooling. All three regimes are rarely seen for a single polymer [120, 121].

Nucleation theory treats the linear growth rate of semicrystalline polymers according to eq 3.3 [91, 111, 116 - 120]:

$$G = G_o \exp[-U^*/R(T_c - T_\infty)] \exp[-K_g/T_c(\Delta T)f] \tag{3.3}$$

In eq 3.3, G is the radial growth rate, G_o is a pre-exponential factor, R is the gas constant, U^* is taken as the activation energy for diffusion to the growth face, and T_∞ is the temperature where crystallization ceases and is generally taken as $T_g - 30$ (K) [111]. T_g is the glass transition temperature. The crystallization undercooling, ΔT, is given by $T_m^\circ - T_c$, where T_m° is the equilibrium melting point and T_c is the crystallization temperature. The factor f accounts for the temperature dependence of the heat of fusion, Δh_f, and is taken as $2T_c/(T_c + T_m^\circ)$. The factor K_g is dependent on the crystallization regime, which is related to the relative rates of surface nucleation and surface spreading. K_g is given by eq 3.4 [111, 118, 120]:

$$K_g(\text{III}) = K_g(\text{I}) = 2{*}K_g(\text{II}) = \frac{4b_o\sigma\sigma_e T_m^\circ}{\Delta h_f k} \tag{3.4}$$

In eq 3.4, $K_g(\text{I})$, $K_g(\text{II})$, and $K_g(\text{III})$ are the values of K_g (Equation 3.3) appropriate to regimes I, II, and III, respectively. The value of b_o is the crystalline layer thickness (see Fig. 3.11), Δh_f

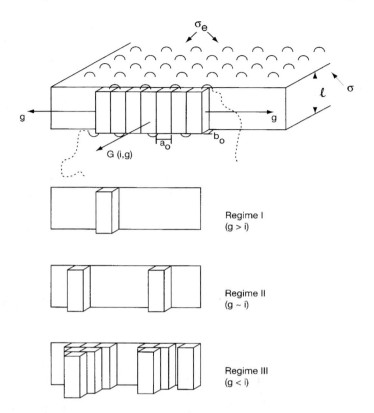

Figure 3.11 Representation of crystallization growth rate kinetics according to regime analysis, as adapted from [91]. See text for description of symbols. The lower portion is adapted from [120] and illustrates growth rate regimes in terms of the relative rates of surface nucleation (i) and crystalline layer growth (g)

is the heat of fusion per unit volume, k is the Boltzmann constant, while σ and σ_e are the lateral and surface fold energies, respectively. The value of σ is often assumed to be governed by eq 3.5 [91, 111, 116]:

$$\sigma = \alpha \Delta h_f (a_o b_o)^{1/2} \qquad (3.5)$$

In eq 3.5, α is given a numerical value of 0.1 [91, 111], a_o is the lateral stem width, and $(a_o b_o)$ is the cross sectional area of a polymer chain (taken for the 110 plane for α-iPP).

　　Equation 3.3 suggests a bell-shaped dependence of the crystallization rate on crystallization temperature. At high temperature, the crystallization rate is nucleation-controlled, and the rate increases with decreasing temperature. At low temperature, crystallization is diffusion-controlled, and the rate decreases with decreasing temperature. The analysis of growth rate data of semicrystalline polymers according to eq 3.3 has been well documented [91, 111, 112, 116, 119, 120], as well as applications to the crystallization of α-iPP [56, 58, 74, 77, 96, 97, 108 - 115].

　　Hoffmann and Clark analyzed a large body of isothermal crystallization data for iPP in the literature with a self-consistent set of governing parameters (U^*, T_∞, Δh_f, T_m°, and lattice parameters) [111]. Based on this work, a regime II–III transition was noted to occur at an approximate undercooling of $\Delta T = 48\,°C$. Lateral and surface free energies of iPP were estimated to be $\sigma = 11.5$ erg/cm^2 and $\sigma_e = 65$ erg/cm^2 to 70 erg/cm^2, respectively. The work for chain folding in iPP was estimated to be 26.8 kJ/mol to 28.5 kJ/mol. Numerous other estimates are available for these parameters [56, 58, 74, 77, 96, 97, 108 - 115]. Compilations of the surface fold energy, σ_e, are in the range of 55 erg/cm^2 to 120 erg/cm^2 [56, 97, 111].

When comparing values of σ_e (and related parameters) from other literature applications of regime analysis, care should be taken to assess the input parameters chosen in the specific analysis. For example, the analysis of K_g depends on the assumed value for U^*, T_g, and T_∞. Variations in T_g and T_∞ are most common. The reported values of σ_e depend not only on the values influencing K_g but also on the assumed values for the lattice parameters, equilibrium melting point (T_m°), and assumptions relating to the lateral surface energy (σ). The assumed value of Δh_f does not influence σ_e if eq 3.5 is used in conjunction with eq 3.4. This latter set of parameters is relatively easy to scale for the purposes of comparison by eq 3.4, while the former set of parameters (U^*, T_g, and T_∞) are more difficult to scale, since raw growth rate numbers are not often reported. The work of Hoffmann and Clark showed that, for a given set of input parameters, the analysis of regime transitions gives reasonably consistent results for α-iPP. In certain cases, the analysis of σ_e by regime analysis has been shown to be of the proper order of magnitude when compared to alternative measures, such as the scaling of lamellar thickness with undercooling through eq 3.1 [56].

The occurence of regime transitions may be affected by the molecular structure of iPP. The regime I–II transition has been noted in low molecular weight fractions [112], and all three regimes have been observed in low molecular weight fractions of high isotacticity [56]. The regime II–III transition is often observed in high molecular weight fractions [56, 74, 96, 111, 113, 115, 120, 121]. Transitions between the proposed α_1 and α_2 crystallographic forms near regime transitions have only been observed in less stereoregular material [115]. Anomolies in the three-regime description have also been noted in materials with low isotacticity [113]. More than three apparent "regimes" were observed. No changes in the spherulite-/macromorphology have been observed for undercoolings at the regime transitions of iPP [56, 112].

Reducing the tacticity not only reduces the melting point [57 - 63, 101] but also has been shown to reduce the experimentally observed linear growth rates and influence the extent of cross-hatching [113]. Corresponding increases in the product of the lateral surface and fold surface energies with decreasing tacticity have been observed [113]. This latter result suggests that a reduction in isotacticity may be analogous to increased surface fold energies and interfacial fractions reported for some random copolymers with increasing co-unit content [122 - 124].

3.2.5.2   Isothermal Crystallization: Isotactic PP/Atactic PP Blends

In the context of nucleation theory, crystallization in a semicrystalline blend, where one component is noncrystallizable, can be viewed as a competition between nucleation at the crystalline growth front and the transport of the noncrystallizable component in the mixture. When the components of the mixture are thermodynamically miscible, the noncrystallizable component influences the crystallization process by 1) affecting the transport properties by modifying both the T_g of the matrix and the rate at which the noncrystallizable component diffuses from the growth front, and 2) modification of the work required to form a critical nucleus on the crystal surface [125]. Linear growth rates require a constant composition in the noncrystalline matrix, which necessitates incorporation of the diluent into the interlamellar regions. Nonlinear growth rates occur when the diluent segregates to the unsolidified matrix, which leads to a sensitivity of the apparent growth rate to the spatial proximity of neighboring spherulite growth centers. The degree of compositional heterogeneity of the amorphous phase during crystallization is governed by the relative rates of crystallization and diluent segregation. This heterogeneity is not phase separation in the context normally applied to multiphase systems, but rather is a physical separation which is inherent to the dynamics of crystallization from all multi-component mixtures.

The effect of a noncrystallizable atactic diluent (aPP) on the crystallization of iPP was investigated in early work [126, 127]. Increasing the content of aPP caused a much more open spherulitic texture due to incorporation of the atactic material in the interlamellar regions [126]. Although the thermodynamics of iPP/aPP mixtures has not been extensively reported in the open literature, this behavior is similar to the morphology of some miscible semicrystalline blends [128]. In a miscible semicrystalline blend, the two components in the blend are not driven to phase separate on the basis of thermodynamic incompatibility, but phase separate due to crystallization of one of the components. When the diluent is of sufficiently low molecular weight in blends with iPP, the spherulite growth has been shown to be markedly nonlinear [127]. In nonlinear growth, the diffusion of the crystallizable species (iPP in this case) to the crystalline growth front is rate limiting.

Similar observations were seen in more recent work with low molecular weight paraffins as the diluent [96, 129]. Crystallization of iPP in a low molecular weight diluent also has been shown to cause the onset of nonlinear behavior in an Avrami analysis at lower crystallinities during crystallization [97]. The effect of aPP addition has also been claimed to reduce the primary nucleation of iPP spherulites, as indicated by an increase in spherulite size with atactic addition [77, 130].

3.2.5.3   *Isothermal Crystallization: Isotactic PP/Rubber Blends*

The blending of iPP with a rubber component is of vital commercial interest. The majority of these blends are incompatible. This behavior is typical in polymer blends, with the resultant morphology being dependent on the individual polymer pair. Figure 3.12 illustrates some general considerations of blend thermodynamics on the development of morphology. The χ-parameter increases as the thermodynamic incompatibility of the polymer pair becomes more severe, and is dependent on temperature. As the χ-parameter or the molecular weight of the blend components increase, the potential exists for a stable two-phase mixture at temperatures above the melting point of the crystallizable component (Immiscible Growth regime). This situation is described by Fig. 3.12 and is appropriate to the case of many binary blends of iPP with ethylene-propylene random copolymers (EPR) [131, 132]. For a miscible blend, crystallization (and subsequent melting) occurs according to Path 3 within the stable one-phase region of the phase diagram (Miscible Growth regime). When the melting point lies within the two-phase region, crystallization can occur simultaneously with phase separation (Path 1) or subsequent to phase separation (Path 2). Path 2 differs from Path 1 by allowing phase separation to occur at temperatures above the melting point prior to crystallization.

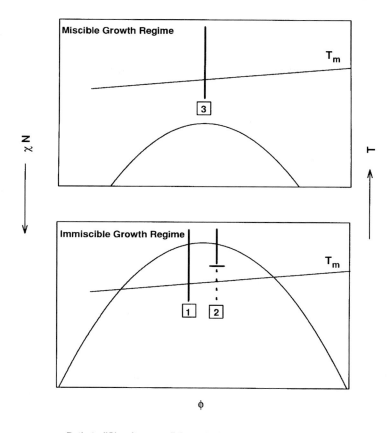

Path 1: "Simultaneous" Domain Growth & Crystallization

Path 2:   "Sequential" Domain Growth & Crystallization

Path 3: Crystallization from Stable Single Phase Melt

Figure 3.12 Potential relationships between the melting point and the thermodynamic phase boundaries in a semicrystalline blend. Within the "Miscible Growth Regime" crystallization and melting occur from within the stable one-phase region of the phase diagram (Path 3). The "Immiscible Growth Regime" describes crystallization and melting within the stable two-phase region (Path 1, 2). Path 2 differs from Path 1 by allowing phase separation to occur in the melt prior to crystallization. χ is the Flory–Huggins interaction parameter, N is the number-average degree of polymerization, T is the temperature, ϕ represents composition

Crystallization of iPP/EPR blends have been examined according to Path 2 for model iPP/EPR blends [131, 132]. Under rapid crystallization conditions, the domain size established for short times in the melt is found to be unchanged following crystallization and contained within the spherulitic macrostructure. Under these conditions, crystallization "locks in" the morphology by preventing further domain growth of the blend components. For longer holding times in the melt, the melt domain structures demix over large size scales, and the spherulitic structures develop within the iPP-rich domains. This case, where crystallization occurs from within a well-developed two-phase melt morphology, is a common case for many iPP/rubber mixtures of commercial interest. Although the nucleation characteristics of iPP can be influenced by the rubber component, the development of crystalline morphology under these conditions is often times very similar to that of the homopolymer. The blend phase morphology in the melt state becomes the critical concern for controlling properties. This aspect is discussed further in Section 3.5.

3.3   Polymorphic Forms of Isotactic PP

Polymorphism is the tendency for a polymer to exhibit more than one crystalline form. As discussed briefly earlier, iPP can crystallize in one of several different forms [25, 41]. All of the different crystalline forms are composed of chains in a 3_1 helical conformation with a common repeat distance (6.5 Å) but differ in unit cell symmetry, inter-chain packing, and structural disorder. As presented in earlier discussions, the α-form is dominant. Other forms include the β, γ, and mesomorphic (smectic) forms. The structure, conditions for formation, melting, and morphological characterization of these various forms are briefly summarized below and serve to illustrate additional important determinants of morphology in iPP homopolymer.

3.3.1   β–Form

3.3.1.1   Crystallographic Symmetry

The existence of the β-form has been known for many years [25, 49, 133 - 138]. Despite the long established presence of the β-form, considerable ambiguity surrounding the crystal structure has remained [138]. Numerous unit cell structures have been reported in the literature [49, 134, 135, 137, 138], and several studies have offered comparative assessments of the various proposed models [137, 138]. Regardless of the detailed crystallographic symmetry, the formation of β-crystallinity is known to result in a unit cell structure with lower density [25, 135, 137, 138], higher rates of crystallization [40, 139, 140], lower apparent melting point [17, 64, 70, 95, 139 - 152], and metastability with respect to the α-form under appropriate conditions of heating [10, 17, 25, 139, 142, 144 - 150, 153, 154] and applied strain [25, 142, 151, 155 - 159]. These observations are all consistent with a lower degree of order in the crystalline state of the β-form relative to that of the α-form [138].

The most common method of quantifying the presence of the β-form is through the use of wide angle X-ray diffraction (WAXD). Turner-Jones et al. defined a relative index which measures the intensity ratio of the strong β-crystalline phase reflection at a d-spacing of 5.5 Å relative to the dominant 110, 040, and 130 reflections of the α-phase [25]. Figure 3.13 compares the WAXS patterns of an iPP sample containing a mixture of β-and α-forms with the same sample of iPP in the α-form. Through the use of special nucleators, the fraction of

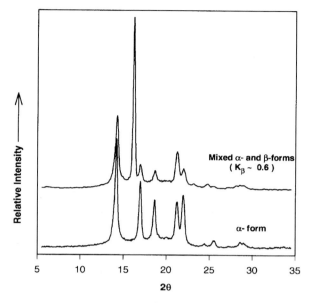

Figure 3.13 A comparison of WAXS patterns for a sample of iPP in the α-form, and a sample with a mixture of α-and β-forms. The latter sample has a value for K_β of approximately 0.6

the crystalline phase which exists in the β-form can be made to approach unity [141, 145, 148, 150, 151, 153, 159 - 162].

3.3.1.2   *Lamellar Morphology*

The internal microstructure of the β-form spherulites is thought to be composed of radial arrays of parallel stacked lamellae [16, 50, 136, 137]. In this regard, the lamellar micro-structure of the β-form exhibits much greater similarity to the "conventional" microstructure of semicrystalline homopolymers than does the α-form with it's unique tendency for cross-hatch formation. Various studies have suggested that the preferred radial growth direction of lamellae within spherulites of the β-form is along the crystallographic a-axis direction, assuming a hexagonal unit cell [16, 49, 137]. Additionally, a strong link between the lamellar microstructure and the optical classification of β-containing spherulites has been made, as discussed below.

3.3.1.3   *Spherulitic Morphology*

Early studies have suggested the formation of two types of β-form spherulites [10, 49]. Keith and Padden classified the two types of β-form spherulites as type β_{III} and β_{IV} [10]. Both β-type spherulites are identified by a negative birefringence that is more pronounced than the α-form. The β_{III}-type exhibits uniform radial birefringence, and the β_{IV}-type concentric banding [10, 16, 17, 49, 137]. As with the variation of spherulite type in the α-form, various authors report different temperature ranges for formation of the β_{III}- and β_{IV}-types [10, 16, 17, 137].

Norton and Keller suggest the formation of β_{III} below 142 °C and β_{IV} in the range of 126 °C to 132 °C [16].

Samuels and Yee measured the intrinsic birefringence of the crystal a-and c-axis in β-form spherulites, as well as the tangential and radial birefringence for the different spherulite types [137]. The optical classification of the β-form spherulites has been linked to the detailed lamellar microstructure [16, 137]. The concentric banding of the β_{IV} spherulites has been associated with a periodic orientation of the lamellae about the radial direction of the spherulite, while the β_{III}-type spherulite has been associated with a random orientation [16, 137]. Both types have the a-axis direction coincident with the radial spherulite growth direction [16, 49, 137]. A simple microscopic examination with cross-polarized light usually shows that β-form spherulites are brighter, due to their higher birefringence, and have concave boundaries with the α-form spherulites because of a higher linear growth rate.

3.3.1.4   Melting Behavior

Estimates of the equilibrium melting point of the β-crystalline, T_m° (β), vary from 170 °C [70], 200 °C [139], 182.9 °C to 184 °C [17, 144, 147], 176 °C [140], 183.3 °C [95], and 174.4 °C [152]. Most of these studies utilized a Hoffmann–Weeks determination of T_m°. Although, collectively, a slightly reduced equilibrium melting point of the β-form relative to the α-form may be suggested, a definitive statement is difficult at present. In part, this difficulty is due to the thermally induced transformation of the β-form to the α-form, which limits the range of undercoolings accessible to a Hoffmann–Weeks analysis. This transformation also adds complications to the interpretation of multiple endotherm behavior, in addition to those factors already discussed for the α-form. However, under practical crystallization conditions, it is well established that the presence of the β-crystalline form is often associated with a low melting point [17, 64, 70, 95, 139 - 152] and multiple endotherm behavior due to the conversion of the β-crystalline phase to the α-form on heating [10, 17, 25, 139, 144 - 150, 153, 154]. The low melting point associated with β-crystallinity has important commercial consequences for temperature-dependent forming processes. Consequently, considerable literature has been devoted both to selective additives for β-crystallinity formation [50, 140, 141, 143, 145, 148, 151, 159, 161, 162] and to crystallization conditions required for the formation of β-crystallinity [10, 16, 17, 25, 64, 135, 137 - 139, 143, 145, 147, 148, 156, 162 - 165].

The conversion of the β-form to the α-form is thought to require a melt/recrystallization step, versus a scenario invoking a solid-state transition, because of the marked differences of the two unit cells [25, 137, 138]. During annealing at elevated temperature, the β-crystallinity has, in most cases, been observed to decrease rapidly from the initial value at short times to a relatively constant level [25, 145, 148, 160]. The level of β-crystallinity at each annealing temperature decreases as the temperature is increased through the β-crystalline melting range [25, 145, 148, 160]. This behavior suggests that β-crystallites have a distribution of stabilities. The presence of varying degrees of β-crystallite stability [17, 145 - 150, 154] has also been shown to influence the conversion of the β- to the α-form on application of applied strain [159].

Various mechanisms have been postulated for β-form melting and the β- to α-form recrystallization process. Many of the associated effects bear close resemblance to general

Table 3.4 Proposed Mechanisms for Beta-Form to Alpha-Form Conversion

Proposed mechanism	References
α-Form nuclei from secondary crystallization	[17, 146, 147, 149, 154]
β–α Conversion within crystallites	[148, 149]
Melt & recrystallization of β-form, no conversion	[17, 146, 147, 149, 154]
Stable β-lamellae nucleate conversion to α-form	[148]
β–α Growth transition during partial melting of β-form	[149]
α-Nuclei within β-spherulites on cooling. Seed conversion.	[17, 146, 147, 149, 154]
β–α Conversion by MRM	[153]

reorganization phenomena in semicrystalline polymers. Details of proposed mechanisms are listed in Table 3.4.

Varga and co-workers have extensively investigated and reviewed the transition of β-form to α-form crystallinity in optical microscopy and DSC experiments [17, 146, 147, 154]. Using preferentially nucleated materials, these studies suggested that the optimum isothermal crystallization temperature for formation of β-crystallinity is between 100 °C and 141 °C [17]. The characterization of the melting process for samples containing β-crystallinity has been claimed to be sensitive to the post-crystallization thermal history [17, 146, 147, 149, 150, 154]. It was proposed that recrystallization of the β-form to the α-form is promoted if the temperature is lowered, following crystallization, below a critical temperature. This critical temperature, TR^*, was in the range of 100 °C to 110 °C [17, 146, 147, 149, 150, 154]. The proposed mechanism was thought to occur by formation of α-form nuclei within the β-spherulite after cooling below TR^*. The α-form nuclei act as sites for α-form recrystallization following melting of metastable β-form crystallites on heating. Other related X-ray and electron diffraction studies are consistent with this view [138].

3.3.1.5   Crystallization Kinetics/Morphology Development

Formation of the β-form can be induced by the addition of specific nucleators or additives [50, 140, 141, 143, 145, 148, 151, 159, 161, 162], controlling the crystallization conditions for the "morphological window" appropriate for a specific resin [10, 16, 17, 25, 64, 135, 137, 138, 139, 143, 145, 147, 148, 156, 162 - 165], crystallization under controlled temperature gradients [95, 138, 139, 143, 147, 156, 163], and under certain circumstances, crystallization under shear [164, 165]. Nucleating agents can be used to either promote β-crystallinity or to prevent formation of β-crystallinity by overwhelming the crystallization with α-form crystals. This latter approach is effective when a few β-form spherulites cause undesirable side effects and nucleation is tolerable.

Studies of β-crystallinity formation in the presence of a temperature gradient have suggested that β-crystallinity is favored by slow growth rates (low velocities through a temperature gradient), high temperature gradients, and a large degree of superheat in the melt [139]. These results are related to the lower incidence of nucleation and faster growth rates of the β-form relative to the α-form [10, 139, 140]. The growth rate of the β-form may eventually be less than that of the α-form at low undercooling [139, 140], although the prediction is complicated by conversion of the β-form to the α-form at elevated temperature. Some experimental evidence has suggested the presence of regime transitions for the β-form [140] and a lower surface free energy relative to the α-form [95, 139]. Both conclusions are at present not definitive, however.

The β-form also exhibits sensitivity to external factors such as applied shear in the melt [164, 165] and, as mentioned earlier, imposed temperature gradients [95, 138, 139, 143, 147, 156, 163]. Such conditions are common to commercial fabrication processes, and considerable attention has been devoted to the characterization of β-crystallinity in moldings and extrusions [8, 9, 164, 167 - 170]. Work on extruded pipe has implied a critical shear rate for the formation of the β-crystalline form [164], although recent synchrotron WAXS studies have indicated an enhancement of β-crystallinity even at very low shear rate [165]. This sensitivity of the β-crystallinity to shear is dependent on the specific resin characteristics.

3.3.2   γ-Form

The presence of γ-phase crystallinity is relatively uncommon for samples of iPP homopolymer formed under typical commercial processing conditions. Due to relatively specialized conditions for formation, the γ-form is probably the least understood of all the crystalline states of iPP. However, studies of the γ-form have taken on some renewed interest, from a scientific standpoint, due to recent proposals relating to the crystallographic symmetry in this polymorphic form [47, 171-173].

3.3.2.1   Crystallographic Symmetry

It has long been recognized that unique X-ray and electron diffraction patterns are associated with the γ-form of iPP [25, 47, 54, 142, 152, 171 - 179]. Comparative X-ray patterns of the α-form and γ-form have been published elsewhere [25, 174, 176, 178]. Early work assigned the X-ray pattern of the γ-form to a triclinic unit cell of similar or slightly higher density than the α-form structure [175]. The γ-form triclinic structure was thought to be related to the α-form by a shear of the α-phase along the a-axis [175].

Recent crystal structure refinements on low molecular weight iPP crystallized to the γ-form have proposed a novel crystal structure with nonparallel chains [47, 171 - 173]. This structure is based on Rietveld refinement of X-ray diffraction data [171, 172], electron diffraction studies of thin film low molecular weight fractions [173], and packing energy calculations [47]. The structure invokes a large orthorhombic cell with bilayer structures. The bilayers maintain the 3_1 helix as a basic building block. Qualitative considerations of this structure suggest that the γ-form crystal is built up of layers of chains in a crossed pattern, with the chains in adjacent layers at an 80° angle to each other rather than parallel. Figure 3.14 depicts this arrangement schematically. The presence of nonparallel chains in the proposed crystal structure is unique among crystallizable synthetic polymers. However, similarities of the γ-form structure with the cross-hatched crystallographic branching of the α-form have been noted [172, 173]. The implications of this structure to the lamellar morphology, melting/temperature stability, and crystallization kinetics of the γ-form have not been fully explored or tested. Some of these aspects are addressed briefly below.

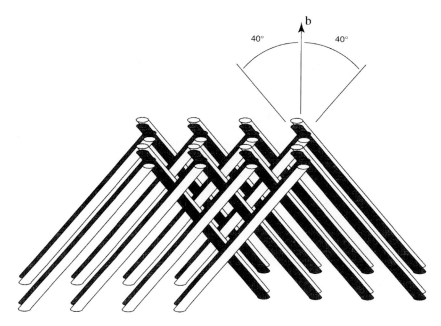

Figure 3.14 Schematic of proposed chain arrangements within lamellae of γ-form iPP [172]. The model suggests layers of pairs of parallel chains, with those chains inclined at 80° to the chains in the next layer, and at 40° with respect to the lamellar surface, alternating directions with each layer. The white bars represent chains of the same chirality, while the gray bars represent chains of the opposite chirality. Where chains of the same chirality cross at the 80° angle, the methyl groups face each other, and a high degree of interdigitation of the methyl groups is suggested

3.3.2.2   Lamellar/Spherulitic Morphology

The γ-form is observed relatively infrequently in commercial PP polymers under normal crystallization conditions. The corresponding morphological details of this minority phase with regard to the lamellar organization, chain orientation, fold surfaces, and relation to the α-form lamellae are not well-known. For these aspects, inferences must be drawn from rather special types of samples studied in the literature. The cross-hatching phenomena common to the α-form has not been observed in the γ-form [54, 173]. Electron diffraction/microscopy experiments on low molecular weight polymers suggested that the γ-form lamellae could nucleate on the 010 face of the parent α-form crystal in thin films. In contrast with the near perpendicular relationship of the chain axes in the cross-hatched pattern of the α-form, a nearly parallel relationship between the chain axis of the nucleated γ-form and parent α-form can occur [54, 172, 173]. An approximate 40° angle between the corresponding lamellae was suggested that requires a relatively pronounced, and unique, amount of tilting of the chain axis with respect to the γ-form lamellar surface [54, 172, 173]. This observation has been reconciled for the above-mentioned crystal structure (with nonparallel chains) by assigning a lamellar surface orthogonal to the b-axis direction with chains inclined 40° with respect to the b direction, and 80° between respective bilayers [172].

The observation of low angle γ-form branching on the α-form lamellae [54, 172, 173] may provide an alternative explanation of early observations by Morrow et al. [142, 175]

regarding the apparent coexistence of the α-form and γ-form in single lamellae. Recent work [179] on pressure-crystallized iPP has suggested the possibility of coexistence of the two phases within the lamellae in concurrence with the original work of Morrow. An abnormal tilt angle of the α-form was suggested as a possible mechanism [179]. These studies also suggested apparent lamellar thinning during the continuous conversion of the α-form to the γ-form with increasing crystallization pressure [179]. Folded chain lamellar morphologies of iPP following crystallization at high pressure in the γ-form has been claimed by other authors, as well [174, 179, 180]. The detailed morphological organization of the α-form and γ-form, particularly following crystallization at elevated pressure of high molecular weight iPP, remains an open and interesting question [179].

The model of chain tilting and nonparallel chains may also be consistent with the observation of a γ-form to α-form transition on application of strain [25, 181]. It would seem very difficult to retain the novel γ-form organization on application of an applied strain, with the consequent approach to parallel chains. While this could imply an intrinsic instability of the γ-form under strain, direct experiments of crystallographic transformations on application of strain have not been performed in the context of the proposed γ-form chain arrangement [47, 171 - 173].

3.3.2.3   Melting Behavior

A definitive comparison of the equilibrium melting point for the γ-and α-forms is difficult due to limited experimental information. A summary of literature observations is given in Table 3.5. These observations suggest, in a general sense, that the melting behavior of γ-and α-forms are similar.

The relative stability of the γ-form and α-form on heating has been addressed [142, 174, 176, 181]. The presence of a low observable γ-form melting temperature and subsequent conversion to the α-form has been observed on heating [142, 174, 176]. Conversion of the γ-form to the α-form on heating was noted following pressure crystallization of low molecular weight samples at high undercooling [142], but the γ-form was stable on heating following crystallization at low undercooling [142]. Similar sensitivity to the initial undercooling has been noted with respect to the conversion of the γ-form to the α-form on application of mechanical stress [142, 176]. Early work suggested the possibility of a solid-state transition during the transformation of the γ-form to α-form on heating [142, 174]. This mechanism has not been demonstrated in the context of recent ideas concerning the crystal structure of the γ-form [47, 171 - 173]. The crystallographic reorganization may

Table 3.5 γ-Form Melting Behavior

Effect	References
Pressure crystallization and melting point	[174]
Low MW fractions: similar α- and γ-form melting	[66]
γ- and α-forms have similar melting points	[152]
Equilibrium melting point estimate: 187.6 °C	[182]
γ-Form lattice packing energy similar to α-form	[47]
Low γ-form melting point, converts to α-form on heating; solid-state transition	[142, 174, 176]
γ-Form conversion to α-form depends on initial undercooling	[142]

require a MRM mechanism. In this sense, conversion of the γ- to α-form on heating is reasonable if the initial γ-form crystallites are sufficiently metastable and recrystallization is allowed to occur at atmospheric pressure (which favors the α-form). In the future, studies of γ- and α-form stabilities may provide critical tests of models relating to γ-form organization.

3.3.2.4   *Crystallization Kinetics and Morphology Development*

The formation of the γ-phase has been observed following crystallization of very low molecular weight fractions [54, 66, 142, 173, 175, 177], low molecular weight homopolymer from homogeneous catalysts [171, 172], random copolymers with crystallizable C_3-sequences and various comonomers [25, 152, 178], and following crystallization at high pressure [142, 174, 176, 179 - 181]. Early and subsequent work [25, 178] showed that formation of the γ-phase is favored in samples with a high defect content (or high "stereoblock" fraction) and/or samples of increasing comonomer content [152]. In copolymer samples, the tendency for formation of the γ-phase decreases as the cooling rate increases or the melt residence increases [178]. The latter effect may be due to the inhibition of α-form nuclei, which have been demonstrated to provide a nucleating surface for the γ-form [54, 173]. In copolymer samples formed by isothermal crystallization, the γ-content is favored as the undercooling decreases (increased crystallization temperature) [152].

The exact role of as-polymerized defects (stereoblock and copolymers) on formation of the γ-phase is not well understood. It has long been recognized that crystallization of low molecular weight fractions and low molecular weight degradation products [54, 66, 142, 173, 175, 177] lead to formation of the γ-phase. Much of the detailed structural studies of crystallographic organization and lamellar organization have utilized samples of this type. This observation would seem to suggest that the γ-phase is favored by short average runs of isotactic sequences, either through copolymerization or limited chain length. However, it has long been recognized that crystallization under pressure leads to increased quantities of the γ-form [174, 176, 181], even for high molecular weight, high tacticity iPP [179].

With increasing pressure, the content of the γ-form relative to the α-form has been observed to continuously increase under isothermal crystallization conditions [174, 179]. The possibility of equilibrium ratios of the γ/α content as a function of pressure was suggested [179]. Study of the crystallization kinetics for the γ-phase is difficult because of the specialized formation conditions. Only a few studies of the isothermal crystallization kinetics at elevated pressure have been performed. These studies utilized high pressure dilatometry over the range of 10 MPa to 200 MPa [183]. No strong dependence of the Avrami exponent on temperature or pressure was noted that might be associated with a change in the crystallization mechanism with increasing γ-crystallinity content. The analysis of the crystallization kinetics of iPP in the γ-form at elevated pressure according to regime theory appears to be still in the formative stages [184].

3.3.3   Mesomorphic (Smectic) Form

Many commercial fabrication processes utilize rapid cooling conditions. Under these conditions, it is common to observe the crystallization of iPP into the mesomorphic form

[41, 185 - 195], also commonly referred to as the smectic form. The mesomorphic form has important commercial implications, and various aspects of this morphology are discussed below.

3.3.3.1   Crystallographic Symmetry

The mesomorphic phase represents a state of order intermediate between the amorphous and crystalline states. Figure 3.15 shows a comparison of the wide angle X-ray pattern of the mesomorphic form compared to the patterns of atactic PP (amorphous) and the α-form of iPP.

Early work suggested a hexagonal crystallographic symmetry in the mesomorphic form [188, 189]. This assignment of the hexagonal structure was based on the observation that the primary diffraction intensity maxima of the mesomorphic form more closely corresponded to the two most intense reflections of the β-form, which was classified as a hexagonal unit cell. This hypothesis is in agreement with solid-state ^{13}C NMR work, which noted that chemical shifts and relaxation times were comparable to that of β-form crystallinity [193]. Caldas et al. [195], however, associated the quench cooled morphology and corresponding ^{13}C NMR observations to a microcrystalline α-form and a disordered α-form symmetry with a larger unit cell dimension. The hypothesis of a mixture of unit cell dimensions and ordering was used to explain the lack of splitting of the $-CH_2-$ and $-CH_3$ resonances in quenched PP relative to a well-ordered α-form. Much earlier work also suggested that the mesomorphic form may be the result of deviations from the α-form symmetry due to lattice disorder ("paracrystallinity") [41, 187]. It has generally been agreed that the mesomorphic phase maintains the 3_1-helical conformation [41, 187, 190 - 195].

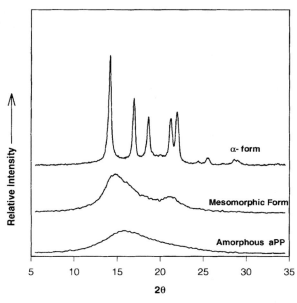

Figure 3.15   A comparison of WAXS patterns for aPP which is amorphous, iPP in the mesomorphic form, and iPP in the α-form

Corradini et al. [192, 194] derived X-ray patterns from various models of aggregates of sequences with helical conformation. The derived patterns were compared with experimental X-ray intensities. This comparison suggested parallel chain organization into bundles with correlational order restricted to 30 Å to 40 Å [192], but the structure could not be described by any one type of unit cell [192, 194]. Infrared experiments suggested that the mesomorphic regions consisted of aggregates of helices lacking three-dimensional order [190, 191]. Indirect measurements have suggested a very low density (0.916 g/cm^3) of the ordered regions with respect to the other polymorphic crystal forms of iPP [196].

With regard to the crystallographic registry in mesomorphic PP, some insight can be drawn from the work of Osawa and Porter on the compressive deformation of iPP in the α-form [197]. This work and other related work [198 - 200] suggest that the mesomorphic form could be induced by compressive deformation of iPP in the α-form, provided that the deformation temperature was below the upper stability limit of the mesomorphic form. Similarly, some experiments have suggested that an oriented mesomorphic form results from drawing samples with β-form crystallinity at low temperature [158]. The results of these deformation experiments reaffirm the viewpoint that the mesomorphic form is disordered relative to the standard crystalline unit cell symmetries [192, 194]. This disorder can be induced either by rapid quenching from the melt or, under certain conditions, the disruption of existing crystallites by deformation forces. The detailed nature of this disorder is not fully resolved.

3.3.3.2   Lamellar Morphology

As with the nature of the crystallographic ordering, the detailed morphological ordering in the mesomorphic form has not been fully resolved. Early work noted nodular structures on the order of 125 Å [189]. Grubb and Yoon claimed morphologies resembling spherical "lumps" of diameter 100 Å to 350 Å [201]. This work suggested that the reorganization of this morphology occurred at temperatures above the temperature at which the α-form diffraction pattern first became evident. Caldas et al. proposed regions of α-form symmetry with variable unit cell dimension and 100 Å to 200 Å in size [195]. Similar nodular structures were noted by Hsu et al. [202]. The lack of a well-defined SAXS maxima in the mesomorphic form has been associated with the absence of well-defined lamellar ordering [202, 203]. The small size of the ordered structures has also been associated with an increase in constraint in the amorphous regions [41, 204]. The small size, high disorder, and apparent low density of the mesomorphic form morphology is associated with excellent clarity in quenched film applications.

3.3.3.3   Melting Behavior

It has long been recognized that the mesomorphic form is unstable, relative to the α-form, with increasing temperature [41, 185 - 187, 189 - 191, 193, 195, 201 - 208]. Consequently, the melting behavior of samples initially in the mesomorphic form is usually dominated by the melting of α-form crystallites related to the mesomorphic-to-α-form transition on heating. This transition is characterized by an apparent exotherm in DSC scans at temperatures of 65 °C to 120 °C. This exotherm is accompanied by an increase in crystallinity [41, 185, 201 - 205, 207, 208], the appearance of an α-form WAXS pattern [185, 187, 201 - 205, 207, 208], an increase in apparent crystallite dimension [187, 201 - 205, 207, 208], splitting of ^{13}C NMR resonances associated with the α-form [195], and the development of a well-defined SAXS pattern associated with improvements in lamellar scale ordering [202, 203, 209]. Recent work [203] with temperature scanning SAXS/WAXS experiments and synchrotron X-ray radiation indicates that the conversion of the mesomorphic form to the α-monoclinic form was a solid-state transition, accompanied by an increase in long-range ordering [202, 203, 209]. Due to the limited mobility in the solid state, it was suggested that the mesomorphic structure is paracrystalline in nature, possibly with α-form symmetry [203]. Interestingly, isothermal annealing experiments in the solid state have indicated that, for samples initially in the mesomorphic form, a limiting value of α-form crystallinity is reached with increasing time at each temperature [205, 208]. This limiting value increases with increasing annealing temperature. These results indicate that there is a range of organizational stabilities in the mesomorphic form, analogous to the range of stabilities commonly encountered in conventional lamellar crystals.

3.3.3.4   Morphology Development

Due to the rapidity of organization, small organizational scale, and low apparent crystallinity in the mesomorphic form, the kinetics of formation on quenching from the melt has not been extensively evaluated. The analysis according to regime kinetics has not been done, nor may it be appropriate. Regardless of these difficulties, it is clear that the content of mesomorphic phase is favored by rapid quenching [41, 185 - 196, 201 - 210] and can be controlled by the rate of cooling from the melt. Piccarolo et al. found a continuous increase in the content of mesomorphic phase and corresponding decrease in the α-form ordering with increasing cooling rate [210]. Samples of iPP homopolymer were predominantly mesomorphic when the cooling rate exceeded 80 °C/s. Random copolymers and related materials with reduced crystallization rates tend to form mesomorphic structures at somewhat lower cooling rates. In commercial applications, this factor can be an important consideration when the sample experiences a gradient in cooling rate, such as may occur through the thickness direction, for example.

3.4   Morphology of Syndiotactic PP

Aspects of the crystallization behavior of syndiotactic PP (sPP) have been investigated for many years [211 - 238]. Early work was often based on materials of low regioregularity (head-to-head monomer insertion), low stereoregularity, and low molecular weight. At times, sPP was present in combination with iPP. Only recently, through the use of highly stereospecific metallocene catalysts [220], has the polymerization of sPP with stereoregularity comparable to that of iPP been possible. The development of highly regular sPP has generated renewed scientific interest and understanding of this polymer [223 - 225, 229 - 238]. The commercial utilization of sPP remains in the formative stages. Some properties of sPP appear in Chapter 12, Table 12.3.

3.4.1   Crystallographic Symmetry

A comparison of the WAXS patterns of iPP and sPP was previously shown in Fig. 3.4. The semicrystalline nature of sPP was originally observed [212], and the crystal structure indexed [214], in early work by Natta and co-workers. This crystal structure has also been reviewed in detail by Lovinger and co-workers [221, 222, 226, 230, 235, 236] and labeled cell I. The original cell I crystal structure [214, 231] proposed a helical chain conformation [214, 232], with a 7.4-Å repeat on an orthorhombic unit cell. This is shown in Fig. 3.16(a). The proposed unit cell required isochiral packing of helices (packing of helices of the same hand). This, and other details of the inter-chain packing in early structure determinations, has recently undergone revision [221, 222, 230, 231, 235, 236, 238]. Recent studies [230, 231, 235, 236], utilizing electron diffraction, X-ray diffraction, atomic force microscopy, and epitaxial growth

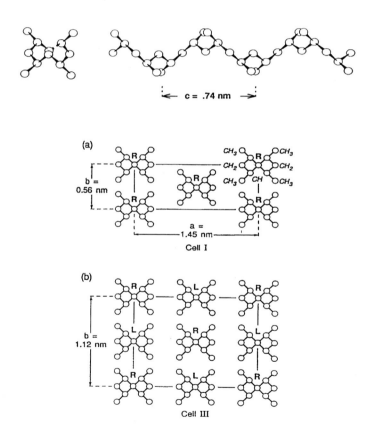

Figure 3.16 Crystalline chain conformation and unit cell structure of sPP. The upper portion of the figure shows the chain conformation looking at the side of the chain. The lower portion of the figure shows the cell I structure of Natta and co-workers, and the revised cell III structure, both viewed in the c-axis direction, along the chains. R = right-handed helix; L = left-handed helix. Upper portion reprinted with permission from Ref. [232], Copyright 1990 American Chemical Society. Lower portion reprinted with permission from Ref. [236], Copyright 1994 American Chemical Society

techniques, have benefited from the availability of highly stereoregular polymers. These studies proposed cell III, also an orthorhombic unit cell, but with fully antichiral packing (packing of helices of opposite hand) [230, 235, 236]. The unit cell dimensions are $a = 14.5$ Å, $b = 11.2$ Å, and $c = 7.4$ Å. This structure is also shown in Fig. 3.16(b).

The cell III unit cell structure [230, 235, 236] is evidenced at high crystallization/annealing temperatures by the appearance of a strong 211 reflection by X-ray diffraction [230, 232, 235]. A similar effect was noted in earlier work [224] but not interpreted in terms of the antichiral chain packing. Crystallization at lower temperatures and higher cooling rates has been shown to lead to isochiral packing defects [230 - 232, 235, 238]. The resulting defect structures can be converted to the cell III structure on heating [235]. Recent work has suggested the presence of the cell I structure in stretched samples [231].

An additional polymorphic structure which results from rapid quenching and cold drawing at low temperature was observed in early work [213]. The presence of this polymorphic structure has been confirmed with similar preparation procedures by other investigators [223]. It has been suggested that chains in this polymorphic form are in a planar zig-zag conformation [213, 223]. This conformation is also characterized by a distinctly different ^{13}C NMR spectra and broader resonances characteristic of decreased order [224]. Recent unit cell assignments from fiber patterns have described the unit cell as orthorhombic with $a = 5.22$ Å, $b = 11.17$ Å, and $c = 5.06$ Å [223]. This form has been shown to convert to the helical conformation on heating [213, 224]. An additional polymorphic form of sPP has been claimed to result from exposing the all-trans form of sPP to solvent vapor [225]. As with the planar zig-zag conformation, the latter study also indicated a conversion to the helical conformation on heating.

3.4.2   Lamellar Morphology

The internal spherulitic morphology of sPP when formed by isothermal crystallization from the melt is seen to be that of radiating lamellae [224]. Generally, no pronounced evidence for cross-hatch formation has been observed in bulk samples following melt crystallization. The lamellar morphology in thin films as a function of temperature has been examined in great detail [226, 234, 235]. At high crystallization temperatures, large rectangular single crystals have been grown with a preferred crystallographic growth direction along the b-axis. These rather special crystals (relative to the bulk) have been shown to exhibit unique fracture behavior, which has been related to the very large anisotropy of the thermal expansion coefficient of sPP with respect to the crystallographic directions [234, 235]. The thermal expansion along the b-axis has been shown to be roughly an order of magnitude greater than the a-axis [234, 235]. A similar anisotropy of the thermal expansion coefficients has been noted in the α-form of iPP, although of somewhat reduced magnitude [45]. In melt crystallized thin films on selected substrates, some tendency for homoepitaxy of sPP has recently been noted [237]. This latter feature might be expected to give rise to qualitatively similar cross-hatching behavior as in the α-form of iPP, but is thought to be of limited importance for the case of bulk crystallization [237].

3.4.3   Spherulitic Morphology

Isothermal crystallization of thin films of sPP have shown, as discussed above, large rectangular single lamellar crystals at high crystallization temperature [226, 234, 235]. As the crystallization temperature is reduced, the morphology progressively changes from axialitic to spherulitic [226, 234, 235]. A similar transition in behaviors has also been noted in bulk specimens [224, 234]. Differences in the characteristic temperature ranges for these transitions may be related to sample thickness or sensitivity to tacticity level. For melt crystallization at lower temperatures, a well-developed Maltese cross pattern (a characteristic of many semicrystalline polymers) is seen under the optical microscope with cross-polarized light [224, 234]. The Maltese cross pattern is not as well developed at higher crystallization temperatures [224, 234]. Although detailed studies are lacking, Fig. 3.17 shows that the bulk polymer morphology is composed of radiating lamellae that resemble those of other semicrystalline polymers [224].

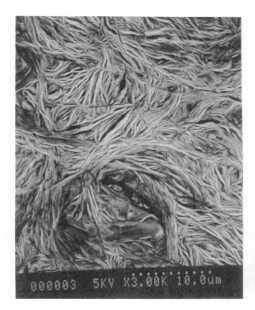 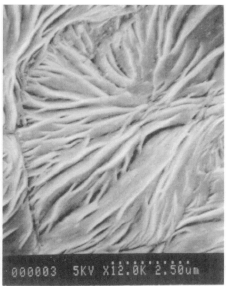

Figure 3.17 Internal lamellar structure of the bulk spherulite morphology for sPP formed by isothermal crystallization at 145 °C and etched

3.4.4   Melting Behavior

The equilibrium melting point of sPP has been evaluated by a number of authors [216, 218, 224, 227, 229, 233, 238]. Reported values are highly sensitive to tacticity level [229, 233] and are difficult to compare due to a lack of common basis for reporting tacticities, although the level of racemic placements in NMR pentads (ξ) is a reasonable measure. For sPP samples with an NMR pentad level exceeding 92% racemic, estimates of T_m° include 171 °C (95% racemic) [224], 168 °C (92% racemic) [238], 166 °C to 186 °C (92% to 95% racemic) [229], and 160 °C to 161 °C (94% racemic) [233].

Various authors have attempted to treat the dependence of the equilibrium melting point on tacticity level, $T_m^\circ(\xi)$, in terms of copolymer melting theory [78, 79, 83, 239]. Extrapolated estimates of the equilibrium melting point (T_m°) for 100% syndiotactic samples are in the range of 208 °C to 220 °C [218, 229]. These values may be overestimated, however. The equilibrium heat of fusion (ΔH°) also can be derived from copolymer melting theory, and is often anomolously low [229]. Galambos et al. [224] noted that the observable melting point, $T_m(\xi)$, is about 10 °C lower for sPP than for iPP at the same pentad percentage (ξ, which would be of meso placements for iPP). Comparison of iPP and sPP melting points is similar to the case discussed earlier with regard to the melting behavior of the α-and β-forms of iPP. While these comparisons are ambiguous, the observed melting point of sPP (for similar tacticity levels) is generally less than that of iPP under practical crystallization conditions. The reported value of $T_m^\circ(\xi)$ for sPP appears to lie between 160 °C and 185 °C at the highest tacticity levels that have been produced [224, 229, 233, 238]. Similarly wide variations for ΔH° have been quoted. These values include 105 to 106 J/g [224, 240], 164 J/g [229], 196 J/g [227], and 190 J/g [233].

As with iPP, multiple melting behavior in sPP can be observed under appropriate conditions. The melting behavior is highly sensitive to the cooling rate from the melt [224], DSC heating rate [233], and isothermal crystallization temperature [229, 233, 238]. The high temperature endotherm increases relative to the low temperature endotherm as the cooling rate increases [224]. An increased tendency for multiple endotherms is observed at lower isothermal crystallization temperatures [229, 233, 238], an effect consistent with the cooling rate dependence. The higher temperature endotherm increases relative to the low temperature endotherm as the heating rate decreases [233]. As with iPP, the upper temperature where multiple melting is no longer observed decreases as the molecular weight increases [233].

Marigo et al. [238] associated the multiple melting behavior of sPP with a reorganization phenomenon. The low temperature peak was associated with structures formed at the crystallization temperature, while the high temperature endotherm was thought to result from reorganization during scanning. In sPP, the reorganization phenomena at elevated temperature are accompanied by the appearance of a strong 211 cell III reflection in variable temperature WAXS experiments [233, 235]. This reflection, as discussed previously, is associated with an increased conversion to fully antichiral packing of chains in the crystalline state. It is not clear at present to what extent some form of "melting" is required for the occurrence of this internal rearrangement of the chains in the crystal. In addition to reorganization of crystals, some degree of morphological heterogeneity cannot be excluded as a possibile contributing factor to multiple melting.

3.4.5   Crystallization/Morphology Development

Hoffmann and Clark analyzed the spherulitic growth rate in terms of regime II growth kinetics [111, 218]. This analysis suggested an interfacial fold energy of 49.9 erg/cm^2, and a work for chain folding of approximately 24.3 kJ/mol. Both values are slightly less than that of iPP. The data was based on sPP samples which by current standards were of relatively low stereoregularity. A regime II–III transition was predicted in the vicinity of $\Delta T \sim 50\,^\circ\mathrm{C}$. More recent work [234] has reexamined the growth kinetics of sPP by regime analysis with samples of substantially improved regularity, and the results were in general agreement with the previous studies. Values of σ_e were in the range of 42 erg/cm^2 to 47 erg/cm^2, and were in approximate agreement with estimates by eq 3.1. The corresponding work for chain folding was quoted in the range of 20 kJ/mol to 24 kJ/mol. Based on the proportionality of the work for chain folding with the equilibrium melting point [111], the results discussed above are consistent with a slightly lower T_m° for sPP relative to iPP, given the current limits on sPP tacticity. A regime II–III transition has been proposed for sPP [234], in approximate agreement with the predictions of Hoffmann and Clark.

3.5   Morphology of Rubber-Modified PP

The addition of rubber to PP has been developed to extend the useful property range of PP resin. The availability of a wide range of PP homopolymers, copolymers, and elastomers with respect to molecular weight and composition has resulted in material with good stiffness and low temperature impact resistance, as well as low modulus, high thermal stability, and improved blush-resistance. This range of properties results from both matrix and dispersed phase composition and part morphology. Illustrative examples of the relationship of morphology to structure, processing, and properties are given below and serve to illustrate the rich variety of morphologies possible from this broad material classification.

3.5.1   Rubber Modification

In the early development of PP, the addition of rubber provided an improvement in impact, but results varied significantly depending on the rubber composition and morphology. The basic requirements for impact-modified brittle plastics were established with the development of high impact polystyrene (PS) [241 - 245]. Similar considerations govern rubber-modified PP, but the crystalline nature of PP complicates the achievement of the desired rubber morphology. From the PS work, it was evident that particles with about 1 micron diameter having good adhesion to the matrix were desired. PP requires a similar morphology [246 - 251].

In PP impact modification, ethylene-propylene rubber (EPR) with 30% to 60% C_2 is often used. The rubber is reactor polymerized or introduced through compounding. As discussed earlier, the rubber composition is sufficiently different from PP homopolymer and random copolymer that it is usually immiscible even in the melt. Thus, the final rubber morphology is strongly affected by shear and deformation during melt process operations.

3.5.2   Morphology

The morphology of rubber-modified PP is determined by the relative chemical composition and molecular weight of the PP and elastomer phases, in addition to the compounding/fabrication process [71, 252 - 258]. Like other rubber-modified polymers, blends of PP with elastomer separate into distinct phases. Immiscible mixtures can result in blends of PP homopolymer with ethylene-propylene copolymers when the comonomer content is as low as 8% ethylene [259]. Recent advances in multistep polymerization technology have added new dimensions to the control of rubber-modified PP morphology. These advances include the ability to polymerize the elastomer phase directly in the matrix, a choice of monomers and monomer ratio, and molecular weight control. The resultant product yields an as-polymerized finely dispersed elastomer phase which allows for the tailoring of rubber phase morphology and interfacial tension.

The morphologies observed in rubber-modified PPs range from dispersed to cocontinuous phase structures. The rubber phase has its own morphological characteristics resulting from its structure, melt processing, and crystallization history. Figure 3.18 shows a transmission electron microscope (TEM) photomicrograph of the dispersed phase structure of a typical reactor polymerized rubber-modified PP homopolymer. The product contains approximately 14% rubber phase with a rubber composition of 40 mole-percent C_2, and was injection molded at 193 °C with a five-minute barrel hold time. The morphology is viewed at the core of the plaque. The properties of this material can be greatly influenced by molding conditions, which cause large changes in rubber particle size. The same material injection molded at 215 °C with a barrel hold time of 10 minutes yields the morphology shown in Fig. 3.19. Note that coalescence and growth of the rubber phase has led to an increase in the

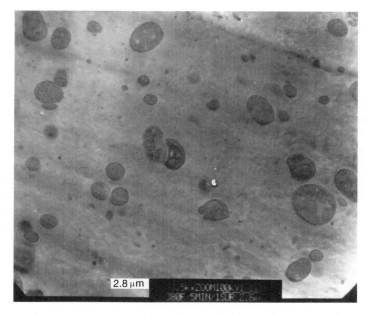

2.8 µm

Figure 3.18   TEM image of reactor polymerized rubber-modified PP injection molded at 193°C

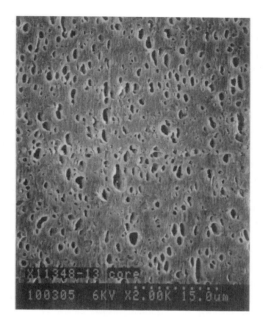

Figure 3.25 SEM image of compounded PP/EPR blend with low viscosity ratio

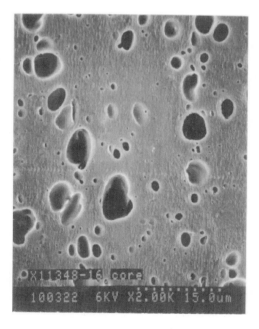

Figure 3.26 SEM image of compounded PP/EPR blend with high viscosity ratio

dispersed phase is high (greater than 10), toughness-related properties will also be anisotropic. Craze formation initiated parallel to the dispersed phase propagates with low probability of arrest, leading to premature failure. An example of this failure mechanism would be the lack of crush resistance in cylindrical geometries where deformation is parallel to the extrusion direction. The morphology in Fig. 3.27 is an example of this type of anisotropy.

Another aspect of processing/morphology relations is the degree to which melt orientation gradients produce a morphology gradient. This is a combined effect of the imposed flow field and the ability of the matrix to transfer shear stress to the dispersed phase. Differences in the morphology gradient from surface to core as a function of η_r are shown in Fig. 3.28 and 3.29 [271]. The similarly molded plaques are viewed perpendicular to the flow direction. It is clearly seen that the plaque with the low η_r (Fig. 3.28) exhibits a highly oriented rubber phase near the surface ("skin layer") and a more spherical shape at the core. The blend with higher η_r exhibits a more isotropic morphology throughout the part cross section (Fig. 3.29). The specific type of morphology has advantages and disadvantages, depending upon the end-use application. In external fascia molding applications [272 - 275] where painting is required, the high surface area of the dispersed phase in the skin layer of a material with low η_r can improve permeation of the paint system into the substrate.

This morphology is shown in greater detail for a rubber-modified PP containing 25 wt% dispersed phase in Fig. 3.30 and 3.31. These figures show TEM photomicrographs of the surface and core morphology, respectively. Quantitative image analysis of these micrographs show approximately 50% of the surface area is covered by the rubber phase, whereas 25% of the core area is rubber. This is an advantage of a blend with low η_r. The disadvantage of the

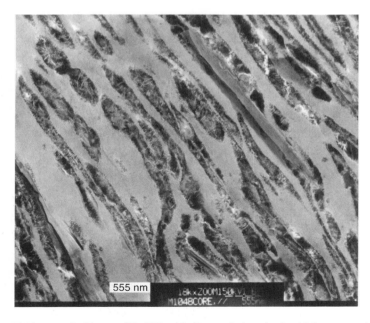

Figure 3.27   TEM image of rubber-modified PP with dispersed phase having high aspect ratio

Figure 3.28 SEM image of morphology gradient in injection molded plaque of rubber-modified PP with a low viscosity ratio

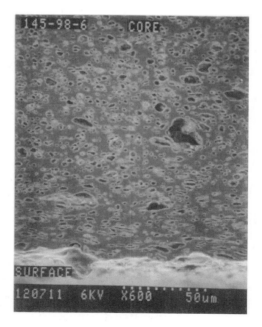

Figure 3.29 SEM image of morphology gradient in injection molded plaque of rubber-modified PP with a high viscosity ratio

highly oriented skin morphology is that it results in a lowering of the shear strength of the material in an anisotropic manner.

Stresses parallel to the flow direction, such as "bump and rub impacts," may result in cohesive failure in the oriented surface when the material strength in this zone is low. Figure 3.32 shows an SEM photomicrograph of such a cohesive failure in a highly oriented morphology. If the morphological structure is more isotropic, as shown previously in Fig. 3.29, then one can expect improved cohesive strength, but at the expense of reduced adhesive strength of the coating layer. This balance of properties is due to the reduction in surface area of the dispersed phase at the coating-substrate interface. The challenge is to provide a blend whose viscosity ratio gives morphologies which provide an optimum balance of coating adhesion and physical properties.

3.5.5   Crystallinity in the Rubber Phase

Under some circumstances, it is desirable to have some crystalline material within the normally amorphous rubber phase. As a practical example, the resistance of an injection molded piece to voiding when deformed (blushing) is improved with inclusion of crystallizable material. This is often achieved by incorporation of high-density polyethylene (HDPE) crystallinity within the rubber phase. The blushing phenomenon has been widely studied. The improvement in blushing characteristics with incorporation of HDPE crystallinity arises from the modification of relative volume changes in the matrix and dispersed

Figure 3.30   TEM image of surface morphology of injection molded rubber-modified PP with 25 wt% EPR

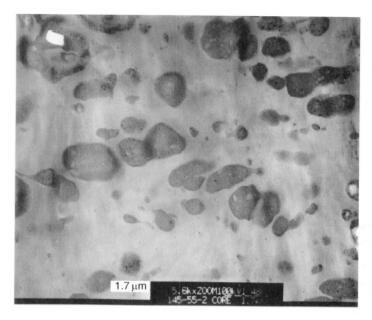

Figure 3.31 TEM image of core morphology of injection molded rubber-modified PP with 25 wt% EPR

Figure 3.32 SEM image of rubber-modified PP showing delamination due to highly oriented surface morphology

phases during cooling and aging, and the resulting reduction in the residual stresses of the matrix phase [276].

The internal morphology of the rubber phase can be varied by changing the chemical composition in situ via polymerization, or by downstream compounding of polymer additives. Variation in rubber composition can also affect the interfacial tension between rubber and matrix, thus influencing dispersive mixing and physical properties. Reactor grade Ziegler–Natta catalysts can produce EPR compositions with sufficiently random comonomer incorporation to give an amorphous rubber, as shown previously in Fig. 3.18. To contrast this case, Fig. 3.33 and 3.34 show the result of incorporation of crystalline structure (HDPE) within the rubber phase. A PE crystalline phase is seen dispersed in the amorphous rubber. The resultant micromorphology of the rubber phase influences the shrinkage of the rubber phase and the final stress state of the matrix, thus making the article more blush resistant [277].

Similar morphologies can be obtained by downstream addition of HDPE. Figure 3.35 shows a TEM photomicrograph of 10% HDPE compounded into a PP/EPR blend. Adding components downstream requires an understanding of melt solubility behavior of the blend components, as well as the influence of the added components on the different phase viscosities. For example, the 10% HDPE blend in Fig. 3.35 lowered the viscosity of the rubber phase at processing temperatures to the extent that the dispersed phase morphology at the core of the sample became highly oriented. Figure 3.36 shows that the surface skin becomes even more oriented (fibrillar) when compared to the same system without added HDPE (Fig. 3.30). This can result in significant changes in properties, such as the propensity to delaminate or a decrease in environmental resistance in critical applications [278, 279].

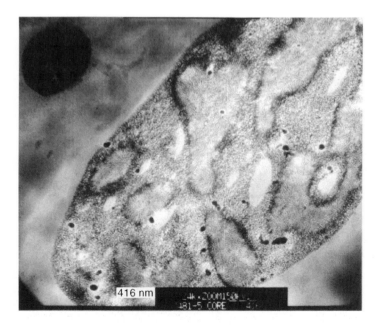

Figure 3.33 TEM image of rubber-modified PP with crystalline PE dispersed in rubber phase, reactor polymerized

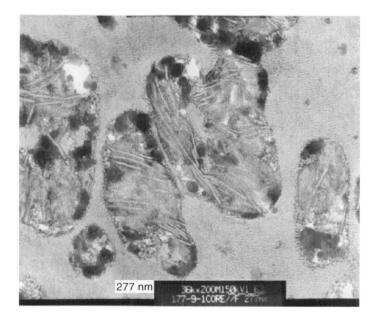

Figure 3.34   TEM image of reactor polymerized rubber-modified PP with crystalline PE dispersed in rubber phase

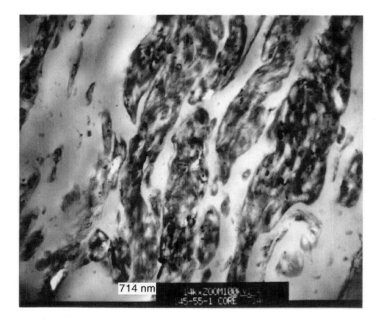

Figure 3.35   TEM image of PP/EPR blend with 10 wt% added HDPE

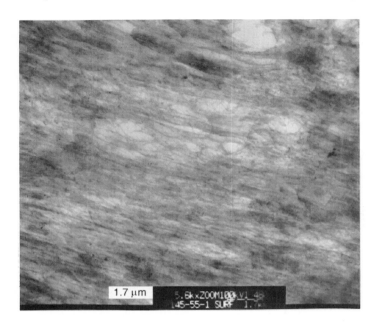

Figure 3.36 TEM image of highly fibrillar surface resulting from injection molding rubber-modified PP with 10 wt% HDPE added

3.5.6   High Alloy Copolymers

As the volume fraction of rubber phase increases to 70%, it can be either the dispersed or continuous phase, depending on η_r. A PP homopolymer with a much lower viscosity than the elastomer will tend to be the continuous phase at low shear (extrusion) conditions. Figure 3.37 is a photomicrograph of a cross section of an extruded pellet of a reactor grade rubber-modified PP containing 65% elastomer. In applications with materials at high elastomer levels, the final forming process can cause dramatic changes in the morphology. In blown film applications, such materials can form microlaminate cocontinuous morphologies, as shown in Fig. 3.38. The entire cross section of this film is less than 25 μm thick. The resulting layer thickness of the individual phases are on the order of hundreds of angstroms. Because of the high surface area of the layered structure, interfacial tension plays a significant role during development of the final morphology.

   Figures 3.39 and 3.40 show cross sections of blown films with the same elastomer level and similar processing conditions, but differing in composition of the PP-rich phase. Figure 3.39 shows the morphology when the PP-rich phase is homopolymer, and Fig. 3.40 shows the morphology when the PP-rich phase is a random copolymer with a small percentage of ethylene comonomer. The change in surface tension between the phases with comonomer addition to the PP-rich phase results in a finer and more regular structure. This results in an improved property balance of puncture and tear resistance [280 - 284].

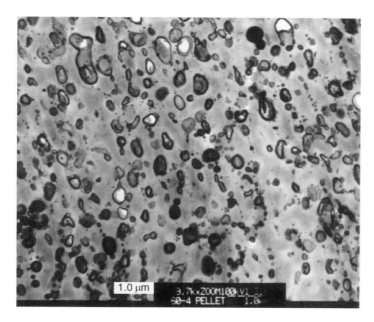

Figure 3.37 TEM image of cross section of extruded pellet of reactor polymerized rubber-modified PP containing 65% elastomer

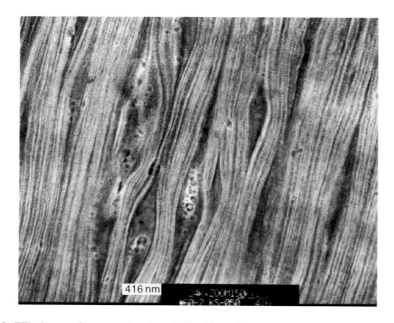

Figure 3.38 TEM image of cross section through film blown from rubber-modified PP with 65% elastomer

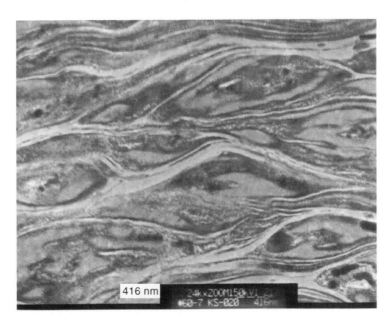

Figure 3.39 TEM image of cross section through blown film of rubber-modified PP with homopolymer in first stage reactor

Figure 3.40 TEM image of cross section through blown film of rubber-modified PP with 3% C_2 random copolymer in first stage reactor

3.6   Injection Molded Homopolymer

3.6.1   Injection Molding Process

The injection molding process provides an additional illustrative example of the strong interrelationship between structure, processing, morphology, and final polymer properties. In the injection molding process, molten polymer is injected into a cold mold cavity with a geometry of desired shape. The final morphology of a molded part is a direct result of flow processes during mold filling and subsequent solidification. The specific characteristics of the bulk morphology result from competitive and interdependent dynamic processes related to the

1. Coupling of the orientation (and subsequent relaxation) of polymer chains in the melt with the imposed flow field,
2. heat transfer between the hot melt and the cold mold walls, and
3. crystallization kinetics under flow conditions.

During filling of the mold, molten polymer chains are oriented by a combination of shear and elongational flow [285, 286]. The induced orientation is partially lost through relaxation of the initially stretched polymer chains. The extent of relaxation is governed by the time elapsed prior to crystallization, which effectively "freezes in" the instantaneous orientation state. The time and extent of relaxation are influenced by molding conditions. This occurs through the coupling of the flow field with the rheological characteristics of the resin, and the imposed temperature gradient between the cold mold walls and the hot molten core. Both the crystallization kinetics and the orientation/relaxation of the polymer chains are sensitive to the localized and time-dependent melt strain and temperature in the mold. The total degree of crystallinity also can be coupled to the temperature gradient. Subsequent to the filling stage, the mold is "packed" under pressure to account for shrinkage due to crystallization and thermal contraction.

3.6.2   Macromorphology

Injection moldings of iPP exhibit skin-core macrostructures and frozen-in orientations which are sensitive to molding conditions [5 - 9, 167 - 170, 287 - 297]. An illustrative example of the skin-core macrostructure is shown in Fig. 3.41, which views a cross section of a molded part with an optical microscope. The dark featureless banding, or "skin-layer," is due to highly oriented flow-induced microstructures which are frozen-in by the crystallization process. The morphology becomes spherulitic moving away from the part surface towards the "core layer." The effective cooling rate is much lower in the core layer, allowing more time for relaxation of flow-induced orientation prior to solidification. These factors lead to less orientation in the core layer relative to the skin layer [6, 7, 167 - 169, 290, 293, 295, 297].

The spatial distribution of orientation in an injection molded part is important because of the sensitivity of properties to frozen-in orientation. Depending on molding conditions and flow pattern, a continuous decrease of orientation or a local orientation maxima moving away from the surface to the core is observed [8, 168, 169, 293, 297]. A sharp transition in orientation is not always observed at the macroscopic skin-core boundary. Qualitative

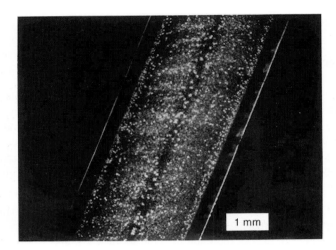

Figure 3.41 Skin-core morphology of injection molded iPP under cross-polarized light with an optical microscope. View is across the flow direction

consideration of flow during mold filling suggests a local maxima in the orientation distribution through the part thickness which is related to the superposition of elongational orientation near the mold walls and shear flow orientation in the central region behind the advancing melt front [285, 286]. Consequently, the macromorphology of injection molded parts has been further subdivided [6, 167, 168, 289, 290, 297]. A featureless skin layer near the surface, a shear zone with row-nucleated spherulites, and a spherulitic core region with lower orientation is often described [6, 167, 168, 297]. Frozen-in orientation and the skin layer thickness decrease with increasing distance from the gate [6, 8, 9, 169, 287] due to the relaxation of melt strain during filling [8, 169]. Additional factors related to the shorter effective fill time prior to packing and the dependence of pressure on crystallization temperature and rate [168, 286, 288] also can play a role.

The bulk crystallinity of injection moldings is strongly influenced by the resin tacticity [9]. A slightly lower degree of crystallinity near the surface relative to the core can be observed [8, 169, 293] and is consistent with a higher effective quench rate at the part surface. The crystallinity gradient through the part thickness is not pronounced [287], as evidenced by similar densities in the skin and core regions [7]. Crystallinity gradients through the part thickness that exhibit maxima [168] and minima [293] have been noted, although the relative crystallinity variation is small. Separation of cooling rate and flow effects is difficult, but considering the substantial orientation gradients, these observations suggest the influence of melt orientation on bulk crystallinity is not pronounced. Melt orientation clearly has a strong influence on the crystallization kinetics [165, 287, 298 - 301] which can partially compensate for the effect of cooling rate on crystallinity.

3.6.3   Morphology Hierarchy

The macrostructure of an injection molded part can be subdivided on a hierarchy of scales. On the "crystallographic" scale, WAXS patterns from injection moldings exhibit a mixture of

a^*- and c-axis orientations [8, 9, 167, 169, 290, 296, 302]. Similar orientation behavior is observed for iPP samples formed by other fabrication methods under conditions of melt strain [15]. The "bimodal" orientation balance of the crystallographic axes is associated with the melt orientability of the resin [9]. For injection molding, the melt orientability acts like a melt draw ratio, and strongly influences the orientation balance in the solid state. "Melt-orientability" is used here as a general term relating to the tendency for orientation in the solid state. This tendency for orientation is governed by the rheological characteristics of the resin (related to molecular weight and MWD), the response of the resin crystallization kinetics to melt strain, and the specific molding conditions. Portions of chains contained within the amorphous regions are also oriented [168, 293, 304]. Infrared dichroism techniques [15, 303 - 305] can be applied to both thick [304] or microtomed sections of injection molded parts. The absolute magnitude of the amorphous orientation is less than the corresponding value of the crystalline orientation function [168, 293, 304]. The amorphous and crystalline orientation functions show similar tendencies with respect to macroscopic gradients and processing conditions [168, 293]. Both orientation functions are relevant to the crystallographic distance scale, yet show similar response to processing and material variation as the skin-core macrostructure.

Lamellar structures show high orientation in the skin layers relative to the core. The "lamellar" scale microstructure common to many semicrystalline polymers formed by crystallization under conditions of shear is that of highly oriented fibriller cores with lateral overgrowths [6, 298]. In this sense, the lamellar morphology of injection molded iPP is similar to that of other semicrystalline polymers, but exhibits unique features associated with the bimodal crystalline orientation. A mixture of lamellar populations containing chains with either c-axis or a^*-axis crystallographic orientations is observed in the skin layers [7, 296, 302]. The representative model of Fujiyama and co-workers [7] proposes that the normal to the surface of lamellae containing c-axis crystalline orientation is parallel to the flow direction and perpendicular for lamellae with a^*-axis oriented crystals. Lamellae containing the a^*-axis oriented crystals are thought to be disordered and of small size.

The morphology of injection molded parts becomes increasingly spherulitic with distance from the surface towards the core [6, 8, 9, 167 - 169, 289] due to a lower cooling rate and comparatively strain-free crystallization conditions. Accordingly, the spherulite size is generally expected to increase closer to the core [167] and with increasing mold temperature and melt temperature [306]. A transitional "shear-zone" morphology can be observed between the featureless skin layer and the unoriented core [6, 167, 168, 289]. The β-crystalline form, and associated β-form spherulites, are also observed in some cases [8, 9, 167 - 170]. Some studies suggest that the β-form spherulites are concentrated in shear zones at depths intermediate between the surface and core of the molded part [8, 167 - 169]. Regardless of the precise morphological location, β-crystallinity can exist in regions of appreciable melt strain. High crystallographic orientation of the β-crystals are observed under the same conditions as that of the α-form crystals [9]. This observation is interesting, considering the metastability of the β-form with respect to the α-form on application of strain in the solid state [25, 142, 151, 155 - 159]. In the absence of preferential nucleators, the content of the β-form is normally observed to be less than 15% of the total crystalline fraction [9]. Consequently, the presence of the β-crystalline spherulites is generally a second-order effect in terms of the correlation of morphology to properties.

3.6.4   Structure/Processing/Morphology/Property Relations

Crystallinity and frozen-in orientation are dominant features of the morphology of injection molded PP. The dependence of these "bulk" morphology variables on processing parameters gives significant variation of properties for a specific resin. Orientation measured on either the crystallographic or macroscopic scale exhibit similar response to process and resin variation. Although quantitative application to large molded parts is difficult, several qualitative generalizations can be made. Generally, the skin layer thickness decreases with increasing melt temperature [6, 8, 9, 167, 169, 170, 289, 291, 292], increasing distance from the gate in the flow direction [8, 9, 169, 170], decreasing resin molecular weight (and increasing melt flow rate) [5, 9, 291, 292], and decreasing resin polydispersity [9, 291]. The skin layer thickness has also been observed to decrease with increasing injection speed [287, 289], although this process parameter has contributions from both the extent of shear (increasing with increasing speed) and the shearing time (increasing with decreasing speed). Other related effects include a decrease in the skin layer thickness with increasing mold temperature [6] and increasing crystallinity with decreasing molecular weight (increasing melt flow rate) [169]. Variables more directly related to the packing stage also have been studied [5, 6, 167, 297]. Crystallinity is strongly influenced by resin tacticity [9].

   The frozen-in orientation influences the impact characteristics of injection moldings [5, 6, 167, 170, 292], although intrinsic contributions from the polymer structure (such as molecular weight) and test geometry are important. The molded-in morphology influences heat distortion characteristics, as evidenced by higher softening temperatures in the skin layers relative to the core during dynamic mechanical testing [7, 170]. Frozen-in orientation strongly influences the mechanical anisotropy [5, 7, 9]. Mechanical anisotropy refers to the property difference when measured in the flow direction relative to the measurement at an angle different from the flow direction. Anisotropy in moldings can exhibit a complicated dependence on this angle [5]. The flexural modulus anisotropy at room temperature increases with increasing orientation level [5, 7, 9] and tends to become more pronounced at reduced test temperature. A strong correlation of part shrinkage in the direction of flow to the area fraction of the skin layer has been observed [6, 167, 291]. Less sensitivity of shrinkage to orientation level is suggested by measurements transverse to the direction of flow [291].

   The tensile modulus and yield strength of injection moldings in the direction of flow increase with increasing orientation [6, 7, 167, 170, 291], as does the flexural modulus [9, 170, 291]. These properties generally show a qualitatively similar response to processing and structural variables as the skin-core macrostructure (or crystallographic orientation). Approximate correlation of the flexural modulus to bulk crystallinity and bulk orientation can be made for a wide range of molding conditions and resin characteristics [9]. This relationship is shown in Fig. 3.42. The flexural modulus of iPP moldings can be varied over a wide range through tailored resin characteristics (tacticity, molecular weight, MWD), molding conditions, and proximity to the gate inlet [9, 170, 291]. For the case shown in Fig. 3.42, the injection moldings exhibit lower crystallinity relative to the compression moldings (along a line of zero orientation), but higher modulus. This reinforces the important role of orientation on properties of injection moldings. Both crystallinity and orientation contribute to the final modulus. The shape of the three-dimensional surface shown in Fig. 3.42 also enables the prediction that higher modulus resins (corresponding to high orientation and high crystallinity) will exhibit increased sensitivity to process variation [9]. The correlation of

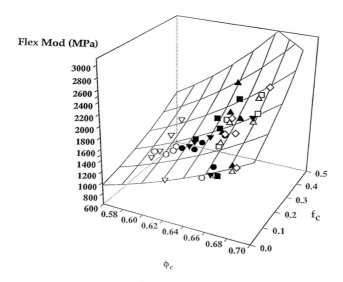

Figure 3.42   The response of flexural modulus in injection molded iPP homopolymer to the volume fraction crystallinity, ϕ_c, and the c-axis crystalline orientation function, f_c. Each symbol corresponds to a different resin molded with different melt temperatures and location from the gate, or by compression molding. Reprinted with with permission from Ref. [9], Copyright 1994 Society of Plastics Engineers

morphology to properties in Fig. 3.42 is greatly simplified by the use of bulk morphology parameters. This approach neglects the effect of *both* crystalline and amorphous orientation, gradients through the part thickness, effects of intercrystalline connectivity, and contributions from crystallinity and orientation to the final property that may not be independent. Regardless, Fig. 3.42 reinforces the strong effect of crystallinity and orientation on the final properties of iPP moldings, as well as the role of morphology as a unifying principle for the wide variation of properties possible through process and polymer structure variation.

3.7   Concluding Comments

Historically, the connection between the application of polymer physics to PP solid-state morphology and the commercial development of new PP chemistries has been inseparable. The determination of the helical chain conformation of iPP in the crystalline state was a critical confirmation of the high stereospecificity of Ziegler–Natta polymerizations. Subsequent studies of the solid-state morphology of iPP were driven by the increased crystallinity and corresponding property enhancement made possible through the improvements in the regulation of stereochemistry and the associated rapid emergence of iPP in the marketplace.

The discussion of the open literature with regard to homopolymer morphology, although admittedly incomplete, illustrates the remarkable morphological versatility of PP in the solid state. Many of the gross features of this morphology have been known since the late 1950s and early 1960s. These features include the basic helical building block of the crystalline structure, the existence of all of the major polymorphic forms, the presence of a variety of spherulite types, and the recognition of cross-hatched lamellae. Subsequent work has built on these early studies and filled in many details. These included details of the crystal structure refinements, details of the cross-hatching mechanism, the correlation of lamellar structures and spherulite optical characteristics, many studies relating to the conditions for formation of the various polymorphic forms, correlation of melting behavior with polymer structure, and the development and application of regime analysis to the crystallization kinetics, to name only a few. With the advent of new experimental techniques and theoretical developments, many of these areas remain remarkably current.

The rich morphology of PP homopolymer exhibits even further complexity when coupled with the variations in structural parameters of the chain and processing history. While this is true for all the PP polymer types, it is particularly evident in the multiphase, rubber-modified systems, as discussed in Section 3.5. Establishment of the specific relation-ships among polymer structure, processing, morphology, and end-use properties, which accounts for all of the morphological complexity in a processed part, is a formidable task. Although we have made considerable progress on the key relationships, it is important to try, where possible, to reduce these complexities into a few basic rules of behavior to establish the global interrelationships. This is expected to be a continuing challenge.

The advent of new polymerization chemistries for PP, such as the relatively recent development of syndiospecific catalysts and investigations into sPP morphology, will continue to challenge our knowledge of the solid-state morphology. Other critically important and rapidly advancing areas, to a large degree neglected here due to space limitations, include chemistries and technologies related to copolymerization, reactor blend technologies, and grafting technologies. The efficient utilization of the expanding range of PP properties possible from these emerging catalyst and polymerization technologies demand an increas-ingly vigorous application of polymer physics at the industrial level. These new advancements further emphasize the important role of polymer physics and polymer morphology as the critical bridge among structure, processing, and properties.

References

1. *Lieberman, R.B., Barbe, P.C.:* Encyclopedia of Polymer Science and Engineering, John Wiley & Sons, Vol 13, New York (1988) 464
2. *Hutchinson, R.A., Chen, C.M., Ray, W.H.:* J. Appl. Polym. Sci. 44 (1992) 1389
3. *Noristi, L., Marchetti, E., Barussi, G., Sgarzi, P.:* J. Polym. Sci. Polym. Chem. Ed. 32 (1994) 3047
4. *Galli, P., Haylock, J.C., Simonazzi, T.:* Polypropylene: Structure, blends and composites, Karger-Kocsis, J., Ed.; Chapman & Hall, London (1995) 1
5. *Fujiyama, M., Awaya, H., Kimura, S.:* J. Appl. Polym. Sci. 21 (1977) 3291
6. *Katti, S.S., Schultz, J.M.:* Polym. Eng. Sci. 22 (1982) 1001
7. *Fujiyama, M., Wakino, T., Kawasaki, Y.:* J. Appl. Polym. Sci. 35 (1988) 29
8. *Fujiymama, M., Wakino, T.:* J. Appl. Polym. Sci. 43 (1991) 97
9. *Phillips, R., Hebert, G., News, J., Wolkowicz, M.:* Polym. Eng. Sci. 34 (1994) 1731
10. *Padden, F.J., Keith, H.D.:* J. Appl. Phys. 30 (1959) 1479
11. *Stein, R.S., Rhodes, M.B.:* J. Appl. Phys. 31 (1960) 1873
12. *Khoury, F.:* J. Res. Nat. Bureau Stnds. 70 (1966) 29

13. *Samuels, R.J.:* J. Polym. Sci. (C) 13 (1966) 37
14. *Samuels, R.J.:* J. Polym. Sci. (A2) 6 (1968) 1101
15. *Samuels, R.J.:* Structured Polymer Properties: The Identification, Interpretation, and Application of Crystalline Polymer Structure, John Wiley & Sons: New York, 1974
16. *Norton, D.R., Keller, A.:* Polymer 26 (1985) 704
17. *Varga, J.:* J. Matr. Sci. 27 (1992) 2557
18. *Sauer, J.A., Morrow, D.R., Richardson, G.C.:* J. Appl. Phys. 36 (1965) 3017
19. *Padden, F.J. Jr., Keith, H.D.:* J. Appl. Phys. 37 (1966) 4013
20. *Balta-Calleja, F.J., Peterlin, A.:* Die Makromol. Chem. 141 (1971) 91
21. *Padden, F.J. Jr., Keith, H.D.:* J. Appl. Phys. 44 (1973) 1217
22. *Lovinger, A.J.:* J. Polym. Sci. Polym. Phys. Ed. 21 (1983) 97
23. *Bassett, D.C., Olley, R.H.:* Polymer 25 (1984) 935
24. *Natta, G., Corradini, P.:* del Nuovo Cimento XV (1960) 40
25. *Turner-Jones, A., Aizlewood, J.M., Beckett, D.R.:* Makromol. Chem. 75 (1964) 134
26. *Mencik, Z.:* J. Macromol. Sci. 6 (1972) 101
27. *Hikosaka, M., Seto, T.:* Polym. J. 5 (1973) 111
28. *Immirzi, A.:* Acta Cryst. 36(B) (1980) 2378
29. *Miller, R.L., Nielsen, L.E.:* J. Polym. Sci. XLVI (1960) 303
30. *Youngman, E.A., Boor, J.:* Macromol. Rev. 2 (1967) 33
31. *Zambelli, Z., Gatti, G., Sacchi, C., Crain, W.O. Jr., Roberts, J.D.:* Macromolecules, 4 (1971) 475
32. *Zambelli, A., Tosi, C.:* Adv. Polym. Sci. 15 (1974) 32
33. *Wolfsburger, C., Zannoni, G., Rigamonti, E., Zambelli, A.:* Makromol. Chem. 176 (1975) 2765
34. *Zambelli, A., Locatelli, P., Zannoni, G., Bovey, F.A.:* Macromolecules 11 (1978) 923
35. *Schilling, F.C., Tonelli, A.E.:* Macromolecules 13 (1980) 270
36. *Doi, Y., Suzuki, T., Keii, T.:* Makromol. Chem. Rapid Commun. 2 (1981) 293
37. *Zhu, S.N., Yang, X.Z., Chûjô, R.:* Polym. J. 15 (1983) 859
38. *Ewen, J.A.:* J. Am. Chem. Soc. 106 (1984) 6355
39. *Paukkeri, R., Väänänen, T., Lehtinen, A.:* Polymer 34 (1993) 2488
40. *Farina, M., DiSilvestro, G., Terragni, A.:* Macromol. Chem. Phys. 196 (1995) 353
41. *Miller, R.L.:* Polymer 1 (1960) 135
42. *Corradini, P., Napolitano, R., Oliva, L., Petraccone, V., Pirozzi, B., Guerra, G.:* Makromol. CHem. Rapid Commun. 3 (1982) 753
43. *Guerra, G., Petraccone, V., Corradini, P., DeRosa, C., Napolitano, R., Pirozzi, B.:* J. Polym. Sci. Polym. Phys. Ed. 22 (1984) 1029
44. *DeRosa, C., Guerra, G., Napolitano, R., Petraccone, V., Pirozzi, B.:* Eur. Polym. J. 20 (1984) 937
45. *Napolitano, R., Pirozzi, B., Varriale, V.:* J. Polym. Sci. Polym. Phys. Ed. 28 (1990) 139
46. *Corradini, P., Petraccone, V., Pirozzi, B.:* Eur. Polym. J. 19 (1983) 299
47. *Ferro, D.R., Bruckner, S., Meille, S.V., Ragazzi, M.:* Macromolecules 25 (1992) 5231
48. *International Tables of Crystallography,* Kynoch Press: Birmingham, 1962, Vol. II
49. *Keith, H.D., Padden, F.J. Jr., Walter, N.M., Wyckoff, H.W.:* J. Appl. Phys. 30 (1959) 1485
50. *Binsbergern, F.L., de Lange, B.G.M.:* Polymer 9 (1968) 23
51. *Lotz, B., Wittmann, J.C.:* Polym. Sci. Polym. Phys. Ed. 24 (1986) 1541
52. *Awaya, H.:* Polymer 29 (1988) 591
53. *Mezghani, K., Anderson-Campbell, R., Phillips, P.J.:* Macromolecules 27 (1994) 997
54. *Lotz, B., Graff, S., Wittmann, J.C.:* J. Polym. Sci. Polym. Phys. Ed. 24 (1986) 2017
55. *Idrissi, M.O.B., Chabert, B., Guillet, J.:* Makromol. Chem. 187 (1986) 2001
56. *Cheng, S.Z.D., Janimak, J.J., Zhang, A., Cheng, H.N.:* Macromolecules 23 (1990) 298
57. *Wunderlich, B.:* Macromolecular Physics, Academic Press: New York, 1980, Vol. 3
58. *Martuscelli, E., Pracella, M., Crispino, L.:* Polymer 24 (1983) 693
59. *Burfield, D.R., Loi, P.S.T., Doi, Y., Majzik, J.:* J. Appl. Polym. Sci. 41 (1990) 1095
60. *Janimak, J.J., Cheng, S.Z.D., Zhang, A., Hsieh, E.T.:* Polymer 33 (1992) 729
61. *Paukkeri, R., Lehtinen, A.:* Polymer 34 (1993) 4075
62. *Paukkeri, R., Lehtinen, A.:* Polymer 34 (1993) 4083
63. *Paukkeri, R., Iiskola, E., Lehtinen, A., Salminen, H.:* Polymer 35 (1994) 2636
64. *Cox, W.W., Duswalt, A.A.:* Polym. Eng. Sci. 7 (1967) 309

65. *Pae, K.D., Sauer, J.A.:* J. Appl. Polym. Sci. 12 (1968) 1901
66. *Sauer, J.A., Pae, K.D.:* J. Appl. Polym. Sci. 12 (1968) 1921
67. *Fatou, J.G.:* Eur. Polym. J. 7 (1971) 1057
68. *Kamide, K., Yamaguchi, K.:* Die Makromol. Chem. 162 (1972) 205
69. *Kamide, K., Yamaguchi, K.:* Die Makromol. Chem. 162 (1972) 219
70. *Samuels, R.J.:* J. Polym. Sci. Polym. Phys. Ed. 13 (1975) 1417
71. *Martuscelli, E., Silvestre, C., Abate, G.:* Polymer 23 (1982) 229
72. *Petraccone, V., DeRosa, C., Guerra, G., Tuzi, A.:* Makromol. Chem. Rapid Comm. 5 (1984) 631
73. *Petraccone, V., Guerra, G., DeRosa, C., Tuzi, A.:* Macromolecules 18 (1985) 813
74. *Monasse, B., Haudin, J.M.:* Colloid Polym. Sci. 263 (1985) 822
75. *Yadav, Y.S., Jain, P.C.:* Polymer 27 (1986) 721
76. *Passingham, C., Hendra, P.J., Cudby, M.E.A., Zichy, V., Weller, M.:* Eur. Polym. J. 26 (1990) 631
77. *Bartzak, Z., Galeski, A.:* Polymer 31 (1990) 2027
78. *Flory, P.J.:* J. Chem. Phys. 17 (1949) 223
79. *Flory, P.J.:* Principles of Polymer Chemistry, Cornell University Press: Ithaca (1953)
80. *Flory, P.J., Vrij, A.:* J. Am. Chem. Soc. 85 (1963) 3548
81. *Wunderlich, B., Czornyj, G.:* Macròmolecules 10 (1977) 906
82. *Mandelkern, L., Stack, G.M.:* Macromolecules 17 (1984) 871
83. *Flory, P.J.:* Trans. Faraday Soc. 51 (1955) 848
84. *Nishi, T., Wang, T.T.:* Macromolecules 8 (1975) 909
85. *Flory, P.J.:* J. Am. Chem. Soc. 78 (1956) 5222
86. *Krigbaum, W.R., Roe, R.J.:* J. Polym. Sci. 2(A) (1964) 4391
87. *Yan, R.J., Jiang, B.:* J. Polym. Sci. Polym. Phys. Ed. 31 (1993) 1089
88. *Sanchez, I.C., Eby, R.K.:* Macromolecules 8 (1975) 638
89. *Lauritzen, J.I., Hoffman, J.D.:* J. Res. Nat. Bur. Std. 64(A) (1960) 73
90. *Hoffman, J.D., Weeks, J.J.:* J. Res. Nat. Bur. Std. 66(A) (1962) 13
91. *Hoffman, J.D., Davis, G.T., Lauritzen, J.I.:* Treatis on Solid State Chemistry, Hannay, N.B., Ed., Plenum Press: New York 3 (1976)
92. *Runt, J., Harrison, I.R.:* Methods of Experimental Physics 16(B) (1980) 287
93. *Rim, P.B., Runt, J.P.:* Macromolecules 17 (1984) 1520
94. *Krigbaum, W.R., Uematsu, I.:* J. Polym. Sci. 3 (1965) 767
95. *Fujiwara, Y.:* Colloid Polym. Sci. 265 (1987) 1027
96. *Okada, T., Saito, H., Inoue, T.:* Macromolecules 23 (1990) 3865
97. *Wang, Y.F., Loyd, D.R.:* Polymer 34 (1993) 4740
98. *Gauer, U., Wunderlich, B.:* J. Chem. Phys. Ref. Data 10(4) (1981) 1051
99. *Bu, H.S., Cheng, S.Z.D., Wunderlich, B.:* Makromol. Chem. Rapid Comm. 9 (1988) 75
100. *Quirk, R.P., Alsamarraie, M.A.A.:* Polymer Handbook, Immergut, E.H., Ed., John Wiley & Sons: New York (1989)
101. *Martuscelli, E., Pracella, M., Zambelli, A.:* J. Polym. Sci. Polym. Phys. Ed. 18 (1980) 619
102. *Busfield, W.K., Blake, C.S.:* Polymer 21 (1980) 35
103. *Bassett, D.C., Olley, R.H., Raheil, I.A.M.:* Polymer 29 (1988) 1945
104. *Chung, J.S., Cebe, P.:* Polymer 33 (1992) 2312
105. *Hsiao, B.S., Gardner, K.C.H., Wu, D.Q., Chu, B.:* Polymer 34 (1993) 3986
106. *Avrami, M.:* J. Chem. Phys. 8 (1940) 212
107. *Heiber, C.A.:* Polymer 36 (1995) 1455
108. *Godovsky, Y.K., Slonimsky, G.L.:* J. Polym. Sci. Polym. Phys. Ed. 12 (1974) 1053
109. *Goldfarb, L.:* Makromol. Chem. 179 (1978) 2297
110. *Wlochowicz, A., Eder, M.:* Polymer 22 (1981) 1286
111. *Clark, E.J., Hoffman, J.D.:* Macromolecules 17 (1984) 878
112. *Allen, R.C., Mandelkern, L.:* Polym. Bull. 17 (1987) 473
113. *Janimak, J.J., Cheng, S.Z.D., Giusti, P.A., Hsieh, E.T.:* Macromolecules 24 (1991) 2253
114. *Lim, G.B.A., Loyd, D.R.:* Polym. Eng. Sci. 33 (1993) 522
115. *Celli, A., Fichera, A., Marega, C., Paganetto, G., Zannetti, R.:* Eur. Polym. J. 29 (1993) 1037
116. *Hoffman, J.D., Frolen, L.J., Ross, G.S., Lauritzen, J.I.:* J. Res. Nat. Bur. Std. 79(A) (1975) 671
117. *Hoffman, J.D.:* Polymer 23 (1982) 656

118. *Hoffman, J.D.:* Polymer 24 (1983) 3
119. *Hoffman, J.D., Miller, R.L.:* Macromolecules 21 (1988) 3038
120. *Phillips, P.J.:* Rep. Prog. Phys. 53 (1990) 549
121. *Hoffman, J.D., Miller, R.L.:* Macromolecules 22 (1989) 3501
122. *Mandelkern, L.:* Polym. J. 17 (1985) 337
123. *Alamo, R.G., Viers, B.D., Mandelkern, L.:* Macromolecules 26 (1993) 5470
124. *Darras, O., Seguela, R.:* Polymer 34 (1993) 2946
125. *Alfonso, G.C., Russell, T.P.:* Macromolecules 19 (1986) 1143
126. *Keith, H.D., Padden, F.J.:* J. Appl. Phys. 35 (1964) 1270
127. *Keith, H.D., Padden, F.J.:* J. Appl. Phys. 35 (1964) 1286
128. *Khambatta, F.B., Warner, F., Russell, T., Stein, R.S.:* J. Polym. Sci. Polym. Phys. Ed. 14 (1976) 1391
129. *Okada, T., Saito, H., Inoue, T.:* Polymer 34 (1993) 4752
130. *Bartzak, Z., Martuscelli, E., Galeski, A.:* Polypropylene: Structure, blends, and composites, Karger-Kocsis, J., Ed. Chapman & Hall: London (1995)
131. *Inaba, N., Sato, K., Suzuki, S., Hashimoto, T.:* Macromolecules 19 (1986) 1690
132. *Inaba, N., Yamada, T., Suzuki, S., Hashimoto, T.:* Macromolecules 21 (1988) 407
133. *Geil, P.H.:* J. Appl. Phys. 33 (1962) 642
134. *Addink, E.J., Beintema, J.:* Polymer 2 (1961) 185
135. *Turner-Jones, A., Cobbold, A.J.:* Polym. Lett. 6 (1968) 539
136. *Fujiwara, V.Y.:* Kolloid Z.Z. Polymere 226 (1969) 135
137. *Samuels, R.J., Yee, R.Y.:* J. Polym. Sci. (A2) 10 (1972) 385
138. *Meille, S.V., Ferro, D.R., Bruckner, S., Lovinger, A.J., Padden, F.J.:* Macromolecules 27 (1994) 2615
139. *Lovinger, A.J., Chua, J.O., Gryte, C.C.:* J. Polym. Sci. Polym. Phys. Ed. 15 (1977) 641
140. *Shi, G-y., Zhang, X-d., Qiu, Z-x.:* Makromol. Chem. 193 (1992) 583
141. *Leugering, V.H.J.:* Die Makromol. Chem. 109 (1967) 204
142. *Morrow, D.R.:* J. Macromol. Sci. Phys. 3(B) (1969) 53
143. *Duswalt, A., Cox, W.W.:* Polymer Characterization-Interdisciplinary Approaches, Craver, C.D., Ed., Plenum Press: New York (1971)
144. *Varga, J.:* J. Therm. Anal. 31 (1986) 165
145. *Zhou, G-e., He, Z-q., Yu, J-m., Han, Z-w., Shi, G-y.:* Makromol. Chem. 187 (1986) 633
146. *Varga, J.:* J. Therm. Anal. 35 (1989) 1891
147. *Varga, J.:* J. Therm. Anal. 35 (1989) 1891
148. *Rybnikar, F.:* J. Macromol. Sci.-Phys. 30 (B3) (1991) 201
149. *Fillon, B., Thierry, A., Wittmann, J.C., Lotz, B.:* J. Polym. Sci. Polym. Phys. Ed. 31 (1993) 1407
150. *Shi, G-y., Zhang, X-d., Cao, Y-h., Hong, J.:* Makromol. Chem. 194 (1993) 269
151. *Zhang, X., Shi, G.:* Polymer 35 (1994) 5067
152. *Mezghani, K., Phillips, P.J.:* Polymer 36 (1995) 2407
153. *Garbarczyk, J., Sterzynski, T., Paukszta, D.:* Polym. Comm. 30 (1989) 153
154. *Varga, J., Toth-Schulek, F., Ille, A.:* Colloid Polym. Sci. 269 (1991) 655
155. *Asano, T., Fujiwara, Y.:* Polymer 19 (1978) 99
156. *Asano, T., Fujiwara, T., Asano, T.:* Polym. J. 11 (1979) 383
157. *Yoshida, T., Fujiwara, Y., Asano, T.:* Polymer 24 (1983) 925
158. *Shi, G-y., Chu, F., Zhou, G-e., Han, Z-w.:* Makromol. Chem. 190 (1989) 907
159. *Chu, F., Yamaoka, T., Ide, H., Kimura, Y.:* Polymer 35 (1994) 3442
160. *Forgacs, P., Tolochko, B.P., Sheromov, M.A.:* Polym. Bull. 6 (1981) 127
161. *Garbarczyk, J., Paukszta, D.:* Colloid Polym. Sci. 263 (1985) 985
162. *Filho, D.d.S., Oliveira, C.M.F.:* Makromol. Chem. 194 (1993) 279
163. *Crissman, J.M.:* J. Polym. Sci. 7(A2) (1969) 389
164. *Dragaun, H., Hubeny, H., Muschik.:* J. Polym. Sci. Polym. Phys. Ed. 15 (1977) 1779
165. *Moitzi, J., Skalicky, P.:* Polymer 34 (1993) 3168
166. *Zachmann, H.G., Wiswe, D., Gehrke, R., Riekel, C.:* Makromol. Chem. Supp. 12 (1985) 175
167. *Kantz, M.R., Newman, H.D. Jr., Stigale, F.H.:* J. Appl. Polym. Sci. 16 (1972) 1249
168. *Trotignen, J.-P., Verdu, J.:* J. Appl. Polym. Sci. 34 (1987) 1
169. *Fujiyama, M., Wakino, T.:* J. Appl. Polym. Sci. 43 (1991) 57
170. *Fujiyama, M.:* Int. Polym. Proc. VIII (1993) 245

171. *Bruckner, S., Meille, S.V.:* Nature 340 (1989) 455
172. *Meille, S.V., Bruckner, S., Porzio, W.:* Macromolecules 23 (1990) 4114
173. *Lotz, B., Graff, S., Staupe, C., Wittmann, J.C.:* Polymer 32 (1991) 2902
174. *Kardos, J.L., Christiansen, J.L., Baer, E.:* J. Polym. Sci. (A2) 4 (1966) 777
175. *Morrow, D.R., Newman, B.A.:* J. Appl. Phys. 39 (1968) 4944
176. *Pae, K.D.:* J. Polym. Sci. (A2) 6 (1968) 657
177. *Kojima, H.:* J. Polym. Sci. (A2) 6 (1968) 1255
178. *Turner-Jones, A.:* Polymer 12 (1971) 487
179. *Campbell, R., Anderson, Phillips, P.J., Lin, J.S.:* Polymer 34 (1993) 4809
180. *Pae, K.D., Morrow, D.R., Sauer, J.A.:* Nature 211 (1966) 514
181. *Newman, B.A., Song, S.J.:* J. Polym. Sci. (A2) 9 (1971) 181
182. *Mezghani, K., Phillips, P.J.:* Bull. Am. Phys. Soc. 40(1) (1995) 288
183. *He, J., Zoller, P.:* J. Polym. Sci. Polym. Phys. 32 (1994) 1049
184. *Campbell, R.A. Ph.D.:* Thesis-U. Tennessee: Knoxville (1991)
185. *Slichter, W.P., Mandell, E.R.:* J. Appl. Phys. 29 (1958) 1438
186. *Natta, G.:* SPE J. 15 (1959) 373
187. *Wyckoff, H.W.:* J. Polym. Sci. 62 (1962) 83
188. *Gailey, J.A., Ralston, P.H.:* SPE Trans. 4 (1964) 29
189. *Gezovich, D.M., Geil, P.H.:* Polym. Eng. Sci. 8 (1968) 202
190. *Glotin, M., Rahalkar, R.R., Hendra, P.J., Cudby, M.E.A.:* Polymer 22 (1981) 731
191. *Hendra, P.J., Vile, J., Willis, H.A., Zichy, V., Cudby, M.E.A.:* Polymer 25 (1984) 785
192. *Corradini, P., Petraccone, V., DeRosa, C., Guerra, G.:* Macromolecules 19 (1986) 2699
193. *Gomez, M.A., Tanaka, H., Tonelli, A.E.:* Polymer 28 (1987) 2227
194. *Corradini, P., DeRosa, C., Guerra, G., Petraccone, V.:* Polym. Comm. 30 (1989) 281
195. *Calda, V., Brown, G.R., Nohr, R.S., MacDonald, J.G., Raboin, L.E.:* Polymer 35 (1994) 899
196. *Vittoria, V.:* J. Polym. Sci. Polym. Phys. Ed. 24 (1986) 451
197. *Osawa, S., Porter, R.S.:* Polymer 35 (1994) 545
198. *Osawa, S., Porter, R.S., Ito, M.:* Polymer 35 (1994) 551
199. *Saraf, R.F.:* Polymer 35 (1994) 1359
200. *Saraf, R.F., Porter, R.S.:* Polym. Eng. Sci. 28 (1988) 842
201. *Grubb, D.T., Yoon, D.Y.:* Polym. Comm. 27 (1986) 84
202. *Hsu, C.C., Geil, P.H., Miyaji, H., Asai, K.:* J. Polym. Sci. Polym. Phys. Ed. 24 (1986) 2379
203. *O'Kane, W.J., Young, R.J., Ryan, A.J., Bras, W., Derbyshire, G.E., Mant, G.R.:* Polymer 35 (1994) 1352
204. *Alberola, N., Fugier, M., Petit, D., Fillon, B.:* J. Matr. Sci. 30 (1995) 1187
205. *Zannetti, R., Celotti, G., Fichera, A., Francesconi, R.:* Die Makromol. Chem. 128 (1969) 137
206. *Fichera, A., Zannetti, R.:* Die Makromol. Chem. 176 (1975) 1885
207. *Vittoria, V.:* J. Macromol. Sci. Phys. 38(B) (1989) 97
208. *Vittoria, V.:* J. Macromol. Sci. Phys. 38(B) (1989) 489
209. *Zannetti, R., Fichera, A., Celotti, G., Martelli, A.F.:* Eur. Polym. J. 4 (1968) 399
210. *Piccarolo, S., Saiu, M.:* J. Appl. Polym. Sci. 46 (1992) 625
211. *Natta, G., Corradini, P., Ganis, P.:* Makromol. Chem. 39 (1960) 238
212. *Natta, G., Pasquon, P., Zambelli, A.:* J. Am. Chem. Soc. 84 (1962) 1488
213. *Natta, G., Peraldo, M., Allegra, A.:* Makromol. Chem. 75 (1964) 215
214. *Corradini, P., Natta, G., Ganis, P., Temussi, P.A.:* J. Polym. Sci. (C) 16 (1967) 2477
215. *Zambelli, A., Natta, G., Pasquon, I., Signorini, R.:* J. Polym. Sci. (C) 16 (1967) 2485
216. *Youngman, E.A., Boor, J. Jr.:* Macromol. Rev. 2 (1967) 33
217. *Marchetti, A., Martuscelli, E.:* J. Polym. Sci. Polym. Phys. Ed. 12 (1974) 1649
218. *MMiller, R.L., Seeley, E.G.:* J. Polym. Sci. Polym. Phys. Ed. 20 (1982) 2297
219. *Corradini, P., Napolitano, R., Petraccone, V., Pirozzi, B., Tuzi, A.:* Macromolecules 15 (1982) 1207
220. *Ewen, J.A., Jones, R.L., Razavi, A., Ferrara, J.D.:* J. Am. Chem. soc. 110 (1988) 6255
221. *Lotz, B., Lovinger, A.J., Cais, R.E.:* Macromolecules 21 (1988) 2375
222. *Lovinger, A.J., Lotz, B., Davis, D.D.:* Polymer 31 (1990) 2254
223. *Chatani, Y., Maruymama, H., Noguchi, K., Asanuma, T., Shiomura, T.:* J. Polym. Sci. Polym. Lett. 28 (1990) 393

224. *Galambos, A., Wolkowicz, M., Zeigler, R.:* Catalysis in Polymer Synthesis, Vandenberg, E.J., Salamone, J.C., Eds., ACS Symposium Series (1991), Vol. 496
225. *Chatani, Y., Maruymama, H., Asanuma, T., Shiomura, T.:* J. Polym. Sci. Polym. Phys. 29 (1991) 1649
226. *Lovinger, A.J., Davis, D.D., Lotz, B.:* Macromolecules 24 (1991) 552
227. *Haftka, S., Kannecke, K.J.:* J. Macromol. Sci.-Phys. 30 (1991) 319
228. *Pirozzi, B., Napolitano, R.:* Eur. Polym. J. 28 (1992) 703
229. *Balbontin, G., Dainelli, D., Galimberti, M., Paganetto, G.:* Makromol. Chem. 193 (1992) 693
230. *Lovinger, A.J., Lotz, B., Davis, D.D., Padden, F.J. Jr.:* Macromolecules 26 (1993) 3494
231. *DeRosa, C., Corradini, P.:* Macromolecules 26 (1993) 5711
232. *Sozzani, P., simonutti, R., Galimberti, M.:* Macromolecules 26 (1993) 5782
233. *Rodriquez-Arnold, J., Zhang, A., Cheng, S.Z.D., Lovinger, A.J., Hsieh, E.T., Chu, P., Johnson, T.W., Honnell, K.G., Geerts, R.G., Palackal, S.J., Hawley, G.R., Welch, M.B.:* Polymer 35 (1994) 1884
234. *Rodriquez-Arnold, J., Bu, Z., Cheng, S.Z.D., Hsieh, E.T., Johnson, T.W., Geerts, R.G., Palackal, S.J., Hawley, G.R., Welch, M.B.:* Polymer 35 (1994) 5194
235. *Lovinger, A.J., Lotz, B., Davis, D.D., Schumacher, M.:* Macromolecules 27 (1994) 6603
236. *Stocker, W., Schumacher, M., Graff, S., Lang, J., Wittmann, J.C., Lovinger, A.J., Lotz, B.:* Macromolecules 27 (1994) 6948
237. *Schumacher, M., Lovinger, A.J., Agarwal, P., Wittmann, J.C., Lotz, B.:* Macromolecules 27 (1994) 6956
238. *Marigo, A., Marega, C., Zannetti, R.:* Macromol. Rapid Comm. 15 (1994) 225
239. *Miller, R.L.:* J. Polym. Sci. 57 (1962) 975
240. *Gee, D.R., Melia, T.P.:* Polymer 10 (1969) 239
241. *Dunn, J.R.:* Rubber Chem. Tech. 49 (1976) 978
242. *Behan, P., Thomas, A., Bevis, M.:* J. Matr. Sci. 11 (1976) 1207
243. *Bucknell, C.B.:* Toughened Plastics, Applied Science: London (1977)
244. *Retting, W.:* A. Makromol. chem. 58/59 (1977) 133
245. *Donald, A.M., Kramer, E.J.:* J. Appl. Polym. Sci. 27 (1982) 3729
246. *Speri, W.M., Patrick, G.R.:* Polym. Eng. Sci. 15 (1975) 668
247. *Fernando, P.L., Williams, J.G.:* Polym. Eng. Sci. 21 (1981) 1003
248. *Stehling, F.C., Huff, T., Speed, C.S.:* J. Appl. Polym. Sci. 26 (1981) 2693
249. *Hodgkinson, J.M., Savadori, I., Williams, J.G.:* J. Matr. Sci. 18 (1983) 2319
250. *Jang, B.Z., Uhlmann, D.R., VanderSande, J.B.:* J. Appl. Polym. Sci. 10 (1985) 643
251. *Jang, B.Z., Uhlmann, D.R., VanderSande, J.B.:* J. Appl. Polym. Sci. 30 (1985) 2485
252. *Spenadel, L.J.:* J. Appl. Polym. Sci. 16 (1972) 2375
253. *Danesi, S., Porter, R.S.:* Polymer 19 (1978) 448
254. *Karger-Kocsis, J., Kallo, A., Szafner, A., Boder, G., Senyei, Z.:* Polymer 20 (1979) 37
255. *Takahashi, T., Mizumo, H., Thomal, E.J.:* J. Macromol. Sci.-Phys. B22(3) (1983) 425
256. *Noel, O.F., Carley, J.F.:* Polym. Eng. Sci. 24 (1984) 488
257. *Galeski, A., Prucella, M., Martuscelli, E.:* J. Polym. Sci. Polym. Phys. Ed. 22 (1984) 739
258. *Martuscelli, E.:* Polypropylene: Structure, blends and composites, Karger-Kocsis, J., Ed., Chapman & Hall: London (1995)
259. *Lohse, D.J.:* Polym. Eng. Sci. 26 (1986) 1500
260. *Hahn, C.D.:* Multiphase Flow in Polymer Processing, Academic Press: New York (1981)
261. *Grace, H.P.:* Chem. Eng. Commun. 14 (1982) 225
262. *Han, C.D.:* Polymer Blends and Composites in Multiphase Systems, ACS Symposium Series 206 (1984)
263. *Sundararaj, U., Macosko, C.W.:* Macromolecules 28 (1995) 2647
264. *Doran, A.Y., Patel, R.:* Rubber Chem. Tech. 53 (1980) 141
265. *D'Orazio, L., Mancarella, C., Martuscelli, E., Polato, F.:* Polymer 32 (1991) 1186
266. *Fujiyama, M. and Wakino, T.:* Intern. Polym. Processing VII (1992) 97
267. *D'Orazio, L., Mancarella, C., Martuscelli, E., Sticotti, G., Massari, P.:* Polymer 34 (1993) 3671
268. *Gonzalez-Nunez, R., Favis, B.D., Darreau, P.J., Lavallee, C.:* Polym. Eng. Sci. 33 (1993) 851
269. *Sova, M., Raab, M., Slizova, M.:* J. Matr. Sci. 28 (1993) 6516
270. *Chu, L.H., Guo, S.H., Chiu, W.Y., Tseng, H.C.:* J. Appl. Polym. Sci. 49 (1993) 1791
271. *Blank, D., Dwyer, S., Frazier, D., Mosier, D., Shu, C., Wolkowicz, M., Wong, A.:* Conference on TPOs in Automotive, Ann Arbor, MI (1994)

272. *Nishio, T., Nomura, T., Yokoi, T., Iwai, H., Kawamura, N.:* Toyota Tech. Rev. 41 (1992) 13
273. *Ryntz, R.A., Ramamurthy, A.C., Mihora, D.J.:* J. Coatings Tech. 67 (1995) 35
274. *Jancar, J., Dibenedetto, A.T.:* J. Matr. Sci. 29 (1994) 4651
275. *Jancar, J., Dibenedetto, A.T.:* J. Matr. Sci. 30 (1995) 1601
276. *Kojima, M.:* J. Macromol. Sci. B19 (1981) 523
277. *Galli, P., Ziminazzi, T., DelDuca D.:* Acta Polym. 39 (1988) 81
278. *White, J.R., Turnbull, A.:* J. Matr. Sci. 29 (1994) 584
279. *Ogier, L., Rabello, M.S., White, J.R.:* J. Matr. Sci. 30 (1995) 2364
280. *Dharmarajan, N., Hazelton, D.R., Kaltenbacher, E.J.:* SPE ANTEC (1990) 1225
281. *Lyngaae-Joergensen, J., Duta, A., Soendergaard, K., Poulsen, K.:* Polym. Networks Blends 3 (1993) 1
282. *Lau, E., Goodman, J.:* J. Elastomers Plast. 25 (1993) 322
283. *Pufka, S.J., Giacobbe, J.:* SPE Laminations and Coatings Conf. (1994) 147
284. *Giacobbe, J.:* SPE ANTEC (1992)
285. *Tadmor, Z.:* J. Appl. Polym. Sci. 18 (1974) 1753
286. *Tadmor, Z., Gogos, C.G.:* Principles of Polymer Processing, John Wiley & Sons: New York (1979)
287. *Isayev, A.I., Chan, T.W., Gmerek, M., Shimojo, K.:* SPE ANTEC (1994) 587
288. *Chen, B.S., Liu, W.H.:* Polym. Eng. Sci. 34 (1994) 835
289. *Fitchmun, D.R., Mencik, Z.:* J. Polym. Sci. Polym. Phys. Ed. 11 (1973) 951
290. *Mencik, Z., Fitchmun, D.R.:* J. Polym. Sci. Polym. Phys. Ed. 11 (1973) 973
291. *Fujiyama, M., Kimura, S.:* J. Appl. Polym. Sci. 22 (1978) 1225
292. *Fujiyama, M., Azuma, K.:* J. Appl. Polym. Sci. 23 (1979) 2807
293. *Houska, M., Brummell, M.:* Polym. Eng. Sci. 34 (1987) 1
294. *Fleischmann, E., Zipper, P., Janosi, A., Geymayer, W., Koppelmann, J., Schurz, J.:* Polym. Eng. Sci. 29 (1989) 835
295. *Fujiyama, M., Wakino, T.:* J. Appl. Polym. Sci. 42 (1991) 9
296. *Wenig, W., Herzog, F.:* J. Appl. Polym. Sci. 50 (1993) 2163
297. *Sjonell, Y., Terselius, B., Jansson, J.-F.:* Polym. Eng. Sci. 35 (1995) 950
298. *Peterlin, A.:* Polym. Eng. Sci. 16 (1976) 126
299. *Lagasse, R.R., Maxwell, B.:* Polym. Eng. Sci. 16 (1976) 189
300. *Hsiung, C.M., Cakmak, M.:* Polym. Eng. Sci. 31 (1991) 1372
301. *Liedauer, S., Eder, G., Haneschitz-Kriegl, H., Jerschow, P., Geymayer, W., Ingolic, E.:* Int. Polym. Proc. 8 (1993) 236
302. *Clark, E.S., Spruiell, J.E.:* Polym. Eng. Sci. 16 (1976) 176
303. *Stein, R.S.:* J. Polym. Sci. 31 (1958) 327
304. *Huber, J.E., Samuels, R.J.:* Interrelations between Processing, Structure, and Properties of Polymeric Materials, Seferis, J.C., Theocaris, P.S., Eds., Elsevier Publishing: Amsterdam, 1984
305. *Karacan, I., Taraiya, A.K., Bower, D.I., Ward, I.M.:* Polymer 34 (1993) 2692
306. *Reinshagen, J.H., Dunlap, R.W.:* J. Appl. Polym. Sci. 17 (1973) 3619

4   Additives

Ronald F. Becker, Lester P. J. Burton, Stephen E. Amos

Many fine papers, conference proceedings, and books covering specific and general aspects of the degradation and stabilization of polymers exist [1 - 5]. In this chapter we present a summary of the mechanism of degradation and stabilization, effective stabilizers, and current practice in major applications areas with respect to stabilization and other additives. Besides the stabilizers, there exists a wide selection of other additives which add to the versatility of PP.

From the perspective of PP stabilization chemists, PP leaving a reactor is a relatively useless product if it is not stabilized. The addition of a small amount of the correct chemical transforms a useless material into a durable raw material suitable for use in a wide variety of applications. Various additives are used not only to impart stability during the processing and use of PP but also to modify various properties and characteristics.

4.1   Role of Additives in PP

Virgin PP directly from a commercial process is very susceptible to air oxidation. If stored unstabilized at ambient temperature, the physical properties of the product deteriorate rapidly over a period of weeks or months depending on the physical form, temperature, available oxygen, and other considerations. If held at slightly elevated temperatures, as during summer storage, the accelerated rate of degradation can result in severe problems, beyond loss of physical properties, in a matter of days. This uncontrolled oxidation is exothermic, and the released heat and gases can lead to melting of the polymer mass, as actually occurred occasionally in the early production years. Luckily, this exothermic reaction can be prevented by the addition of a few parts per million of an antioxidant to the reactor product before drying and storage. This is often referred to as an "in-process" stabilizer.

For the fabrication of useful PP articles, the concentration of stabilizers will range from several hundred parts per million (ppm) to several percent. The exact concentration needed is highly application-dependent.

Beyond the need for stabilization, additives are used in PP for the following reasons:

- Adjust color: Polypropylene is whitish in color. Pigments are used to add color to the manufactured articles. Pigments may also have an impact on stability and physical properties.
- Alter stiffness: Polypropylene homopolymers and copolymers are typically semicrystalline materials which are manufactured to obtain various degrees of stiffness. The stiffness can be further adjusted through the addition of plasticizers, nucleators, or fillers.
- Control transparency: Polypropylene is translucent. Its transparency is dramatically improved with clarifying additives. It can also be rendered opaque with pigments and fillers.

- Lower molecular weight and molecular weight distribution: Additives can be used to reduce the molecular weight and narrow the molecular weight distribution. This alters processing characteristics and physical properties.
- Decrease static buildup: Polypropylene is a natural insulator and can build static charge. Several types of additives are used as antistats.
- Control surface properties: Various additives can be used to modify the frictional and adhesion properties of PPs.
- Neutralize catalyst residues: Acid scavengers are routinely incorporated to neutralize catalyst residues and prevent equipment corrosion.
- Suppress transition metal catalyzed oxidation: The oxidation of PP is accelerated by certain metals. Several types of metal chelators successfully suppress this phenomenon.
- Enhance whiteness: Fluorescent whitening agents are used to enhance whiteness or brilliancy of pigmented and unpigmented articles.
- Prevent biological growth: Biocides are used to prevent biological growth on the surface of PP articles.

4.2   Mechanism of PP Oxidation and Degradation

The oxidative processes of PP are rather complex. The oxidation and degradation products formed are dependent on a variety of factors, including oxygen availability, impurities, residual catalyst form, physical form (molten versus solid), crystallinity, storage temperature, air pollutants, radiation exposure, metal exposure, chemical exposure, part thickness, stress in the part, comonomer content, and other additives present. The traditional description of oxidation and degradation of PP shows the initiation, propagation, branching, and termination steps.

The following definitions will be used in this section:

- RH = polypropylene; the H is any available hydrogen on the PP
- $RO\cdot$ = alkoxy radical
- $R\cdot$ = alkyl radical
- $ROO\cdot$ = peroxy radical
- $HO\cdot$ = hydroxy radical
- ROH = alcohol
- $ROOH$ = hydroperoxide

4.2.1   Initiation

Traditionally, most treatments on the subject begin with the initiation reaction (eq 4.1), depicted as

$$RH \underline{\quad\quad} energy \longrightarrow R\cdot + H\cdot \tag{4.1}$$

Equation 4.1 does not take into account the reaction between hydrocarbons and molecular oxygen. The oxidation of hydrocarbons is well-known [6, 7] and is depicted in eq 4.2 and 4.3.

$$RH + O_2 \rightarrow R\cdot + \cdot OOH \tag{4.2}$$

Since this oxidation reaction occurs in a polymer cage, the products may recombine (eq 4.3) to form a hydroperoxide or stay separate as in eq 4.2.

$$R\cdot + \cdot OOH \rightarrow ROOH \tag{4.3}$$

4.2.2   Propagation

Following these equations, the traditional autoxidation scheme can be entered, as follows. Propagation steps cause the radical sites to move, but there is no overall increase in the number of radicals from these reactions.

$$R\cdot + O_2 \rightarrow ROO\cdot \tag{4.4}$$
$$ROO\cdot + RH \rightarrow ROOH + R\cdot \tag{4.5}$$
$$RH + H\cdot \rightarrow H_2 + R\cdot \tag{4.6}$$
$$R\cdot + R'H \rightarrow RH + R'\cdot \tag{4.7}$$

We must not forget the contribution of the small free radical fragments:

$$\cdot OOH + RH \rightarrow R\cdot + H_2O_2 \tag{4.8}$$
$$\cdot OH + RH \rightarrow R\cdot + H_2O \tag{4.9}$$
$$H\cdot + RH \rightarrow R\cdot + H_2 \tag{4.10}$$

4.2.3   Branching

The branching reactions cause an increase in the number of radical sites

$$ROOH \rightarrow RO\cdot + \cdot OH \tag{4.11}$$

The hydroperoxide can be formed either during the propagation, as in eq 4.5, or in the initiation step from the recombination of the radical species, as in eq 4.3. The homolytic cleavage of the hydroperoxide enables an additional radical to be formed. This is the crucial step toward increasing the concentration of radicals in the polymer. This can be considered a secondary initiation.

While other branching steps have been recorded, they are also based on the hydroperoxide cleavage.

4.2.4   Termination

These reactions reduce the number of radicals by combining two radical sites to form a nonradical product.

$$RO\cdot + \cdot H \rightarrow ROH \tag{4.12}$$

$$ROO\cdot + \cdot H \rightarrow ROOH \tag{4.13}$$

$$R\cdot + R'\cdot \rightarrow R{-}R' \tag{4.14}$$

$$RO\cdot + R\cdot \rightarrow ROR \tag{4.15}$$

$$2ROO\cdot \rightarrow ROOR + O_2 \tag{4.16}$$

$$2RO\cdot \rightarrow ROOR \tag{4.17}$$

$$2R\cdot \rightarrow {-}HC{=}R + {-}H_2C{-}R \tag{4.18}$$

Bimolecular disproportionation reactions are also reported in the literature for carbon-centered radicals [8]. If we assume that the reaction is intramolecular, then this would need to be classified as a termination reaction depicted in eq 4.18. The disproportionation reaction also enables two radicals to be removed from either propagation or branching reactions. As with any termination reaction, this will have the overall effect of stabilizing the polymer. The reaction can occur either intra- or intermolecularly. Regardless of the path followed, the result is still the same: a decrease in the overall number of radicals. When an unsaturated site is formed, it will be more prone to oxidation than the saturated site, regardless of the pathway.

The radical pair formed in the initiation eq 4.1 or 4.2 is affected by the viscous environment provided by PP relative to other nonpolymeric hydrocarbons. The high viscosity should make recombination to the hydroperoxide (eq 4.3) highly likely. If the radicals recombine, the propagation is delayed until enough energy is available to cause homolytic cleavage of the hydroperoxide, as shown in eq 4.11. From that point, the reaction proceeds to the propagation stage. If the alkyl and hydroperoxy radicals remain separate, as in eq 4.1 or 4.2, then a path exists for immediate propagation as in eqs 4.5 to 4.8.

These reactions do not occur haphazardly. In eqs 4.5 through 4.10, we see that a common feature is the formation of a carbon-based radical. Once this carbon- based radical is formed, one of two reactions can occur:

1.   A peroxy radical will form as in eq 4.4, or
2.   a hydrogen can be abstracted (eq 4.7) intramolecularly.

If a peroxy radical is formed, then the next step can be the intramolecular abstraction of hydrogen atoms (eq 4.5). The intramolecular hydrogen abstraction is roughly three times more likely than the intermolecular route [9]. The act of intramolecular abstraction will cause the radical site to migrate down the polymer chain [10]. This migration provides a mechanism for radicals to "find" another radical or antioxidant molecule (as seen in later sections) which can terminate the chain reaction. If termination does not occur, then a mechanism exists for the buildup of hydroperoxide concentration in the polymer.

During this migration, the free radical has a choice of hydrogens to abstract: primary, secondary, or tertiary, forming the corresponding radical. A tertiary sterically hindered carbon radical is thermodynamically favored. The hindered nature of these radicals lowers the probability of forming a cross-link between molecules. This characteristic differentiates PP from unbranched types of polyethylene, wherein cross-linking is a very common phenomenon leading to an initial viscosity increase.

4.2.5   Chain Scission

In none of the reactions above have we seen any degradation (i.e., chain scission or loss of molecular weight) of the molecules. If anything, the termination reactions depicted in eqs 4.14 through 4.17 indicate an increase in the molecular weight. However, experience with PP teaches us that this is not the case; we know that severe degradation will result.

There are various paths which can lead to chain scission. By far the most common in PP is a unimolecular β-scission of carbon- [11] and oxygen-centered [12] radicals. This cleavage is illustrated in Fig. 4.1. The resulting products from the carbon-centered radicals are an olefin (a) (which is even more susceptible to oxidation than a saturated hydrocarbon) and a new carbon radical (b), which can reenter the oxidation cycle as PP·. From the alkoxy radical, a

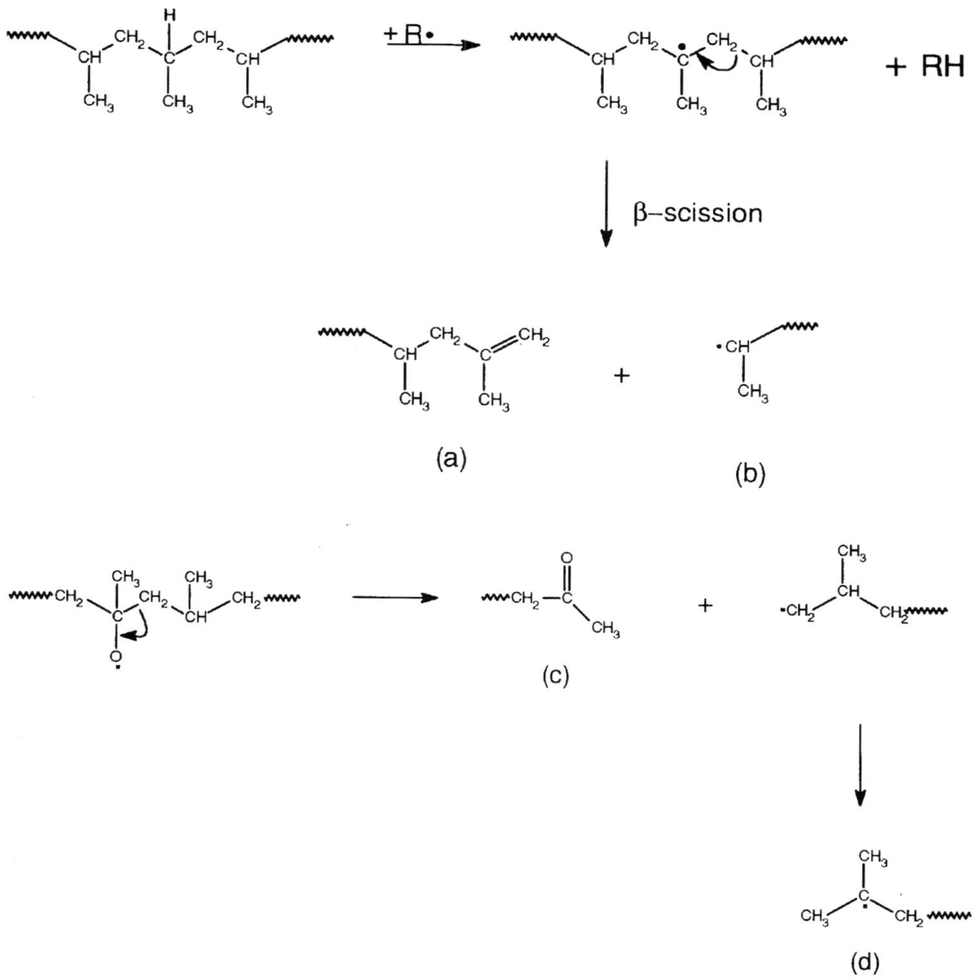

Figure 4.1 β-scission of PP from carbon-centered and oxygen-centered radicals

carbonyl-containing molecule (c) and another carbon-centered radical (d) are formed. As a simple result of probability, the fragments tend to be long since the original chain typically contains several thousand propylene units.

Other chain scission reactions would include the Norrish I and II types of carbonyl "backbiting" mechanisms, which would be accelerated by UV light and which would only begin to be significant when the carbonyl concentration had built up appreciably. As that would only occur after oxidation had proceeded to a relatively advanced stage, it usually represents only a small fraction of the molecular weight degradation in PP.

The reduction in the molecular weight of the polymer leads to a change in many of its corresponding properties. One of the most detrimental is the loss of toughness of the polymer, which is discussed further in Section 6.3.1. In addition, the scission will produce products which will tend to cause an increase in the color of the polymer and the generation of oxygenated compounds, which will adversely effect the taste and odor properties of the degraded resin.

The availability of oxygen and temperature are also key factors in the oxidation scheme. At PP processing temperatures of 200 °C to 300 °C, the reaction rates are extremely rapid. Fortunately, a very limited amount of air has access to the melt during the extrusion or molding of PP. Further, a nitrogen purge at the throat of an extruder has an additional marked effect on the maintenance of molecular weight.

In the solid form, PP is a semicrystalline polymer with a crystalline content that is normally between 40% and 60%. The crystalline regions are essentially impervious to oxygen, so the oxidation only occurs in the amorphous region. In accelerated testing, the oxygen diffusion rate through PP articles is slow enough that the oxidation process appears as a surface phenomenon [13]. The surface can become dull, crazed, or powdery with little loss of physical properties of the manufactured article. Beyond a millimeter of depth, oxygen starvation can severely suppress degradation [14]. However, in practical exposures times, the oxygen availability would not be limited by diffusion rate. Any preferential surface degradation would be attributed to acceleration by exposure to light. Regardless of the cause, such cosmetic effects are usually aesthetically unacceptable and require counter-measures in stabilization. In articles with higher surface to volume ratios, such as film and fibers, the physical properties deteriorate more rapidly upon oxidation.

Obviously, unstabilized PP is very prone to oxidation and degradation in the presence of air. Fortunately, this situation is easily corrected by adding appropriate stabilizers. A small amount of the correct additive will yield a durable, useful material.

4.3   Stabilizing PP

Simply stated, the stabilization of PP is just a matter of proper management of radical products or potential radicals by using the correct additive. There are numerous stabilizers available commercially which provide the needed protection. They are typically classified as primary, secondary, or UV (ultraviolet) antioxidants (AOs). Several UV stabilizers could be classified as primary or secondary AOs, and some secondary AOs have some primary characteristics. Unfortunately, the detailed mechanisms are complex and difficult to study in

PP because of nature of the medium and the transient nature of oxidation intermediates, but we present below the major recognized mechanisms.

4.3.1   Primary Antioxidants

Primary antioxidants are defined as additives that interfere with the oxidation cycle described in eqs 4.2 through 4.11 by reacting with the formed radicals and interrupting the cycle. Thus, they are called "radical scavengers." Primary antioxidants perform well when used by themselves in their intended application. Both hindered phenols (HP) and hindered amines (HA) function as primary antioxidants. Enough of a difference exists between the HPs and HAs to treat them separately.

4.3.1.1   Hindered Phenols

The HPs can react with the radical species generated in eqs 4.2 through 4.11. Specifically, the HP is able to transfer it's phenolic hydrogen to the generated radical, causing a nonradical product to be formed. In transferring the hydrogen, the hindered phenol itself becomes a radical known as a hindered phenoxy. This is a stable radical which will not abstract a hydrogen from the polymer matrix. The specific mechanism for a common HP, butylated hydroxytoluene (BHT), is shown in Fig. 4.2.

HPs enable the radicals to be managed in two different ways, depending on the radical being quenched. Equations 4.19 through 4.21 outline the potential reactants and products.

$$PP \cdot + AH \rightarrow PPH + A \cdot \qquad (4.19)$$
$$PPO \cdot + AH \rightarrow PPOH + A \cdot \qquad (4.20)$$
$$PPOO \cdot + AH \rightarrow PPOOH + A \cdot \qquad (4.21)$$

The reactions depicted in eqs 4.19 and 4.20 both result in stable molecules being formed. By so doing, the initial radical species is effectively removed from participation in the propagation steps. While the formation of a hydroperoxide in eq 4.21 removes a radical species from the propagation steps, the effect may not be as permanent as in eqs 4.19 and 4.20; the newly formed hydroperoxide can undergo homolytic cleavage with the formation of two more radicals, as in eq 4.11.

The abstraction of the hydrogen from the HP prevents another initiating event from occurring on the polymer backbone. This step immediately results in at least one less radical being formed. Regardless of the radical being quenched, the overall effect of the HP is to delay the oxidation and, eventually, the degradation of the PP, for almost any radical can eventually result in chain scission.

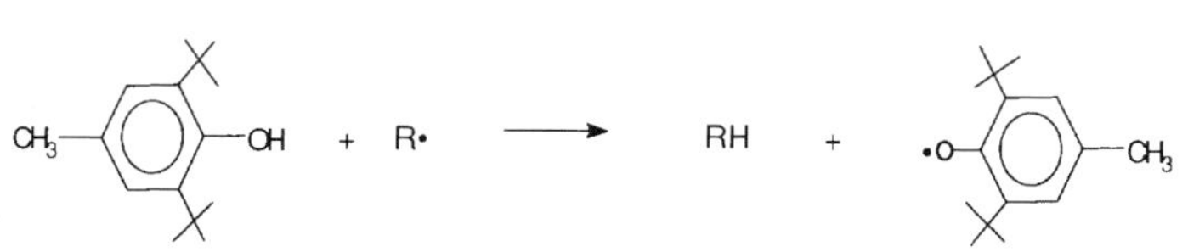

Figure 4.2 Radical scavenging mechanism of typical HP

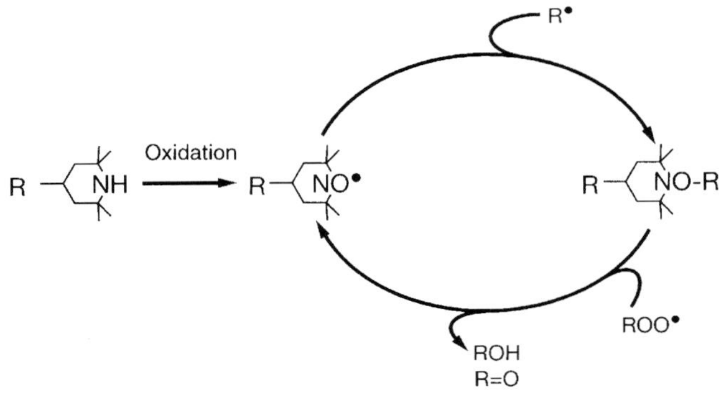

Figure 4.4 Regenerative mechanism of HA free radical scavengers

An important point about HAs is that the nitroxyl species is regenerative. However, the cyclic regeneration eventually ends. Some of the regenerated products are inefficient radical scavengers, and some of the stabilizer is lost during exposure [20].

HAs find the bulk of their use as stabilizers against the oxidative degradation initiated by UV light. More recently, the high molecular weight compounds have been shown to be effective as thermal stabilizers [21]. This class of compounds plays an important role in the commercial uses and success of PP.

4.3.2   Secondary Antioxidants

The secondary antioxidants decompose hydroperoxides and prevent new oxidation cycles from beginning. Consequently, they are often described as "peroxide decomposers." This class of compounds is termed "secondary" because their best performance occurs in the presence of primary AOs. When used in a resin by themselves, secondary AOs do not exhibit appreciable activity. The value of these compounds comes when they are combined with the correct primary antioxidant. When the correct combination is made, a strong synergistic effect results. The two most common classes of secondary AOs are phosphites (the term "phosphite" is meant to include phosphonites) and thio compounds, listed in Table 4.3.

One of the most common examples of this synergism is seen in the performance of a phosphite with a hindered phenol. Table 4.4 shows the synergism quite well. It is evident that, when used alone, the phosphite does not stabilize the melt well, while the hindered phenol imparts a relatively good degree of stability. When used together, the combination exhibits a high degree of melt stability.

Another example of secondary stabilizers is the use of distearyl thiodipropionate (DSTDP) for long-term heat aging (LTHA). At oven temperatures of 150°C, a typical test temperature for LTHA, the use of a thioester by itself fails in a few days. A typical hindered phenol can give lifetimes of 20 to 35 days. When used in a ratio of 1:4, the hindered phenol/thioester combination yield lifetimes of 80 to 100 days. Figure 4.5 shows an example of the synergism. The exact values depend on the type and concentration of the phenol/thioester combination used.

Table 4.3 Examples of Commercially Available Phosphites, Phosphonites, and Thiocompounds

Trade name	Manufacturer	Type	MW
Phosphites			
Weston® 399	General Electric	Aromatic phosphite	688
Ultranox® 618	General Electric	Aliphatic diphosphite	732
Ultranox® 626	General Electric	Aromatic diphosphite	604
Irgafos® 168	CIBA	Aromatic phosphite	647
Ethanox® 398	Albemarle Corp.	Fluorophosphite	487
Phosphonite			
Sandostab® P-EPQ	Sandoz	Aromatic phosphonite	1035[a]
Thiocompounds			
DSTDP	Various	Thioester	683
DLTDP	Various	Thioester	514
SE-10	Hoechst Celanese	Disulfide	571

[a] MW of major component

Table 4.4 Synergism of Secondary Antioxidants

	MFR of Re-extruded PP		
Pass number	Phenolic[a]	Phosphite[a]	Both[a]
1	4	3.9	2.5
3	6.3	6	3
5	10	16	6

[a] 0.05 pph, each stabilizer

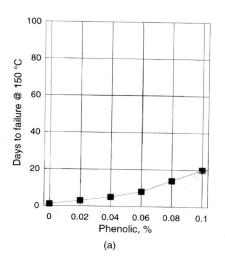

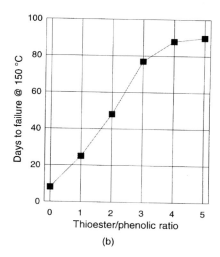

(a)   (b)

Figure 4.5 Effect of DSTDP on oven aging at 150 °C: (a) Effect of HP alone, (b) Synergistic effect of thioester added to HP, phenol at 0.06%. Source: Montell Polyolefins

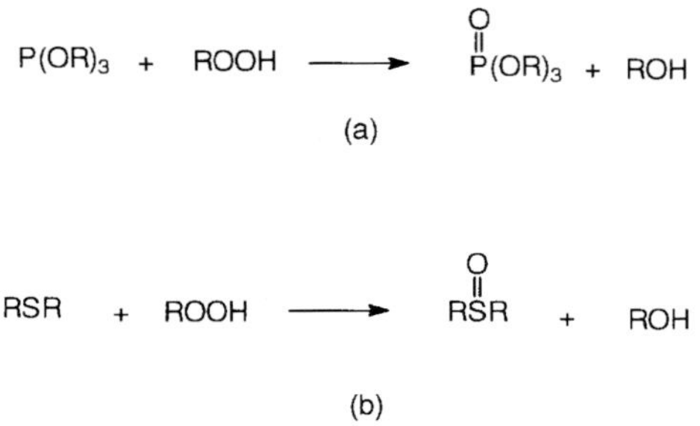

$$P(OR)_3 \ + \ ROOH \ \longrightarrow \ \overset{\displaystyle O}{\overset{\|}{P}}(OR)_3 \ + \ ROH$$

(a)

$$RSR \ + \ ROOH \ \longrightarrow \ \overset{\displaystyle O}{\overset{\|}{R}}SR \ + \ ROH$$

(b)

Figure 4.6 Mechanism of secondary stabilizers. Action of (a) phosphites, (b) thioesters on a hydroperoxide

Both the phosphites and thioesters are synergistic with the hindered phenols because they attack a source of free radicals, the hydroperoxides. As seen in Fig. 4.6, they both reduce a hydroperoxide to an alcohol. By so doing, the opportunity for the homolytic cleavage of the ROOH into two radicals (eq 4.11) is eliminated.

Another example of a secondary antioxidant AO (albeit unconventional) is the general class of UV absorbers. Examples appear in Table 4.5. We could classify these as true UV stabilizers, since their mode of action is to interact directly with UV light, but we will classify them as secondary stabilizers due to their synergism with HA, a primary antioxidant. As a broad class of compounds, UV absorbers will impart only a moderate amount of UV stability to a PP-based resin. When a HA is used in conjunction with the UV absorbers, a more UV-stable resin results. By absorbing the UV light before it has a chance to energize a chromophore, the formation of a radical is prevented [22]. The absorbers do not absorb all the UV light, so some radicals are formed but are neutralized by the HA primary antioxidants.

A well-stabilized PP resin will usually make use of one or two of the above combinations, depending on the intended application. This allows the PP supplier to make a cost-effective resin.

4.3.3   Effects of Flame Retardants

A variety of commercial flame retardants are available for use in PP and propylene copolymers [23 - 26]. When flame retardants are added to a propylene resin, the stability can be affected. Details on flame retardants appear in Section 5.7.

Commercial flame retardant systems can be broken down into the following broad categories: halogens (bromine and chlorine), alumina trihydrate, magnesium hydroxide, phosphates, borates, and antimony oxide. Each of these have their own strengths and

Table 4.5 Examples of Commercially Available UV Absorbers

Trade name	Manufacturer	Type
Tinuvin 328	CIBA	Benzotriazole
LA-34	Asahi Denka	Benzotriazole
Cyasorb UV- 531	Cytex	Benzophenone
UV-CHEK-AM- 340	Ferro	Hydroxy benzoate

weaknesses in the realm of flame retarding PP products, as well as their effect on the stability of the resin.

One of the deleterious effects of halogenated flame retardants on the stabilization occurs in UV-stabilized formulations. Formulations of this type are finding use in roofing and other construction applications. Hindered amines, being basic, are adversely effected by the presence of halogenated flame retardants. The source of this antagonism is an interaction between the basic amine and the acidic [27] by-products of the halogenated (typically brominated) flame retardants that can result from excessive processing temperatures. While the interaction is extremely detrimental, the proper choice of HA and flame retardant can minimize the effect on the UV stability of the polymer.

The inorganic-based flame retardants adversely effect the ability of hindered phenols and thioesters to yield good LTHA values. The effects of some aluminum and zinc compounds can be seen in Table 4.6.

Table 4.6 Effect of Various Flame Retardants on the LTHA of Heterophasic Copolymers

Flame retardant	pph	Heat aging[a]
	control	26
ATH	20	2
Zinc oxide	20	3
Zinc oxide	40	1
ATH/zinc oxide	20/20	1

[a] Days to visual failure at 150 °C

4.3.4   Effects of Fillers

A variety of fillers are used in PP formulations. Some of the fillers commonly used are talc, fiber glass, calcium carbonate, clay, carbon black, and mica. Each of these add a specific property to a given formulation [28, 29], described in more detail in Section 5.6.

Typically, the presence of fillers causes a decrease in stability. The cause of the decrease may be either physical or chemical in nature. The physical aspect of the decrease is due to the adsorption of the antioxidants onto the surface of the inert filler. This effect is particularly evident in resins with high surface area fillers, such as calcium carbonate, carbon black, and silicates. If the antioxidant is immobilized, it is unable to serve its only purpose, to protect the polymer. Usually a modest increase in the amount of stabilizer suffices to overcome the negative influence of the filler.

The oxidation and degradation chemistry of the system can be changed by other fillers. Talc is an excellent example of this effect. Metallic impurities in the talc play a major role in the lack of stability in the final formulation. Talc contains iron-based impurities that catalyze the decomposition of hydroperoxides, accelerating the branching reaction in eq 4.11. This results in a large decrease in the overall stability of an otherwise stable resin. This effect can be handled in several ways:

1. Choose a talc which is lower in iron content. Talcs vary not only from manufacturer to manufacturer, but one manufacturer will have several grades, each differing in their effect on stability.

2. Include a talc deactivator. These are generally epoxy resins which will coat the talc and protect the PP.
3. Add a metal deactivator to the formulation which will complex with the iron in the talc and prevent it from catalytically decomposing hydroperoxides.

In general, when incorporating fillers into an existing formulation, it is reasonable to expect affects on the stabilization performance.

4.4   Other Additives

4.4.1   Acid Scavengers

The inclusion of an acid scavenger is necessary because of the catalyst residues. Even though the amount of catalyst residues is in the low ppm range [30], the need to neutralize acid residues persists. For the processor who runs thousands of pounds of polymer in a month, the potential for the corrosion of a mold surface or die lip can be a very costly proposition. By adding the appropriate antacid, any acidic species will be neutralized or scavenged, eliminating or reducing the potential for corrosion.

The use of antacids also can influence:

- Color of the resultant formulation: The chemistry involved here is complex and beyond the scope of this chapter [31]. The choice of the antacid can affect the overall acidity/basicity of a resin and influence the reactions of many of the organic additives in the system.
- Release properties: The use of metallic stearates will give a resin a certain amount of lubricity, which has the potential for providing a small amount of mold release or slip properties. With time, plate out can form on the mold, die lips, or chill rolls. This is not generally a problem except in situations where an extremely clean surface is needed.

Antacids include metallic stearates, including sodium, calcium, and zinc; zeolite structures (dihydro talcite, both synthetic and natural); calcium and zinc oxides; and other metallic salts based on lactic acid and benzoic acid.

4.4.2   Nucleating Agents

The use of a nucleating agent can affect the physical and/or optical properties of PP products. Regardless of which effect is desired, it is brought about by the same mechanism: increased nucleation of the crystallizing PP.

Commercially available nucleators can be broken down into two classifications, which the authors term "melt sensitive" and "melt insensitive." The melt sensitive nucleators have a melting point which is below or near the normal processing temperatures for PP-based resins. Melt insensitive nucleators do not melt at normal processing temperatures.

Melt sensitive nucleators include the sorbitol-based compounds. As a group, they are characterized by providing the PP with enhanced clarity, and are thus called "clarifiers." They

Table 4.7 Structures and Melting Points of Four Commercial Sorbitol-Based Nucleators

Number	R_1	R_2	Melting pt., °C
1	H	H	220
2	H	CH_3	245
3	H	CH_2CH_3	230
4	CH_3	CH_3	270

The sorbitol compounds are based on the following structure:

also provide increases in physical properties. Table 4.7 lists the four commercial materials currently available.

These compounds are limited by thermal decomposition at elevated temperatures. The decomposition causes two problems. The first is the loss of the nucleating property, with an associated decrease in the clarity of the resultant part. Second is the formation of aldehydes from the thermal decomposition of the sorbitols. Depending on the aldehyde formed by the decomposition, a sweet, cherry-like odor may form which will remain with the final part. While the odor may be pleasant, it is unwanted in most applications. Even the original commercial sorbitols differ in their organoleptic properties. If the neat material has a noticeable odor, then the final part will also contain the odor.

The melt insensitive nucleators include a broad range of compounds, including the benzoate salts. Of particular interest is sodium benzoate. Another class of compounds includes the sodium salts of organic phosphates. Both the sodium benzoate and organic phosphates have melting or decomposition temperatures well above the normal processing temperatures for PP. Sodium benzoate is used primarily as a nucleator. Its primary effect would be to enhance the physical properties of PP; it is less effective (than clarifiers) at improving the transparency. The organic phosphates act both to nucleate and to clarify a PP resin. All clarifiers nucleate, but not all nucleators clarify well.

The actual mode of nucleation differs between the melt sensitive and insensitive nucleators. The melt sensitive nucleators actually set up a "physical gelation network" within the matrix [32]. The formation of this gel network insures a highly dispersed nucleating agent and a high degree of nucleation. The melt insensitive nucleators act as single point nucleation sites within the matrix. This is illustrated in Table 4.8. The clarity of the compounded resin is effected by the dispersion of the finely divided nucleator, as determined by the mixing time in a high-speed mill. Even upon reextrusion, the dispersion and, hence, the clarity is not effected. While the need for adequate dispersion prior to

Table 4.8 Influence of Intensive Mixing on Effectiveness of Melt Insensitive Nucleator

Mixing intensity	Haze, %
Low	32
High, 15 sec	28
High, 2 min	21
High, 4 min	20

Sample: Random copolymer, NA-11 nucleator

compounding is important to both the melt sensitive and insensitive nucleators, it is critical when using a melt insensitive nucleator.

4.4.3   Peroxides

Alkyl peroxides are added to PP to produce controlled rheology (CR) resins by promoting extrusion degradation of the starting resin. The advantages of CR resins lay in their higher melt flows and narrower molecular weight distributions than their parent resins, permitting more output and higher orientation in some fine denier fiber operations. Specific advantages of using a controlled rheology resin appear in Section 9.2.1.2.

The amount of peroxide needed depends on several factors: 1) the melt flow rate (MFR) of the starting resin, 2) the desired MFR of the final resin, and 3) the antioxidant system used in the formulation. Table 4.9 shows the effects of the starting melt flow rate and the peroxide concentration on the melt flow rate of the final resin. The MWD of the degraded resin depends only on the starting MWD and the starting and ending MFRs. Table 4.10 shows the influence of the peroxide degradation on the Polydispersity Index (PI) of a resin, a measure of MWD based on a rheological method discussed in Section 6.5.3.

There are some interactions between the peroxide and the normal stabilization. The introduction of the peroxide, a radical source, adversely effects the stability and color of the resin. Also, the amount or type of antioxidant in a formulation effects to some degree the

Table 4.9 Peroxide-Assisted Degradation of PP

Peroxide concentration, %	Starting MFR		
	0.8	3.5	12
	Final MFR[a]		
0.013			26
0.025		17	44
0.05	8	33	58
0.075	14	51	74
0.1	33	64	
0.125	37		

[a] Extruded at 245 °C

Table 4.10 Effect of Alkyl Peroxides on the PI by Starting and Ending MFR

Starting MFR	Ending MFR	PI
0.1	0.1	4.1
0.1	5	2.5
0.1	46	2.4
0.5	5	2.7
0.5	52	2.3
4	50	2.7
12	70	3.2

efficiency of the peroxide in the degradation step. Table 4.11 shows the influence of the antioxidant system on the final melt flow for varying amounts of peroxide.

4.4.4   Slip Agents

During the use of PP films and laminates, the line speeds and reliability of the packaging machine operations are of utmost importance. To decrease the friction of the film on the processing and conversion equipment, a lubricating agent known as a slip agent is added.

The mode for the reduction of coefficient of friction arises from the migration of the slip agent to the surface of the film. Once on the surface, the slip agent is able to lubricate the processing equipment, which in turn will allow faster line speeds. The migration of the slip agent through the polymer matrix has been related to the development of crystallinity of the polymer [33]. Compounds which have shown usefulness as slip agents include primary amides, secondary amides, and ethylenebisamides. The structure of each of these classes of compounds is shown in Fig. 4.7. Each of these materials offers unique properties which allow the resin to be tailored to meet specific requirements. Two important properties should be considered in evaluating these amides: 1) reduction in the coefficient of friction (COF) and 2) thermal stability of the slip agent.

Table 4.11 Influence of Antioxidant and Peroxide Concentration on the Final MFR of a CR Resin

AO concentration, %	MFR, g/10 min Peroxide concentration, %	
	0.05	0.1
0.05	28	66
0.1	26	61
0.25	22	61
0.5	20	54

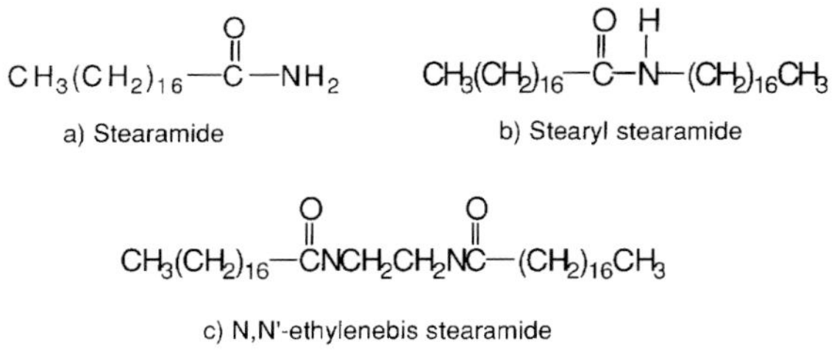

$$CH_3(CH_2)_{16}-\overset{\overset{\textstyle O}{\|}}{C}-NH_2 \qquad CH_3(CH_2)_{16}-\overset{\overset{\textstyle O}{\|}}{C}-\overset{\overset{\textstyle H}{|}}{N}-(CH_2)_{16}CH_3$$

a) Stearamide   b) Stearyl stearamide

$$CH_3(CH_2)_{16}-\overset{\overset{\textstyle O}{\|}}{C}NCH_2CH_2N\overset{\overset{\textstyle O}{\|}}{C}-(CH_2)_{16}CH_3$$

c) N,N'-ethylenebis stearamide

Figure 4.7 General structures of (a) primary-, (b) secondary-, and (c) ethylenebis-amides

Commercially available amides can be classified by two distinct features: molecular weight and unsaturation. Each of these factors has an influence on the mobility of the additive in the polymer matrix. The more similar the fatty section is to PP, the slower its migration to the surface. The selection of a slip agent will depend on the following factors:

- Rapidity of COF drop: Differences in the reduction of the COF can be grouped by saturated and unsaturated compounds regardless of molecular weight; the unsaturated compounds will migrate faster and, therefore, yield lower COF values in a given time period (differences in COF become smaller as the films are allowed to age and the slower slip agents migrate to the surface).
- Thermal stability: Thermal stability increases from primary to bis to secondary amides.
- Time of final conversion (printing, lamination, coating, or heat sealing): If this occurs in-line, the slip needs to be active immediately and must keep its ability to reduce COF. If rolls of film are stored prior to conversion, then the slip can be slower acting.
- Post-production processes: These may include corona treatment or printing. The slip agent cannot interfere with these operations.
- Clarity of final film: The type and amount of the slip agent cannot cause deleterious effects on the clarity of clear films.

In choosing the appropriate slip agent, these factors must be kept in mind. The properties of the slip agent must be balanced with the processing conditions and the end-use application.

4.4.5   Antiblocking Agents

Antiblocking agents, or "antiblocks," are also used in the manufacture of films. Blocking is a term describing the polymer film sticking to itself as a result of storage in roll form. One solution for blocking is the addition of an appropriate antiblock.

Typical antiblocks can be either silica, talc, or diatomaceous earth, the common feature being that they are all inorganic materials and, thus, are not miscible with the polymer. Antiblocks function by creating microscopic roughness to the otherwise smooth film surface. The challenge is to add just the right amount of the correct antiblock with adequate dispersion. Antiblocks are used in the 0.05 pph to 0.2 pph range for unoriented films. Differences in antiblocking performance exist between oriented and unoriented films, with the oriented films needing less antiblock agent and using finer particle sizes than the unoriented films.

Primary amides can also be useful in the prevention of blocking. In contrast to their effectiveness as slip agents, the saturated primary amides have been shown to provide better blocking than the unsaturated amides.

4.4.6 Antistats

Polypropylene, being a good insulator, can accumulate a static charge. Such a charge can cause problems such as dust buildup, small parts hanging up in the mold, and static cling in films. This problem can be solved by either internal or external antistats.

4.4.6.1 Internal Antistats

In the usual internal solution to static charge buildup, an antistatic agent (or "antistat") which has limited solubility in the PP matrix, and with hydrophilic character, is added to the PP. Over a period of time, the antistat migrates to the surface of the PP. The hydrophilic portion is excluded from the polymer matrix and resides on the surface. When sufficient antistat has accumulated at the surface, the static charges may dissipate, as the absorbed moisture provides some conductivity. At a surface resistivity below about 10^{14} ohms/square, the charge will be dissipated in a reasonable time [34]. Below about 10^{10} ohms/square, the charge dissipates rapidly. In polyolefins, typical agents are glycerol monoesters (e.g., glycerol monostearate; GMS) and ethoxylated secondary amines.

The effect of GMS level on the surface resistivity of a propylene copolymer is shown in Fig. 4.8. Ethoxylated amines also show similar effects. Concentrations range from 0.1 pph up to 1.0 pph, depending on the speed and degree of antistatic protection needed.

One particular problem with the surface active antistats is that they are not permanent. With time and continued washing of the surface, the "reservoir" of agent is consumed through the blooming action. Once lost, the antistatic agent is no longer available at sufficient concentrations to reduce static buildup.

Since the antistats need to be on the surface of the polymer to function, care needs to be taken not to add more than is needed, to prevent possible aesthetic and post-production

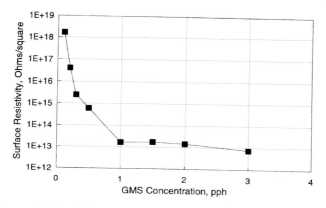

Figure 4.8 Surface resistivity of 2.3 mm (90 mil) plaque. GMS (42% mono) in PRO-FAX 7523. Source: Montell Polyolefins

process problems. Also, the antistats can broadly be classified as "oily" or "waxy" surface deposits, which may pose problems during sealing, printing, or adhesion operations. If the inclusion of an internal antistat may cause such problems, the type and level need to be carefully chosen and suitably tested.

It is also to important to keep in mind the Food and Drug Administration (FDA) regulations when formulating with these compounds. Glycerol monostearate has a broader range of usage allowed under the current FDA regulations than the ethoxylated amines.

Another approach is to add a high concentration of a conductive agent to the PP to lower the volume resistivity to the point where charges may flow through the polymer. This is accomplished only when a sufficient amount of the conductive material is added that the particles touch and are able to make a conductive path through the part. Thus, the high loading needed severely limits the use of this approach; it is only used in situations where static discharges are highly hazardous. Typically, a conductive carbon black is added at 10% to 30%, depending on the grade of the carbon. Figure 4.9 shows the response of a typical PP impact copolymer to varying levels of carbon black in terms of volume resistivity [35].

The traditional antistats also show some additional functionality as mold release agents when used at relatively high concentrations. The glycerol esters can be used in the 0.25 pph to 1.0 pph range to be effective mold release agents. The ethoxylated amines also function as mold release agents at the same concentration ranges.

4.4.6.2   *External Antistats*

These agents are applied topically to the converted part by the either the processor or a downstream operation. The materials need to be hygroscopic; glycerols and polyols are typical of compounds used.

4.4.7   Mold Release Agents

Mold release agents may be classified as internal or external agents. The internal agents are made up from the same class of compounds as the slip and antistatic agents. Generally, the

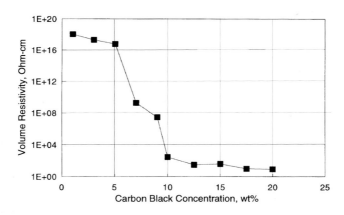

Figure 4.9 Reduction in volume resistivity of PP with carbon black loading. Source: Montell Polyolefins

amides are more effective than the monostearates due to their faster blooming. The mode of action is similar to that of slip agents, but only those with very rapid response times are effective. In fact, release agents can be termed "slip agents for injection molding." The classifications of mold release agents are the same as for the slip agents: the lower the molecular weight, the faster the action, and unsaturated molecules work faster than saturated ones.

External mold release agents are generally spayed on the mold surfaces and consist of silicone compounds. As such, they do not qualify as additives. Great care must be taken with silicone sprays, as trace amounts can destroy the adhesion of ink or paint in subsequent operations.

4.4.8   Pigments

In many applications it is desirable to pigment the resin to a specific color. A wide range of PP products are pigmented. The pigments used range from cadmium- and chrome-containing inorganic compounds to azo and quinacridone organic pigments. The effects on the stabilization of a PP resin vary from pigment to pigment. The major effects are:

- UV light stability: Pigments vary in their light stability. If a pigment which is not light stable is used in a stable formulation for natural resin, the overall affect will be to destabilize the resin. In cases such as this, it is useful to employ additional stabilization to either account for the unstable pigment or to help stabilize the pigment itself. Various UV absorbers usually help in these situations.
- Thermal stability: Pigments also vary in their resistance to elevated temperatures. As in the case of UV stability, an unstable pigment can destabilize the entire resin formulation. Additional amounts of phenolic or thioesters help in stabilizing these systems.

In each of these cases, the best cure lies in the prevention of the problem. By choosing the proper pigments, many of these problems can be eliminated.

Pigments vary considerably in their effects on the stabilization system. Some pigments are more difficult to stabilize than others, requiring additional testing and formulation work.

4.4.9   Fluorescent Whitening Agents

Chemically, these compounds are typically phenyl coumarins or benzoxazoles which can absorb invisible UV radiation and emit it as visible blue light. This has a twofold effect:

1. In a polymer with a yellow cast, the emitted blue light makes up for the absorbed blue light to make the polymer appear whiter, and
2. the polymer appears to glow, even in normal lighting.

The glow is due to the fact that the object is converting the invisible UV light into visible blue light; in so doing, the object is emitting more visible light than is available in the background, and it appears to shine.

4.4.10   Metal Chelators

The term "metal chelator" is a better description of the general classification metal deactivators. The role of transition metals in the catalytic decomposition of hydroperoxides is well documented [36, 37]. Use of a metal deactivator is advised when the PP will contact copper. Specifically, wire and cable applications gain appreciable lifetimes when one of the metal chelators is used. The exact choice of the chelator depends on factors such as cost/performance, solubility in PP, and color considerations.

It is imperative that a chelator be used whenever copper contact is intended. Increasing the concentration of traditional AOs does not approach the performance level of a commercial chelator.

4.4.11   Lubricants

Polyolefins generally do not require lubricants for enhanced processing properties. If needed, paraffinic oils, PP waxes, or fatty amides are used. The purpose of the lubricant is to reduce friction in the die. The overall effect is to increase output and reduce die swell.

4.4.12   Biocides

Biocides have been largely used in plasticized PVC and its related applications [38]. In traditional PP applications, the need for a biocide to control the growth of microorganisms is virtually nonexistent. Some trash cans and other waste disposal containers make use of these compounds to inhibit bacterial growth. The improvement is both aesthetic and sanitary. By incorporating the appropriate agent, the consumer receives a product which is able to resist the formation of unpleasant and unsightly organisms. Table 4.12 lists commercially important antimicrobial agents in use [39].

Table 4.12 Antimicrobal Agents Finding Use Commercially

Chemical name	Industrial name
10,16-Oxybisphenoxy arsine	OBPA
2-n- Octyl-4-isothiazolin-3-one	
N-trichloro-methylthio-4- cyclohexane-1,2-dicarboximide	Folpet

4.5   Additive Requirements for Resin Suppliers

The additive requirements of a resin producer are simple, but essential:

1. Quality: Once a particular additive is included in a formulation, it is imperative that the quality of the additive be high and consistent. Considering the role of these additives, the

reliability of their performance must be without question. Fortunately, suppliers have approached the business with this high quality attitude.

2. Cost-effectiveness: Some additives are far more effective at low concentrations than others. In that situation, a higher price for the additive may be balanced by the high performance, and it can be the most cost-effective material.

3. Food use acceptability: Most PP producers and fabricators prefer to work with grades that have the FDA or other clearances, even if the specific application does not need clearance. Whole production plants prefer to use exclusively FDA-approved grades to avoid contamination with nonaccepted grades. In practice, many of the common additives have a wide degree of acceptability. Conversely, the common monomeric HAs do not have any FDA acceptance, yet they are widely used in non-FDA applications.

4. Technical support: The level of support needed will depend largely on the sophistication and self-reliance of the resin producer. Additive suppliers typically have the extensive technical knowledge, personnel, and equipment necessary to find solutions to a variety of problems. Even when the resin supplier is knowledgeable about additives, the suppliers can be a valuable resource when difficulties arise.

Ultimately, each resin supplier will tailor its additive requirements to meet the needs of its customers, plants, and technical resources. Those needs will change with time, depending on market conditions, customer demands, market segment, and technical commitment. As an industry that is highly dependent on effective additives, PP producers have demanded, and have received, additives of the highest quality, backed by diligent technical service and delivery.

4.6   Additive Requirements for Specific Markets

4.6.1   Fibers

The stabilization of fibers, whether they be staple, bulk continuous filament, melt-blown, or spunbonded, offers considerable challenges. The demands placed on the stabilization system can vary greatly, depending on the conversion process and end-use application.

Fiber producers demand that the resin supplied to them be a product which can be converted with a minimum of interruptions. The stabilization needed for this will vary, depending on the conversion process used. The goal of the stabilization system is to have the proper process stability without sacrificing properties needed for success in the end-use application. The specific aspects of the stabilization needed for particular end-uses and processes are discussed below.

4.6.1.1   Disposable Items

This segment is made up of melt-blown, spunbonded, and carded staple fiber fabrics. The stabilization needed for end-use applications is not that severe, although the demands placed on process stability are often extreme. Melt temperatures in the 270 °C to 290 °C range are common. Traditional stabilization can be used in the manufacture of these resins. It is not uncommon to find hindered phenols used alone or in combination with phosphites. Concentrations are usually kept to a minimum, since many of these items are used once and discarded (hence, the term "disposables"), so low cost is important. An additional reason for keeping the stabilization to a minimum is to reduce the potential for discoloration. As the generation of a color body in a PP resin is generally due to a reaction of one of the additives, low levels minimize the potential for a color problem.

4.6.1.2   Carpet and Upholstery

The need for continuity in the spinning operation is extremely important for this segment of the industry. Filament breaks in a bulk continuous fiber operation can cause an entire line to shut down. A resin with extremely consistent melt stability is needed for this process, which runs at high temperatures and with long residence times. Combinations of hindered phenols and phosphites are typically used in concentration ranges from 0.05 pph to 0.15 pph.

These products are more durable, so we need to be concerned with the stability of the finished product. Criteria for this market include:

- Weatherability: Typically moderate UV stability is needed. Polymeric HAs are used in these applications. Additional protection can be afforded to both the resin and the pigments by the use of a UV absorber.
- Gas fade resistance: Typical HPs, when exposed to certain offending gasses, can cause the phenomenon known as gas fading [40 - 42]. When gas fading occurs, the HP used in the stabilization system forms a compound which can turn the fiber pink, blue, or yellow. Typically, a yellow color is formed, and that discoloration is termed "gas yellowing." The high surface area of fibers and lighter colors possible with PP-based resins can exaggerate the problem. Several solutions exist to eliminate, or at least minimize, the gas fading problem:
    - Use an HP that is resistant to gas fading. Several commercial HPs on the market are gas fading-resistant. The structures of these are given in Fig. 4.10.
    - Use a truly nonphenolic stabilization system. By removing the phenolic, only the phosphite would be left in the resin. This would severely effect melt stability but could be an attractive solution to a gas fading problem.
    - Use hydroxylamines; they have been shown to yield resins that provide both melt stability and low gas fade characteristics [43].

4.6.2   Films

Polypropylene has been converted into film since the beginning of its production, but new catalysts and film processes have helped growth in this area continue. Depending on the type of film and the process by which it is made, the process stability requirement will be moderate to heavy. Process or melt stability is aimed at preventing rheological changes and maintaining film strength. Functionalizing components, additives effecting slip and blocking properties, can be process dependent but are usually more specific to the final film conversion process.

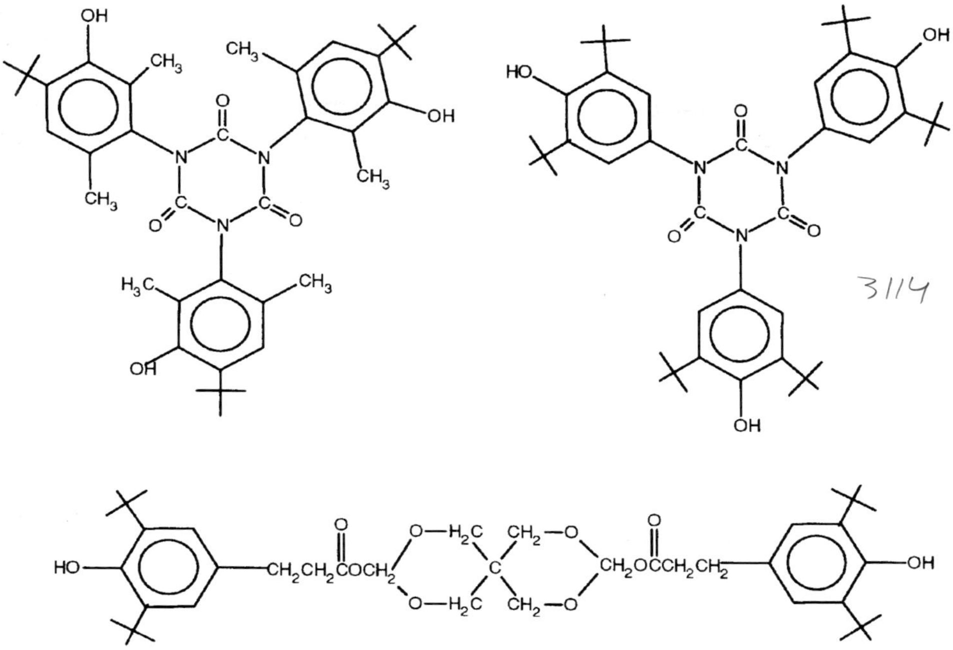

Figure 4.10 Examples of HPs with resistance to gas fading

The most common processes used to produce PP films are chill roll cast, for nonoriented, and tenter frame, for oriented, films. Oriented and nonoriented films also can be made by different blown film processes, but these are not as widely used as the above flat processes. Extrusion temperatures may vary between 210 °C and 300 °C. A stabilization package consisting of moderate levels of phenolic (500 ppm to 1000 ppm) and phosphite (500 ppm to 1500 ppm) antioxidants is usually present in the lower temperature processes (< 250 °C). For higher temperature processes, either both components or just the phosphite will be raised for additional processing stability.

Film resins will usually contain more functionalizing additives (by weight) than stabilizers. The two main functionalizing additives are antiblocking and slip agents. These materials are combined to provide the release of one film from another or from take-off equipment. Since films have large surface areas and may be wound under tension and high-speeds, there can be substantial static charges and compressive forces present between film layers. An antiblock is an inert material, large enough to protrude from the film surface and provide physical separation of the film layers. Antiblocks are essential to prevent blocking during any appreciable film storage time. Probably the most common type of antiblock used in cast PP film is diatomaceous silica. These materials provide good antiblocking properties at between 500 ppm and 2000 ppm. Other types of materials recently used for this application include talc and glass spheres. Certain precautions must be taken with natural materials, such as talc and silica, to insure they do not have high levels of metal impurities that may react with process stabilizers. Oriented films typically use antiblocks with smaller particle sizes, such as clays.

Since antiblocks rely on size to provide the surface separation, particle size and dispersability are two important characteristics. Depending on the film thickness, antiblock average particle size can range from less than 1 micron to 15 microns. Particles or agglomerates larger than 25 microns can appear as optical defects. In addition, the presence of agglomerates indicates that some of the antiblocking agent was not dispersed, and the normal concentration may be ineffective. Thus, antiblocks are often coated to provide better dispersion in the PP. In cast films, particles less than 1 micron are relatively ineffective as an antiblock, while in oriented films these small particle sizes still show functionality.

The presence of these inorganic antiblock materials at the film surface can have a surprising effect on film-handling characteristics. Because static electricity is highly dependent on the nature of the two surfaces being contacted and separated, as when films pass over rolls during any film operation, the nature of the antiblocking agents can cause, or cure, serious problems with static charge generation.

Slip agents are generally materials that tend to bloom from PP and which have some inherent lubricating properties. Since slip agents eventually end up on the film surface, they may increase the haze of the film. Probably the most widely used slip agents for PP film are fatty amides, such as erucamide and oleamide.

The time needed for the surface concentration of slip agent to reach an effective concentration can vary from days to weeks, depending on the agent used and the aging conditions. Other factors such as polymer crystallinity, presence of comonomers, and presence of other additives also can effect the time to reach the effective level.

Corona treatment of the film needs to be considered in determining the slip level. Treatment removes much of the agent at the surface at that time, and the blooming resumes after treatment. Thus, the timing of the treatment can be important.

4.6.3   Medical Applications

Polypropylene is a useful material for medical applications because it is easy to injection mold, maintains good dimensional stability during autoclave sterilization, and is cost-effective for disposable devices. While the majority of molded PP used in medical applications is for disposable devices such as syringes, nonwoven fabrics also are used in items such as surgical masks and gowns.

The manufacturing of medical devices is similar to any other injection molding, thermoforming, or nonwoven operation, and requires similar additive packages. The difference in additive technology for medical applications comes after the manufacturing process, during the sterilization of the article. Devices may be sterilized by one of three main techniques: autoclave, ethylene oxide, or radiation treatment. That order also describes the historical evolution of sterilizing techniques. The popularity of these different sterilization techniques vary among regions, so PP resins produced by a global polymer manufacturer may face any one or a combination of these methods. Of these three techniques, radiation treatment is the most damaging to the PP, as it creates numerous radicals that lead to oxidative degradation. This discussion focuses on stabilization against degradation from radiation sterilization.

To complicate matters, the degradation associated with radiation sterilization takes place in the solid-state, where diffused oxygen has greater mobility to react with the radicals compared to the bulky antioxidant molecules. The stabilization needs of radiation-sterilized PP are similar to that of high temperature exposure, except that the number of radicals produced during the irradiation process is much higher. The sterilized part contains a much higher concentration of radicals than would a nonirradiated part.

Combinations of techniques often are the result of a device being sterilized by the manufacturer and again by the end-user (such as a hospital). The first technique is often radiation sterilization, which creates radicals with little mobility in the solid-state. The article may then be stored for a long period of time, during which, if incorrectly stabilized, the radicals can react with oxygen and eventually cause chain scission and embrittlement of the article, especially if followed by another sterilization treatment. The last treatment may be by autoclave or a second dose of radiation, which would allow these radicals to react and degrade the PP. Currently, most PP articles for medical use are sterilized by high energy radiation, such as gamma-ray or electron beam radiation.

4.6.3.1   *Chemistry and Stabilization of Irradiated PP*

When bombarded with high energy radiation, such as gamma-ray or electron beam radiation, PP can be easily ionized. The ionized molecule is deficient in the number of bonding electrons. This can lead to the breaking of bonds, as depicted in eq 4.22 [44, 45].

$$PP \xrightarrow{\text{radiation}} PP \cdot + + e^- \rightarrow PP' + + PP'' \cdot \qquad (4.22)$$

The secondary electrons produced in eq 4.22 are sufficiently energetic to cause further ionization or radicalization of the PP. In addition, the energy level of the radiating beam is high enough that any "hits" on the carbon-carbon backbone bonds will cause breaking of that bond, which can then recombine (no change in MW), react with some low MW entity (loss of MW), or cross-link (increase in MW). It appears that none of these processes dominates, and the initial net effect on the PP is minor [46]. The above reactions take place very rapidly after irradiation, on the order of fractions of a second. These events will occur solely due to the energy of the radiation in all polymers, regardless of the presence or absence of stabilizers. More important are the events that follow the radiation.

After the initial reactions occur and meta-stable polymer ions and radicals are formed, a new set of reactions begin which can eventually cause embrittlement. The PP radicals created, as seen in Fig. 4.11, are combinations of alkyl and allyl radicals [47]. In thick sections, like an injection molded syringe, the alkyl radical will predominate [48]. The alkyl radicals react with oxygen and are converted to peroxy radicals very rapidly, whereas the more stable allyl radicals undergo oxidation at slower rates but, once oxidized, decay quickly, with chain scission [39].

(a)   (b)

Figure 4.11 Radical products possible from radiation sterilized PP: (a) tertiary alkyl radical, (b) allylic radical

Peroxy radicals generated by radiation undergo similar types of reactions to those generated by lower energy radiation, such as UV light. Though the chemistry may be the same, the rates of some reactions are different, and the penetration of sterilizing gamma radiation is deeper than UV radiation. A higher rate of peroxy radical termination, compared to oxidation in the melt state, can be explained by a cage theory [49]. The theory supposes that peroxy radicals are generated in close proximity to one another and will recombine due to their immobility in the solid-state. Raising the temperature by 20 °C will significantly reduce this cage recombination, and instead of forming dialkyl peroxides, high concentrations of hydroperoxy radicals will result [50]. Consequently, the damage to the irradiated item depends on the storage conditions, which must be part of the test regime.

The degree of oxidation and depth of oxidation in an irradiated sample depends more on the type of radiation than the type of polymer. Studies using chemiluminesence have shown that surface oxidation increases with decreasing dose rate [51]. Since gamma radiation is much lower in dose rate than electron beam (1 megarad/hr vs. 1 megarad/sec), it can cause up to 3 times as much surface oxidation.

Copolymers of propylene with 3% ethylene are becoming more popular for medical applications due to their physical property retention after irradiation. Copolymers are ionized, radicalized, oxidized, and degraded by radiation at comparable rates to homopolymers. Thus, the physical property retention appears to come from different morphology, namely lower crystallinity [52].

As described above, PP is subject to mechanical failure due to oxidative degradation suffered as a result of sterilizing radiation. Various combinations of antioxidants have been tried to prevent this failure. Initially, radiation stabilization utilized the same classes of additives used for process stability, such as combinations of phenolics and phosphites. To provide the additional stability needed for sterilization, higher concentrations of these additives were used. Often this simple increase in antioxidant concentration did not provide the desired stabilization and actually caused other problems, such as discoloration.

Phenolic and phosphite antioxidants often are used in combination to provide a synergistic control of molecular weight and color changes. Phenolic yellowing is accelerated by radiation sterilization but can be minimized by using more phosphite antioxidant. Since radiation occurs when the polymer is in the solid state, oxygen has high mobility compared to these large organic molecules, and the secondary AO synergism may be slowed or prevented. Discoloration is solely due to additives, since PP without stabilizers does not discolor after radiation [53].

Some phenolic antioxidants are very effective stabilizers even at relatively low concentrations (< 500 ppm). Discoloration problems can be minimized by using low levels of these antioxidants without hurting the post-radiation stability of the polymer. This solution, unfortunately, leaves the potential for color problems if additive concentrations and radiation doses cannot be controlled to tight tolerances.

A more desirable solution is to add only noncoloring antioxidants. This was difficult in the case of homopolymer PP, since the phenolic antioxidant was key for molecular weight control during processing. Since the development of more forgiving PP copolymers for medical applications, recent formulations have moved toward replacing the phenolic with HAs.

Hindered amines can scavenge primary radicals similarly to phenolic antioxidants, although their effective temperature range tends to be lower (25 °C to 120 °C vs. 25 °C to

300 °C). The antioxidant activity and lack of yellowing have made hindered amines prominent in medical formulations. Typical formulations include about 1000 ppm of a monomeric hindered amine and other coadditives, including phenolics, phosphites, and mobilizing additives, described below [54 - 57].

Researchers have studied the mobility of PP radicals after gamma radiation treatment [58]. Their studies show that alkyl radical termination was increased during and after radiation treatment with the addition of a "mobilizing" additive such as a hydrocarbon oil. Their theory suggests that the mobilizer increases the free volume of the amorphous phase and allows polymer chains greater mobility to recombine.

In summary, medical applications for PP, and in particular radiation sterilized PP, require unique stabilization packages. Since radiation sterilization causes increased oxidation of the polymer, additive levels are increased. Recent advances in stabilization packages have been achieved through the use of HA stabilizers and mobilizing agents.

4.6.4   Automotive

The consumption of plastic in the manufacturing of automobiles in the USA was over 1.5 million metric tons (3.5 billion lb.) in 1993. Polypropylene and related polymers accounted for 250 k tons (550 M-lb.) of the total. With recent advances in catalyst technology it is expected that PP base resin volumes will continue to grow.

The auto manufacturers place very strict demands on the polymers. Regardless of the specific resin used, the exposure depends on the specific use. For purposes of this discussion we will break the uses into three areas: under the hood, interior, and exterior.

4.6.4.1   *Under the Hood*

In these applications the challenge is heat from the engine. There is also exposure to oil, grease, and various cleaning agents used by the consumer. Ultraviolet light exposure is not a concern.

To stabilize for the heat generated from engine operation, typical quantities of HPs are used, with synergistic amounts of thioesters. The frequent use of carbon black in these parts can jeopardize the overall thermal stability of PP [59, 60]. The amount of additional HP and thioesters will depend on the amount and type of carbon black used. Preference is given to increasing the thioester over the HP to contain costs.

4.6.4.2   *Exterior*

Polypropylene used on the exteriors of automobiles are typically pigmented black or a color coordinated with the body panels. In many cases the parts, bumpers in particular, are painted with the same color as the body panels. In some cases only part of the bumper is painted to help create a trim effect on it. Regardless of the painting scheme used, the bumper needs to be paintable, as well as UV stable.

Other uses would include body side molding and other trim parts, with color schemes as above. All the exterior parts will undergo similar exposures. The combination of heat and UV light will cause the greatest amount of damage to PP.

When pigmented black, the carbon black will afford a substantial amount of UV stability to the resin. Functioning as a UV absorber, the carbon black will adequately protect the bulk of the part. Since automobile manufactures are equally concerned with the aesthetics of a part, as well as mechanical integrity, the surface also needs to be protected. The best way to protect the surface of even a black part is by the addition of a HA. Typically, a monomeric HA at a concentration of 0.2 pph to 0.3 pph will be adequate for these applications. Since HAs function by scavenging radicals, they need to be present at or near the surface of the part. The monomeric HAs can migrate to the surface where they will be active. A problem with the monomeric HAs is that the continued migration will eventually deplete the concentration needed to stabilize [61]. The polymeric HAs migrate slower than monomeric HAs. Parts with a thicker cross section stabilized with only polymeric HAs exhibit a lower UV stability compared to a corresponding resin stabilized with a monomeric HA. Combining the polymeric and monomeric HA gives the polymer the fast protection of the monomeric and the longer lasting effect of the high molecular weight fraction [62].

With a pigmented resin system, the color fastness of the pigments needs attention in addition to the polymer stability. The use of the same HA system as above is usually effective. Additionally, a UV absorber can be added to help protect the pigments. Only by stabilizing both polymer and pigment components can a successful system be developed. Caution is advised when changing colors.

4.6.4.3   *Interior*

The stabilization needs of PP used in interiors are similar to the exterior needs, except that the temperatures of an interior are higher, and the amount of ultraviolet light will be lower, due to the screening effect of the window glass. Combinations of monomeric and polymeric HA in conjunction with a UV absorber will adequately protect the interior parts.

The exposure conditions of the various auto models and individual parts are so different that only close cooperation between PP suppliers and auto companies can assure the development of adequate materials for the these demanding applications.

4.6.5   Housewares

The use of PP-based articles for containers for both food and other household items continues be very successful. The stabilization needs of the resins used in this market are fairly straightforward. The criteria are:

- Processing: Conventional primary and secondary antioxidants give the needed stability.
- Optical properties: Whether for food or nonfood applications, both clarity and color are important. The needed clarity can usually be obtained by adding a clarifier tho a random copolymer. The color is controlled by the choice and level of the primary and secondary antioxidants. A compromise between process stability and lower color is often necessary.
- Food contact: A large number of commercially available additives meet the regulatory requirements.
- Taste and odor: An important criterion is the absence of any taste or odor transference to food contained in the article. This restriction essentially eliminates the use of certain

additives, such as thioesters, for these applications. Similarly, the CR resins, made with alkyl peroxides, also add what is usually an unacceptable level of taste and odor to a resin. However, the CR resins can be used if care is taken to produce a resin which is free of the more volatile decomposition products of the peroxide. Normally, a vacuum vented extruder can accomplish the devolatilization.

- Thermal stability: If the parts are cleaned in a dishwasher or used to heat or cook food in a microwave oven, heat stability needs to be addressed. The conventional means of adding a thioester to the resin cannot be used due to taste and odor considerations. Thus, the HP alone must thermally stabilize the resin. High loadings are not acceptable because of the potential of color formation. This leaves only one choice: a highly effective phenolic compound which can yield the needed thermal stability at a low concentration. Also needed is resistance to aqueous extraction.

4.6.6   Construction

Construction has not been a strong market for PP resins. However, with the advent of high alloy copolymers, there are indications that PP may soon find its place in this application area. The use of high alloy resins is a fairly new development. For a description of the resins used in these markets, see Section 7.1.8.2.

Major concerns for the stability of resins used in this market are:

- UV stability: The need for UV stability is inherent in any outdoor application for construction, including roofing, geomembranes, and geotextiles. Roofing materials also require flame retardancy. For roofing materials pigmented with carbon black, the need for HAs, for UV protection, which are adversely affected by the halogenated flame retardants, is obviated.
- Process stability: The need for process stability is twofold: 1) the use of regrind, and 2) the use of conversion processes which are unconventional for propylene-based resins. In calendering operations, molten polymer is exposed to air for periods as long as 30 minutes, a severe exposure for conventional PP stabilization systems. However, with the selection of a stronger stabilization system, PP can be adequately stabilized for calendering.

4.7   Testing

Various bodies (ASTM, ISO, SAE) have specific test methods and procedures for resin and application testing, and any detailed studies should be pursued with those organizations. The intent of this section is to outline some of the more important test methods for evaluating PP stabilization.

4.7.1   Process or Melt Stability

A resin is repeatedly passed through an extruder at specific conditions. By measuring the melt flow rates of successive passes, the process stability of various formulations can be compared.

Table 4.4 employed this method. Color can also be measured on these multiple passes to evaluate the color stability of the resins.

4.7.2 Long-Term Heat Aging (LTHA)

This evaluation consists of placing a specimen in a forced air oven at the specified temperature and monitoring the time to embrittlement. The criteria for failure needs to be determined by the user, but it is often just a brittle break when bent manually. The onset of failure is usually sudden enough that the criterion is not critical. The specimens are typically molded to specific dimensions and placed on stainless steel racks in the oven. Different temperatures can be used. Typical temperatures for PP resins range from 100 °C to 160 °C, and 150 °C is common.

4.7.3 UV Stability

The UV stability of a resin can be determined by a wide variety of test procedures, each of which has its own strengths and weaknesses. Table 4.13 describes the tests and gives the strengths and weakness of each.

4.7.4 Radiation Resistance

The specimens are exposed to various dosages of radiation (gamma or e-beam), usually in the 3 MRad to 5 MRad range. Following this, a property such as impact strength is measured and tested at intervals. The parts are usually stored at an elevated temperature ($\sim 60\,°C$) to

Table 4.13 Comparison of Tests Used in the Evaluation of UV Resistance

Test equipment	Light source	Strengths	Weaknesses
QUV(1)	Fluorescent bulbs - a variety are available	Inexpensive to buy and operate Ability to vary UV spectrum by choosing different bulbs	No general acceptance, as test method is lacking
Weatherometer	Xenon bulbs with different filter combinations	Ability to change UV spectrum by using various filter combinations Ability to change intensity of light by varying wattage to the bulb General acceptance in a variety of test methods	Expensive to buy and operate
Sunshine weatherometer	Carbon arc	Acceptance in pigment evaluation	Expensive to buy Light source very labor intensive UV spectrum unlike sunlight

accelerate the testing. The testing and failure criteria need to be determined for a specific market and/or customer. The specimens may be laboratory moldings or extrusions, or commercially produced articles.

References

1. *Allen, N., Ed.:* Degradation and Stabilization of Polyolefins, Applied Science Publishers, 1983
2. *Gaechter, R., Ed.:* Plastic Additives Handbook, Hanser Publishers, 1987, 2nd Edition
3. *Rabek, J.F.:* Photostabilization of Polymers Principles and Applications, Elsevier Applied Science, 1990
4. *Jellinek, H., Ed.:* Degradation and Stabilization of Polymers, Elsevier, 1989, Vols. 1 & 2
5. *Gugamus, F.:* Poly. Deg. Stab. 24 (1989) 289–301
6. *Hawkins, W.H., Ed.:* Polymer Stabilization, Wiley–Interscience, 1972, 37
7. *Tudos, E.:* Advances in the Stabilization and Controlled Degradation of Polymers, Patsis, A., Ed., Technomic Publishing Co., Inc., Lancaster, 1989, Vol. 1, p. 86–98
8. *Huyser, E.S.:* Free Radical Chain Reactions, Wiley–Interscience, 1970, p. 13
9. *Grassie, N.:* Developments in Polymer Stabilization, Scott, G., Ed., Applied Science Publishers LTD, 1979, Vol. 1, p. 221
10. *Davies, D.I.:* Free Radicals in Organic Synthesis, Springer-Verlag, 1978, p. 10
11. *Tzoganakis, C.:* Poly. Proc. Eng. 6(1) (1988) 29–60
12. *Carlsson, D.J.:* Polm. Stab. and Degr.: P. Klemchuk E.; ACS, 1984, 367
13. *Mita, I.:* Degradation and Stabilization of Polymers, Jellinek, H., Ed., Elsevier, 1983, Vol 1, p. 277
14. *Mita, I.:* Degradation and Stabilization of Polymers, Jellinek, H., Ed., Elsevier, 1983, Vol 1, p. 282
15. *Pospisil, J.:* Poly. Deg. Stab. 20 (1988) 181–202
16. *Grassie, N.:* Polymer Degradation and Stabilization, Cambridge University Press, 1985
17. *Denisov, E.T.:* Poly. Deg. Stab. 34 (1991) 325
18. *Hodgeman, D.K.C.:* in Developments in Polymer Degradation - 4, Grassie, N., Ed., Applied Science Publishers, 1982, p. 205
19. *Rabek, J.F.:* Photostabilization of Polymers Principles and Applications, Elsevier Applied Science, 1990, p. 318–327
20. *Sedlar, J.:* Advances in the Stabilization and Controlled Degradation of Polymers, Patsis. A., Ed., Technomic Publishing Co., Inc., 1989, Vol. 1, p. 227
21. *Gijsman, P.:* Poly. Deg. Stab. 43 (1994) 171–176
22. *Al-Malaika, S., Scott, G.:* in Degradation and Stabilisation of Polyolefins. Allen, N., Ed., Applied Science, 1983, p. 284
23. *Lyons, John W.:* The Chemistry and Uses of Fire Retardants, Wiley—Interscience, 1970
24. *Pearce, Eli M.:* Pure & Appl. Chem. 6 (1986) 925
25. *Hilado, C.J.:* Flammability Handbook for Plastics, Technomic Publishing Co., Inc., 1994, 4th Ed
26. *Troitzsch, J.H.:* Progress in Organic Coatings, 11 (1983) 41
27. *Carlsson, D.J.:* Journal of Applied Polymer Science, 33 (1987) 875
28. *Gaechter, R., Ed.:* Plastic Additives Handbook, Hanser Publishers, 1987, 2nd Edition, Ch. 9
29. *Steppek, J.:* Additives for Plastics, Springer-Verlag, 1983, Ch. 4
30. *Klender, G.J.:* SPE Retec, Polyolefins V (1987) 225
31. *Kresta, J.E.:* SPE 38th ANTEC (1980) 478
32. *Thierry, A.:* Poly. Comm. 31 (1990) 299–301
33. *Schael, G.W.:* J. Appl. Poly. Sci. 10 (1966) 653–661
34. *Gaechter, R., Ed.:* Plastic Additives Handbook, Hanser Publishers, 1990, 3rd Edition, p. 755
35. *Wright, C.M.:* Montell internal document
36. *Gaechter, R., Ed.:* Plastic Additives Handbook, Hanser Publishers, 1987, 2nd Edition, Ch. 9
37. *Chirinos-Padron, A.J.,* Poly. Deg. and Stab. 20 (1988) 237
38. Plastics Compounding, 1994/1995 Red Book, Advanstar Communications, p. 13
39. *Reilly, C.J.:* Modern Plastics Encyclopedia - 95, Toensmeier, P. Ed.; McGraw Hill, p. C-3
40. *Wagner, H.:* Melliand Textilberichte, 63 (1982), 291–293

41. *Yachigo, S.:* Polym. Degrad. Stab. 37 (1992) 99–106
42. *Speidel, A.:* Chemiefasem Textilindustrie, 33/85 (1983) E81– E83
43. *Cooper, K.:* SPE Retec Polyolefin IX, (1995)
44. *Ranby, B.:* Photodegradation, Photo-oxidation and Photostabilization of Polymers, Wiley–Interscience, New York, 1975
45. *Jellinek, H., Ed.:* Degradation and Stabilization of Polymers; Elsevier, 1989, Vol. 1, p. 359–360
46. *Bradley, R.:* Radiation Technology Handbook, Marcel Dekker, Inc., 1984, p. 114–129
47. *Ohnishi, Y.:* J. Poly. Sci. (1963), A1 625
48. *Dunn, T.:* Pad. Phys. Chem. 14 (1979) 625
49. *Carlsson, D.:* Pure Appl. Chem. 52 (1980) 389
50. *Decker, C.:* J. Poly. Sci. (1973) A1(11) 2847
51. *Yoshii, T.:* J. Appl. Poly. Sci. 31 (1986) 1343
52. *Yoshii, K.:* J. Appl. Poly. Sci. 32 (1986) 5669
53. *Horng, P.:* Plastics Engineering (1984) April 35
54. *Dunn, T.S.:* Radiat. Phys. Chem. 19 (1982) 287
55. *Dunn, T.S.:* J. Indust. Irrad. Tech. 5 (1983) 443
56. *Dunn, T.S.:* J. Indust. Irrad. Tech. 1 (1983) 33
57. *Williams, J.L.:* Radiat. Phys. Chem. 19 (1982) 29
58. *Dunn, T.S.:* Rad. Phys. Chem. 19 (1982) 291
59. *Mwila, J.:* Poly Degrad. Stab. 44 (1994) 351–356
60. *Strengrevics, E.:* PMAD Retec Akron (1986) 98–112
61. *Gugamus, F.:* Poly. Degrad. Stab. 46 (1994) 123–140
62. *Gugamus, F.:* Poly. Degrad. Stab. 44 (1994) 273–297

5   Compounded Polypropylene Products

Stephen M. Dwyer, Omar M. Boutni, Chichang Shu

5.1   Introduction

Physically blending a polymer with other existing polymers or reinforcing agents is a well-established strategy for obtaining new compositions with desirable end-use properties. This approach has been widely used because it is often found to be a more rapid and less expensive route to meet the demands of marketplace than the development of new reactor-based polymers.

Polypropylene is one of the most important commercial plastics for its superior intrinsic properties such as high melting temperature, high chemical resistance, and low density. Polypropylene is also a highly versatile material because it can be compounded with high amounts of fillers, reinforcing agents, and other polymeric materials [1]. The use of mechanical blending technology broadens the property range of PP and makes it possible to tailor the physical properties for particular applications. In addition, these property improvements can often be achieved while maintaining the cost advantages of PP. The result is the growth of a family of compounded PP products, which represents an important segment of the PP industry.

The purpose of this chapter is to present a brief overview of the current state of knowledge in compounded PP products and their applications, starting with the fundamental aspects of compounded products. This is followed by a discussion of compounded PP products, including impact modified PP, thermoplastic olefins, thermoplastic vulcanizates, filled and reinforced PP products, and flame retardant PP.

5.2   Technical Issues

5.2.1   Composition

Compounded PP products usually consist of PP, modifiers, and chemical additives. The goal of the formulation is to achieve specific balanced combinations of properties, processability, and cost.

As the host material, the inherent properties of PP establish the basic characteristics of the compounded products; stiff PP will generate stiffer compounds, and tougher PP favors toughness in the compounded product. As with unmodified PPs, several structural parameters, such as molecular weight, molecular weight distribution, and stereoregularity, can be varied to obtain a good balance of desired properties in the host PP. In addition, the molecular structure can be modified by copolymerization with other monomers. For example, PP randomly polymerized with ethylene reduces stiffness and melting temperature, and increases impact resistance somewhat [2]. Heterophasic copolymers provide high levels of impact that can also be attractive starting points for preparing compounds. Although encountered less frequently, PP can also be modified by grafting on functional groups to improve compatibility with other polymers or materials [3, 4].

We refer to the materials added at high concentrations to the PP compound as modifiers. Polypropylene modifiers include organic polymers, mineral fillers, and reinforcing fibers. The hard, inert fillers and reinforcing agents provide enhanced stiffness and higher use temperatures. The organic polymers, most often elastomers, provide improved impact behavior. Application requirements, which often involve a combination of different properties, dictate the selection and concentration of modifiers that will meet the needs of the applications. Usually, the major required characteristics are obtained at the expense of other properties. For instance, the elastomers are used to improve impact resistance at the cost of reduced modulus and strength, while the fillers, used to gain higher stiffness, heat distortion temperature, and dimensional stability, do so at the cost of reduced impact resistance. Thus, the most effective compound provides the best balance of properties for the particular application. Optimum performance is accomplished by properly choosing the various components and the compounding technology.

Those materials added at low concentrations, but often with major effects, are the additives, which are discussed in Chapter 4. Many remarkable changes in the appearance and performance of PP can be achieved with a small fraction of additives. For instance, pigments provide colorful appearance; antioxidants enhance heat aging stability; and polar additives can improve the interfacial adhesion with PP.

5.2.2   Compounding Process

Compounding is the process of mixing PP with other ingredients to form a PP-based multicomponent product. In practical applications, melt mixing is the most commonly used technique because of energy efficiency, operability, and environmental considerations. The difficulty of the compounding task depends greatly on the starting materials and their physical forms, compared to the size of the desired dispersion. A finely divided material is usually desired for the dispersed phase, so it is usually reduced to the smallest particle size that economics allows prior to extrusion, most frequently by the supplier. At the compounder's facility, those particles are then distributed within the PP particles, usually by dry blending, although a significant fraction of modifiers are metered into the hopper in parallel to the PP. Often, difficult materials may be mixed with other materials as carriers to provide more reliable control of their addition to the extrusion operation.

The compounding operation generally consists of two mechanisms, which can be achieved simultaneously or stepwise [5, 6]. First, the particles of the material to be dispersed, whether fluid or solid, are sheared and broken into smaller ones; this is size reduction. Second, these smaller particles are mixed within the PP matrix to provide a uniform concentration; this is dispersion. The efficiency of mixing, determined by the equipment, the materials, and the process conditions, employing these two mechanisms, size reduction and dispersion, is the key factor that determines the quality and properties of a PP compound.

There is a variety of compounding equipment available for this task [5 - 7]. An internal batch mixer, such as a Banbury mixer, is capable of mixing any size and shape of material that will physically fit into it. The mixing time and the procedure for feeding material can also be freely chosen. Because of the high intensity of mixing, a mix can be completed in this device in a relatively short period of time. A far less intensive mixer, the single screw extruder is the most widely used mixing equipment in the plastics industry. In these machines, the mixing quality is based on the total shear deformation for a given material throughput. Based upon material bulk density, melting behavior, melt viscosity, and desired melt temperature, different screw configurations can be selected. In general, the total shear deformation can be changed by varying the depth of the screw channel or the angle of the pitch helix, and by incorporating mixing devices in the screw or barrel design. Twin screw extruders provide another dimension for extrusion compounding. They provide more control over the shear applied to the melt, so they are more intensive mixers than single screw extruders. They are commonly classified by their rotational direction and intermeshing structure: counterrotational or corotational, and intermeshing or nonintermeshing, with numerous combinations of these available. The advantages of twin screw extruders are: low energy consumption (and associated temperature increase) relative to the shear deformation achieved, greater tolerance to difficult materials to process, and flexibility for producing small quantities of multiple items. For those advantages, they command a higher price.

Clearly, each type of mixer is intended for a particular level of difficulty. In turn, each has its limitations. Each of them must be used within its capabilities, or one of the process objectives, size reduction or dispersion, will likely be compromised. A common temptation in compounding is to increase the mixer output. If done indiscriminately, at some point the uniformity of the compound suffers, and properties lower than those of the average composition are experienced. Thus, there is always a balance of mixing quality and output which must be understood for any given mixing device.

In all of these mixing devices, the heat and shear rates arising during the compounding process may cause polymer degradation and color or odor development. Proper stabilization is the best protection (see Chapter 4), but precautions to exclude oxygen, such as inert gas blanketing, can be effective. Occasionally, volatiles, dust, or other difficulties from the modifiers need to be addressed, for which special accessory equipment is available. At times special processes are employed, such as grafting polar moieties, chemically degrading the polymer, or activating agents providing interfacial enhancements. In addition, the selection of compounder configuration, feeding technique, operating conditions, and appropriate stabilizers all may have effects on the resulting products.

5.2.3   Particle Dispersion

Because compounded PP products are multiphasic in nature, many properties, and consequently applications, depend critically on the uniform and adequate dispersion of the constituent components. The establishment of the dispersed phase morphology-property relationships is an essential step toward achieving effective compounds and in finding the optimum processing window for manufacturing compounded products.

For the binary polymer blends employing PP, the most common phase morphology is one of a continuous matrix within which the other component is dispersed. Clearly, the component which occupies the higher volume fraction in the compound would normally assume the role of a continuous phase. On the other hand, the component with the lower viscosity tends to encapsulate the more viscous component and to become the continuous phase [8, 9, 10]. Thus, the shape, size, and size distribution of the dispersed phase depend strongly on the composition, melt properties, and processing history. Proper balancing of the rheological properties of the components in the melt state by selection of appropriate molecular weight distribution and use of appropriate intensive mixing equipment, such as the various types of twin screw devices, are two important ways to control the nature and scale of phase dispersion to meet product needs [11].

The size and shape of rigid mineral fillers and reinforcing fibers also have a profound influence on the physical and mechanical properties of compounded PP products. While high concentrations of fillers are desirable for their property enhancements, the task of producing a uniform material becomes increasingly severe. This is particularly true for high aspect ratio materials like mica or glass fibers, although very high flow versions of PP have alleviated this difficulty recently. As in all plastics, anisotropy introduced by aligned fibrous filler can also cause variations in shrinkage, modulus, impact, and appearance in different directions.

5.2.4   Interface

The condition of the interface between the phases is often crucial to attractive end-use properties. This is true of both polymeric and mineral fillers.

For multiphase polymer blends, the interfacial adhesion is critical to the effective action of the impact modifiers [11]. An attractive approach to improving interfacial behavior is to employ an interfacial agent, such as a graft or block copolymer, whose parts are compatible with the different phases in the blend [12]. The introduction of this interfacial agent also reduces the interfacial tension and promotes interfacial adhesion. The result of this improvement is a more stable, finer dispersion of the minor component and a great improvement in the mechanical properties.

With fillers, a more oliophilic surface, usually achieved by coating the filler, facilitates the breakup of agglomerates in the PP matrix. Also, the degree of interfacial adhesion between polymer matrix and fillers or reinforcements has strong effects on properties of these composite materials. There are two options available for adhesion improvement. One is to provide surface treatment to the inorganic fillers or reinforcements. For instance, silane coupling agents are frequently used to modify the adhesion of inorganic fillers to PP. The other option is to chemically modify the PP. Grafting of different polar groups, such as acrylic acid, acrylic ester, or maleic anhydride, to PP is often used. Under certain conditions, adopting both options will have enhanced synergistic effects on interfacial adhesion.

5.2.5   Crystallization

As with unmodified PP, crystallization of the PP in compounds dictates many of the end-use property levels reached, such as the modulus, use temperature, and impact strength. To some degree, the crystallinity is, in turn, affected by variations in processing conditions. In compounded products, the situation is sometimes complicated by the effect of the incorporated modifiers on the crystallization of the PP matrix. In a few instances, fillers with surface treatments have unusual effects. For fiber reinforced PP, it has been observed that the nucleation density on the surface of some fibers can be so high that the usual development of the spherulites is obstructed, and the PP crystals grow directly out from the fiber surface, while providing exceptional adhesion.

5.3   Principles of Rubber Toughening

The facts of rubber-toughening have preceded theoretical explanations of them. A rubber-toughened polymer, polystyrene (PS) being the classic case, exhibits the following characteristics, compared to the brittle parent, which illustrates a crazing mechanism for toughening:

• Yielding,
• high elongation to break,
• stress-whitening during elongation,
• high energy to break, and
• somewhat lower modulus.

In this situation, the PS elongation reaches 40% instead of 3%.

5.3.1   Mechanisms

Various mechanisms have been proposed to explain the toughening of elastomer-modified polymers. An early concept of energy absorption by an elastomer was suggested by the stress-whitening in butadiene-styrene elastomer-modified polystyrene [13]. This approach proposed that the elastomer absorbed the energy by carrying the stresses of deformation associated with the development of microcracks, which explained the stress-whitening. The chief weakness of this theory was that it relied on the elastomer phase, which explained only a small portion of the total energy absorbed by the material [14].

Bucknall and Smith [15] proposed the multiple crazing theory, which emphasized the role of the matrix polymer in deformation and energy absorption. They noted that the appearance of stress-whitening was due to the formation of many crazes near the elastomer–matrix interface. They suggested that the function of the elastomer particles was to control craze growth by initiating a sufficiently large number of energy-absorbing crazes of controlled size, and to terminate the crazes before they reached the catastrophic failure size. To achieve termination, adhesion of the dispersed phase to the matrix was essential; systems without adequate adhesion displayed low elongations compared to those reached with good adhesion. While there are some weak spots in this model, the need for good adhesion is clear. The dimension of the dispersed rubber phase is important to both the initiation and termination of crazes. Particles too small would not provide adequate stress concentration to initiate a craze, and ability to terminate crazes also decreases with particle size. While the specific particle size interactions with initiation and termination are also not clear, it is evident that there is an optimum particle size for any given system. It appears that this optimum is more associated with effective craze termination than initiation. This mechanism is an accepted part of most current explanations of rubber toughening of brittle materials [16, 17].

A second theory, shear yielding in the matrix, has also been identified as an energy-absorbing mechanism [14, 18, 19]. The formation of shear bands, caused by localized yielding, involves a change in shape without a change in volume. It may be initiated by the region of high stress concentration due to the presence of elastomer particles, but the role of the rubber particles is less clear. Little stress-whitening is associated with this deformation process, but permanent deformation occurs. Shear yielding is commonly observed in the deformation of rubber toughened PVC. Because this theory has several shortcomings, Bucknall et al. [16, 17, 20] suggested that crazing and shear yielding can occur simultaneously in elastomer-modified polymers. In this case, interactions between the two mechanisms may play a role in toughening. Since shear bands are oriented at an angle to the crazes, they would act as barriers to limit the growth of crazing. Furthermore, when shear bands originate at the craze tip, they relieve the hydrostatic stresses required for craze growth. In either case, the interaction between the two mechanisms acts to reduce the craze size in the matrix [21].

The process of voiding as a toughening mechanism has also been proposed by some researchers. It has been suggested that in some thermoplastics which failed predominantly by shear yielding, the process of voiding can reduce the local buildup of hydrostatic stress at the crack tip. The initiation of voids and their subsequent growth enhance the matrix deformation [22, 23, 24].

The above elastomer modification mechanisms used for glassy polymers have also been applied to semicrystalline polymers for impact enhancement. In the study of elastomer-toughening mechanisms of PP, Jang et al. [25, 26] reported that, depending upon the test temperature or rate of loading, the elastomeric particles may promote crazing or shear yielding, which determine the extent of plastic deformation prior to fracture. Low temperatures or high rates favor the formation of crazes, while high temperatures or low rates promote shear yielding. The role of either mechanism is to provide sufficient elongation to absorb the applied energy without reaching a local stress level that would cause catastrophic failure.

5.3.2   Elastomer Characteristics

In practice, predominantly ethylene-propylene rubber (EPR) and ethylene- propylene-diene monomer elastomer (EPDM) are the two most important types of elastomers in impact modification for PP. Several important factors determine the effectiveness of an elastomer on impact enhancement:

- Amount of elastomer added,
- its particle size and size distribution,
- the glass transition temperature (T_g) of the elastomer, and
- its chemical affinity for the PP matrix.

As might be expected, the extent of impact enhancement increases with elastomer content [27, 28, 29]. In commercial products, levels of elastomer do not usually exceed about 20%, since the addition of greater quantities results in an undesirable softening.

The effect of elastomer particle size is important because it determines the number and spacing of particles at a given concentration. Impact characteristics can be influenced by elastomer particle size, principally through the effect on initiation and termination of crazing and shear yielding [30]. It is recognized that, for a particular polymer pair, there exists a critical particle size that yields optimum toughness. That optimum is about 0.4 μm for PP/EPR.

Martuscelli and co-workers reported the influence of EPR copolymer structure and composition on melt rheology, phase morphology, and impact fracture behavior of PP/EPR blends [29, 31 - 33]. It was found that the degree of dispersion of EPR in the PP matrix was a crucial factor for good impact. The degree of dispersion was, in turn, determined mainly by the melt- phase viscosity ratio (viscosity of dispersed phase/viscosity of matrix).

The range of particle sizes effective for PP toughening varies with test temperature. For the test at room temperature, a quite wide range is effective. Below the T_g of PP, a narrower range is needed, and approaching the T_g of the elastomer, the range is narrowest.

The sensitivity of impact enhancement to the T_g of the elastomer can be clearly demonstrated by the dependence on the test temperature [26]. Below the T_g of the elastomer, it is ineffective. Accordingly, for adequate impact at a particular temperature, the T_g of the elastomer must be below that temperature.

Good adhesion between elastomer particle and PP matrix is also believed to be essential for the effectiveness of elastomer toughening. For example, polyisoprene is not a good impact modifier for PP due to the wide difference in solubility parameters, and thus poor adhesion, between it and PP [27]. However, a significant improvement in the impact strength of this polymer system was achieved by the use of a grafting additive to promote interfacial adhesion [34].

The C_2/C_3 content of the EPR affects the blend in different ways. At high C_3 levels, the high T_g would control, and poor impact would result, although miscibility or interfacial adhesion should be adequate, and some PP crystallinity in the EPR would reduce shrinkage stresses in the PP matrix. As C_2 content increases, PP crystallinity disappears and T_g drops, but shrinkage stresses remain (see Sections 5.5.2 and 3.5.5). At still higher C_2 levels, polyethylene (PE) crystallinity develops, and impact resistance reaches a maximum. The highest C_2 levels reduce the interfacial adhesion, and impact level drops again. The optimum concentration, which is quite sharp, is around 50 to 60 mole% C_2 [35]. Thus, the dispersed elastomer phase must be sufficiently immiscible with the matrix to maintain phase separation, yet adequately miscible to provide for strong adhesion between two phases.

5.4   Impact-Modified PP

Polypropylene homopolymer, while having a number of valuable properties and economic benefits, exhibits a poor low-temperature impact resistance. Such a shortcoming is due to its relatively high glass transition temperature (T_g), about $-15\,°C$. Incorporation of a soft, elastomeric phase as a toughening agent is an effective way to improve the low-temperature impact strength of PP. Various elastomers have been used as impact modifiers, but EPR is the most common. The resulting PP/elastomer polymer systems are normally multiphasic, with the elastomer as the minor, dispersed component. Impact enhancement is usually achieved at the cost of a reduction in modulus and strength. We refer to blends with up to about 20% rubber as impact-modified PP.

5.4.1   Performance

Having about the same rubber content and particle size (in the fabricated part) as a reactor-prepared heterophasic copolymer, the impact-modified PPs display the same ranges of modulus, impact strength, and other basic end-use properties, which are discussed in Chapter 6. However, other additives may be added to the blends with virtually no cost penalty. Thus, pigmented, antistatic, and special stabilization and other additive compositions are readily accommodated in the compounds. In addition, the scale of the reactor operation limits its products to those applications commanding large volumes only, while compounded products may be prepared on a much smaller scale, and in a shorter time frame. In this sense, compounded blends are more specialty products than reactor copolymers.

5.5   Thermoplastic Olefins

Thermoplastic olefin elastomers (TPOs) are basically blends of noncross-linked elastomers with polyolefin polymers such as PP or PE. The distinction between an impact-modified PP and a TPO is somewhat arbitrary; for this discussion, we consider rubber levels over about 20% to be TPOs. We will concentrate on binary blends of PP with EPR or EPDM, and ternary blends of PP, PE, and EPR or EPDM, as they constitute the largest group of TPOs in the market. In addition, the recent advance of in-reactor TPOs will be addressed.

5.5.1   EPR Blends

5.5.1.1   Morphology

In PP/EPR blends, the multiphasic morphology was observed by microscopy and dynamic mechanical tests [36 - 40]. In microscopic studies, three types of dispersed morphology were observed at different compositions. When EPR forms the minor phase, the average size of dispersed EPR particles depended largely on the relative viscosity between PP and EPR; the morphology of a very fine and uniform distribution of the EPR particles could be obtained when the two component polymers had similar melt viscosities. In the intermediate composition range, the blends with a lower viscosity EPR showed cocontinuous morphology in a wider range of concentration than those with higher viscosities. At high elastomer content, as expected, EPR forms the matrix and PP droplets are dispersed in it. Dynamic mechanical analysis (DMA) showed that the transition temperatures of the blends were identical to the pure components, indicating total incompatibility between PP and EPR, in spite of the intimate mingling of the phases. The rules controlling the morphologies in PP/EPR blends are also applicable to PP/EPDM systems [36, 37, 40, 41]. Detailed morphological descriptions of impact-modified PP, reactor-based impact copolymers, and TPOs appear in Section 3.5.

In injection molding of these blends, two distinct morphological layers are generally observed within the cross section [42, 43]. Near the top surface, there exists a shear zone having an elongated elastomer phase. Elastomer particles in this zone are highly stretched and oriented with the injection direction as a result of high shear rates near the wall during mold filling coupled with a high cooling rate. The shear zone is followed by a core zone of a large number of randomly sized spherical elastomer particles. It is also possible that, during injection molding, some elastomer particles in the core zone are elongated by flow, and spherulites nucleate along rows due to the shear. However, the slower cooling rates of polymer melt in this region allow the elastomeric inclusions time to relax, yielding spherical droplets. The morphology of the shear zone has significant effects on surface character, while the physical properties depend more on the morphology of the core zone. Further description of the effects of molding may be found in Section 3.6.

The crystallization behavior of PP-based blends containing EPR or EPDM has also been reported. A substantial increase in the number of nuclei in the blends with increasing elastomer content in the system has been found [8, 44 - 47]. The change in nucleation density was first attributed to nucleation activity by the elastomer on the PP. More recent work has shown that the increased nucleation is the result of a greater number of heterogeneous nuclei (inorganic residues and contaminants) that migrate from the EPR phase into PP during the mixing process. Using EPR copolymers with a reduced number of heterogeneities, D'Orazio et al. reported that the effects of EPR on nucleation behavior of PP/EPR blends disappeared [9].

Although the rubber is clearly immiscible with PP, the character of the PP spherulites has been shown to be affected by the rubber addition. Melting points and heats of fusion (PP basis) were lower, and the spherulites were more irregular in texture and boundaries. At the same time, the crystallization temperatures are raised, based on the nucleation mentioned above. Unfortunately, nucleation, by raising the crystallization temperature, would work to reduce impact; smaller, but more dense and more brittle spherulites would result. Many investigators confuse this behavior with the results of higher quench rate, which gives the smaller, less well-defined, and therefore tougher spherulites of the mesomorphic (smectic) form of PP. Thus, the observation of less regular, lower melting spherulites in EPR/PP blends is more likely to explain the improved impact than nucleation.

5.5.1.2   Properties

In a tensile test, results obtained from a large number of blends have shown that elastic modulus is not very sensitive to structural differences [48]. In fact, its value depends almost entirely on composition and moduli of constituent components. Young's modulus of PP/elastomer systems, as expected, decreases with increasing the EPR or EPDM content [41, 49 - 51]. Chemical modification of EPR or PP by maleic anhydride grafting did not cause any significant effect on concentration dependence of elastic modulus.

Tensile yield strength of the PP/elastomer systems decreases monotonically with increasing EPR or EPDM content due to the reduction of the effective matrix cross section introduced by the elastomer phase [41, 49]. The engineering yield strength of the PP/elastomer blends is a predictable function of elastomer content using the Nicolais–Narkis equation [52]. Since the elastomer does not exhibit the characteristic yielding behavior of the thermoplastics, above a certain elastomer content, a distinct yield point cannot be defined.

5.5.2   Ternary Blends of PP, PE, and EPR

The PP/EPR binary mixtures often exhibit a behavior known as "blushing," where a whitening occurs when the molded part is deformed. It has long been known that addition of HDPE to the PP/EPR blends can reduce this tendency [53, 54]. Studies of the morphology of these ternary mixtures revealed that the HDPE tended to gather within the EPR particles [55 - 61]. Thus, in PP-rich ternary blends, HDPE and EPR have an affinity for each other. They tend to combine within PP to form a characteristic morphology with HDPE particles surrounded by an elastomer shell. About 20 vol% of EPR could accommodate 20 to 30 vol% of HDPE [40, 62].

As illustrated in more detail in Section 3.5.5, the HDPE addition provides a better match between the matrix and dispersed phase shrinkages. The low shrinkage of the amorphous EPR normally creates tensile stresses in the high-shrinking PP matrix during cooling, allowing cracks and crazes to form later at low levels of strain. The HDPE induces higher shrinkage in the dispersed phase particles, lowers the stresses in the PP matrix, and reduces the tendency to form voids or crazes when the item is deformed. The effectiveness of this solution is not sensitive to the source of HDPE; either reactor or compounding can be satisfactory, provided the usual concerns about dispersion and particle size are observed in the compounding approach.

5.5.3   In-Reactor Thermoplastic Olefins

Thermoplastic olefins are traditionally manufactured by mechanical blending. With the development of new catalyst systems and polymerization technology, it is now possible to produce these kinds of blends directly in the reactor [63 - 65]. In-reactor TPOs have several important advantages over conventional, mechanically blended TPOs, namely:

- Products are polymerized directly from monomers. The decreased variability in raw materials imparts better material consistency.
- Fewer manufacturing steps are required to produce materials directly from the reactor. Therefore, cost savings are possible.
- Elastomers are finely dispersed in the olefin matrix. As a result, the in-reactor TPOs exhibit improved physical properties and melt uniformity.
- A wider range of elastomeric compositions are possible, as the viscosity ratio does not restrict the selection as severely as in blends.

Besides the obvious advantages mentioned above, the new technology is also capable of controlling the chemical structure and physical properties of the constituent polymers in the reactor. Therefore, composition and formulation not previously economic or even physically possible can now be produced. Details of this technology appear in Sections 3.5.6 and 7.1.8.2.

5.5.4   Performance of TPOs

TPOs are a class of material with a broad range of compositional variety leading to a diversity of performance characteristics, ranging from soft, flexible to rigid and tough. Selected properties for commercial TPOs including both mechanical blends and in-reactor grades are summarized in Table 5.1.

Applications for these materials can vary from automotive bumper fascias and body side moldings to commercial roofing systems. The following outlines the diversity of their performance capability.

1. Mechanical properties: TPOs are available in a wide range of stiffness. With a flexural modulus as low as 34 MPa (5000 psi), the softer TPOs behave and feel like thermoset rubber or leather-like substances, while flexural modulus values as high as conventional PP copolymers are available. The more rigid TPOs are used in stiff applications, such as automotive body panels. These materials retain good impact and abrasion resistance over the entire property range.
2. Thermal properties: Due to the presence of crystalline PP, heat deflection resistance of TPOs is better than many other olefinics and elastomers. With proper stabilization, TPO grades can endure long-term exposure to high temperature without significant loss of properties. The combination of these thermal capabilities makes TPOs particularly suitable for wire, cable, and automotive applications, especially under the hood. The low temperature properties of TPOs are also excellent at retaining their flexibility. This makes TPOs suitable for many outdoor applications.
3. Environmental: As with conventional PP, TPOs have good resistance to solvents, acids, and alkalis, especially for those harder grades which contain more of the crystalline phase. They do not absorb moisture, so they do not need to be dried before processing. They can be formulated to provide excellent resistance to outdoor exposure.

Table 5.1 Selected Property Ranges for Commercial TPOs

Property	Units	Flexible TPO	Stiffer TPO
Melt flow	g/10 min	0.1 - 20	0.4 - 20
Hardness	Shore D	25 - 50	50 - 75
Flexural modulus	MPa (kpsi)	34 - 550 (5 - 80)	550 - 2070 (80 - 300)
Tensile strength	MPa (kpsi)	5.5 - 21 (800 - 3000)	6.9 - 28 (1000 - 4000)
Elongation	%	300 - 800	25 - 800
Gardner impact at −20 °F	J (in-lb)	> 440 (> 320)	54 - > 440 (40 - > 320)

4. Processability: TPOs are available in a wide range of viscosities for processing by various techniques, such as thermoforming, injection molding, blow molding, and extrusion. Melt temperatures in the range of 230 °C to 250 °C (380 °F to 420 °F) are recommended. Being thermoplastic, TPOs are readily recycled.

5.6   Thermoplastic Vulcanizates

Thermoplastic vulcanizates (TPVs) are a highly engineered class of thermoplastic elastomeric compositions comprising a cross-linked elastomeric phase and a melt-processable thermoplastic polymer. These materials are generally produced by dynamic vulcanization in which both blending and a cross-linking reaction are carried out at the same time in a melt-mixing device. The resulting compounds exhibit more elastomer-like properties, such as lower compression set, lower stiffness, higher ultimate mechanical properties, and better resistance to fatigue, heat, and chemicals, than the corresponding mechanical blends, yet they can be processed by conventional fabrication processes as thermoplastics [66 - 68].

Polypropylene-based compounds which fall in the TPV category are primarily designed to compete with conventional thermoset elastomers such as EPDM, nitrile, butyl, and neoprene, and higher cost thermoplastic elastomers such as thermoplastic urethane and copolyesters [69, 70]. The main driving force for the development of TPVs is the substantial economic advantage with respect to the fabrication of finished products due to the simplicity of thermoplastic processing. Today, PP-based TPVs may be found in a variety of applications ranging from extrusion and blow molding to injection molding.

5.6.1   Dynamic Vulcanization

Dynamic vulcanization is a process of vulcanizing elastomer during its intimate melt mixing with a nonvulcanizable thermoplastic polymer to form a TPV. Gesseler [71] first developed this technology to improve the mechanical properties of elastomer–plastic blends. Fischer [72] then used this process to prepare compositions containing varying amounts of partially cured EPDM elastomer and PP. Coran and co-workers [73, 74] later used this technology to produce highly elastomeric compositions of fully cured EPDM and PP. More recently, Braga et al. [75] developed a dynamic vulcanization process to obtain TPVs from PP and EPR blends.

The dynamic vulcanization process is applicable to various elastomer–plastic combinations [76 - 78]. The procedures for forming a TPV based on the use of a batch-type mixer were given by Coran and Patel [68]. Typically, a larger portion of elastomer (in comparison to impact-modified products), a thermoplastic resin, and other ingredients such as filler, plasticizer, and stabilizer, are first melt-mixed. After forming a homogeneous blend, cross-linking agents are added. The curing reaction then occurs primarily in the elastomer phase while mixing continues. To insure uniform cross-linking of the blend composition, more rapid mixing is required for faster vulcanizations. The progress of cross-linking can then be followed by the changes in the mixing energy requirement. After reaching the maximum consistency, a TPV is formed and can be discharged from the mixer. The TPV containing vulcanized elastomer and the thermoplastic can finally be extruded, pelletized, or processed by normal plastic techniques.

For an elastomer–PP combination, many different vulcanizing agents or their combinations may be used to dynamically cure the elastomer. However, the cross-linking system chosen can have significant effects on the end-use properties. For instance, the EPDM–PP based TPVs cured by dimethylol phenolic resin have better compression set values and oil resistance than those vulcanized by sulfur or peroxide curing systems [79, 80].

In addition to the type of cross-linking system chosen, the cross-link density also has marked effects on the TPV properties. The cross-link density is controlled by the amount of curing agent used during dynamic vulcanization. Only a small number of cross-links is required for a large improvement in tension set, while tensile strength increases rather continuously as the cross-link density of the elastomer phase increases [74, 80].

The effects of incorporating a compatibilizer during dynamic vulcanization have also been reported [81]. The compatibilizer, typically block or graft copolymer, can be formed in situ during melt mixing. Even a small amount of compatibilizer can cause the formation of smaller elastomer particles during melt mixing and improve the mechanical properties of dynamically vulcanized elastomer–PP blends.

5.6.2   Morphology

Morphology of the blend is a major variable in controlling physical and rheological properties. Unlike thermoset elastomers, the PP-based TPVs form a two-phase system. The final morphology depends on both the nature of the blend before cross-linking takes place and the mechanism of cross-linking.

Abdou-Sabet and Patel reported the effects of composition and extent of cross-linking on morphological changes in EPDM–PP-based TPVs [80]. For uncured EPDM–PP blends, three main morphological forms are possible, depending on composition:

1. Elastomer particles dispersed in the continuous PP matrix,
2. cocontinuous PP and elastomer phases, and
3. PP particles dispersed in the continuous elastomer phase.

For the EPDM–PP blends with PP as the major component, dynamic vulcanization retains the morphology of dispersed EPDM in PP matrix. However, for EPDM–PP blends in the intermediate composition range, the use of phenolic curing agent generates two cocontinuous phases in the early stages of the dynamic curing process, even when well-defined, dispersed-phase uncured blends are used as the starting material. As the cure progresses, phase inversion takes place, and, at the end of the process, the elastomer exists as cured particles dispersed in the PP matrix. The morphology of dispersed elastomer particles is also observed for the fully cross-linked EPDM–PP blend, even with 80 wt% EPDM.

Thus, depending upon the state of cure, the cross-linked elastomer forms a continuous or discrete phase. In either case, PP forms somewhat more of a continuous phase. This morphological characteristic of having a continuous PP phase with the cross-linked elastomer is the key to obtaining a blend that exhibits physical properties comparable to a vulcanized elastomer and the processability of a thermoplastic.

Table 5.7 Comparison of PP Modified with 40% Mica and Other Fillers

Property	PP Homopolymer[a]	40% filled polymer				
		Suzorite mica 200 HK (untreated)	Suzorex mica 200 NP (treated)	Talc	Calcium carbonate	30% Glass fibers
Tensile strength, MPa (kpsi)	32 (4.7)	28 (4.1)	43 (6.2)	30 (4.3)	19 (2.8)	43 (6.3)
Flexural strength, MPa (kpsi)	31 (4.5)	45 (6.5)	65 (9.5)	44 (6.4)	32 (4.7)	70 (10.1)
Flexural modulus, MPa (kpsi)	1240 (180)	6400 (930)	7600 (1100)	4700 (680)	2900 (420)	6400 (930)
Izod impact strength, J/m (ft-lb/in)						
Notched	24 (0.45)	32 (0.60)	35 (0.65)	24 (0.45)	40 (0.75)	74 (1.4)
Unnotched	no break	200 (3.8)	230 (4.4)	240 (4.5)	1200 (23.0)	500 (9.4)
Heat deflection temperature at 264 psi, °C	56	89	108	78	84	125

[a] PP = Profax 6523, Montell Polyolefins

Source: Montell Polyolefins

Table 5.8 Properties of Coupled, Glass-Reinforced PP

Property	ASTM	Units	Injection molding GR PP grades					
			Low density[a]	Stiff[b]	High flow[c]	High stiffness & flow[d]	Max stiffness & flow[e]	High impact[f]
Glass content		%	10	30	20	40	44	30
Melt flow rate	D 1238	g/10 min	6	5	18	16	12	5
Density	D 792A	g/cm^3	0.97	1.13	1.04	1.24	1.26	1.13
Flexural modulus	D 790	MPa (kpsi)	2070 (300)	4830 (700)	3800 (550)	6900 (1000)	7250 (1050)	4340 (630)
Tensile strength	D 638	MPa (kpsi)	54 (7.8)	88 (12.7)	78 (11.3)	97 (14)	83 (12)	64 (9.3)
Notched Izod impact strength	D 256A	J/m (ft-lbs/in)	85 (1.6)	107 (2.0)	75 (1.4)	96 (1.8)	107 (2.0)	213 (4.0)
Heat deflection temp. at 66 psi	D 648	°C	141	150	149	152	143	136
Mold shrinkage	D 955	in/in	0.006	0.003	0.004	0.003	0.002	0.004

[a] HiGlass PF072-1, Montell Polyolefins
[b] HiGlass PF072-3, Montell Polyolefins
[c] HiGlass PF062-2, Montell Polyolefins
[d] HiGlass PF062-4, Montell Polyolefins
[e] HiGlass BJ44A, Montell Polyolefins
[f] HiGlass SB224-3, Montell Polyolefins
Source: Montell Polyolefins

reinforcing efficiency may be sacrificed if a critical fiber length is not maintained, and thus regrind levels in injection molding becomes an issue [95, 96].

5.8   Flame Retardant PP

Fireproofing of polymeric materials is clearly aimed at reducing the risks resulting from the burning of these materials. The major goal has been to reduce the rate of burning to prevent loss of human life and property damage. Recent developments have attempted to address other issues, such as smoke emission and toxicity of gases produced upon burning. The growth of plastic use in a multitude of applications, in place of metals and wood, has accelerated the development of strict regulations. These vary depending on the intended end-use of the polymeric materials in specific applications and region of use, and by customers. As a result, there are requirements which flame retardant polymeric materials must meet to be qualified for use in certain applications. Thus, test standards have been developed that vary among applications and regions. Some flammability test standards are discussed in Section 11.5.1.

Flame retardancy of PP has relied predominately on the use of combinations of organohalogen and metal oxide additives. In general, high loadings of mixtures of brominated or chlorinated organic compounds and antimony trioxide have been found to be effective. In some cases, NONEN 52 (Marubishi Yuka), decabromodiphenyl oxide available from many suppliers, hexabromocyclododecane (Saytex HBCD-SF), ethylenbistetrabromophthalimide (Saytex BT-93, Ethyl), and dodecachlorodimethano dibenzocyclooctane, a chlorinated alicyclic additive such as Dechlorane Plus (Occidental Chemical Corporation) were successfully used with antimony trioxide as a synergist [97, 98]. Combinations of Dechlorane Plus, antimony oxide and zinc borate were also reported to impart good flammability rating in PP homopolymer and copolymer types [99].

Halogenated flame retardant additives are not thermally stable and, hence, generate corrosive gases such as hydrogen chloride and hydrogen bromide during combustion or high temperature processing. Recent emphasis on lower smoke evolution and elimination of potentially harmful by-products generated during the decomposition of organohalogen compounds has lead to the exploitation of other flame retardant additives. Chief among these additives are alumina trihydrate and magnesium hydroxide, which have been commercially promoted for use in PP. Although these additives are nonvolatile, nontoxic, and noncorrosive, they are only effective at much higher concentrations than their halogenated counterparts, and consequently have an adverse effect on the impact strength and melt flow of the compound. In addition, a major drawback of these additives is their dissociation temperatures, which are well within the normal PP processing range. Some manufacturers of flame retardant PP have successfully resolved these issues by developing proprietary compounding techniques to achieve good dispersion and produce useful products, but the fabricated articles are still limited to those that can be processed at low temperatures.

Char formation during burning is an important mechanism used by polymers to resist burning. Charring is the formation of incombustible matter which hinders the polymer from burning. A correlation exists between the limiting oxygen index (the concentration of oxygen needed to sustain combustion) of a polymer and the amount of char formed during its pyrolysis in an inert atmosphere, for a number of common engineering polymers [100, 101]. While many polymers yield a significant amount of char, unmodified PP yields none.

Recently, a series of intumescent flame retardants, which generate char, have been evaluated in PP. The most notable ones are ammonium polyphosphate and polytriazinilpi-perzine. Used alone, these additives are not very effective, but in conjunction with other co-additives, substantially improved burning behavior and flammability ratings were observed which correlated with increased char during pyrolysis [102]. In general, the benefits of intumescent flame retardants in PP are the absence of dripping and bloom, and less smoke than halogenated FR, plus a UL94 V-O rating. Nonetheless, some of these additives have the same limitations as the halogenated additives, mainly their thermal stability and corrosive and hygroscopic nature. Therefore, care must be taken during the compounding and fabrications steps to avoid premature degradation of these additives.

References

1. *Galli, P., Danesi, S., Simonazzi, T.:* Polym. Eng. Sci. 24 (1984) 544
2. *Burkle, M.D.H.:* Plast. Mod. Elast. (1979) Oct., 76
3. *Lohse, D., Datta, S., Kresge, E.:* Macromolecules 24 (1991) 561
4. *Chung, T.C.:* New Advances in Polyolefins, Chung, T.C., Ed., Plenum, New York, 1993, p. 59
5. *Cheremisinoff, N.P.:* Guidebook to Mixing and Compounding Practices, PTR Prentice Hall, Englewood Cliffs, New Jersey, 1994
6. *Manas-Zloczower, I., Tadmor, Z. Eds.:* Mixing and Compounding of Polymers, Hanser, New York, 1994
7. *Curry, J.E.:* Polymer Blends and Alloys, Folkes, M.J., Hope, P.S., Eds., Blackie, New York, 1993, p. 7
8. *Speri, W.M., Patrick, G.R.:* Polym. Eng. Sci. 15 (1975) 668
9. *D'Orazio, L., Mancarella, C., Martuscelli, E., Sticotti, G.:* J. Mater. Sci. 26 (1991) 4033
10. *Karger-Kocsis, J., Kallo, A., Kuleznev, V.N.:* Polymer 25 (1984) 279
11. *Paul, D.R.:* Multicomponent Polymer Materials, Paul, D.R., Sperling, L.H., Eds., ACS, Washington, D.C., 1986, p. 1
12. *Flaris, V., Wasiak, A., Wenig, W.:* J. Mater. Sci. 28 (1993) 1685
13. *Merz, E.H., Claver, G.C., Baer, M.J.:* J. Polym. Sci. 22 (1956) 325
14. *Newman, S., Strella, S. J.:* J. Appl. Polym. Sci. 9 (1965) 2297
15. *Bucknall, C.B., Smith, R.R.:* Polymer 6 (1965) 437
16. *Bucknall, C.B.:* Toughened Plastics, Applied Science Publishers Ltd., London, 1977
17. *Bucknall, C.B.:* Polymer Blends, Paul, D.R., Newman, S., Eds., Academic, New York, Vol. II, 1978, p. 91
18. *Newman, S.:* Polymer Blends, Paul, D.R., Newman, S., Eds., Academic, New York, Vol. II, 1978, p. 63
19. *Hobbs, S.Y., Bopp, R.C., Watkins, V.H.:* Polym. Eng. Sci. 23 (1983) 380
20. *Bucknall, C.B., Clayton, D., Keast, W.E.:* J. Mat. Sci. 7 (1972) 1443
21. *Donald, A.M., Kramer, E.J.:* J. Mat. Sci. 17 (1982) 1739
22. *Yee, A.F.:* J. Mat. Sci. 12 (1977) 757
23. *Maxwell, M.A., Yee, A.F.:* Polym. Eng. Sci. 21 (1981) 205
24. *Borggreve, R.J.M., Gaymans, R.J., Eichenwald, H.M.:* Polymer 30 (1989) 78
25. *Jang, B.Z., Uhlmann, D.R., Vander Sande, J.B.:* J. Appl. Polym. Sci. 29 (1984) 3409
26. *Jang, B.Z., Uhlmann, D.R., Vander Sande, J.B.:* J. Appl. Polym. Sci. 30 (1985) 2485
27. *Karger-Kocsis, J., Kallo, A., Szafner, A., Bodor, G., Senyei, Z.:* Polymer 20 (1979) 37
28. *Kumbhani, K.J.:* Elastomerics 110 (1978) 17
29. *Bull, A.L.:* Plast. Rubb. Int. 6 (1981) 240

30. *Jang, B.Z., Uhlmann, D.R., Vander Sande, J.B.:* Polym. Eng. Sci. 25 (1985) 643
31. *Greco, R., Mancarella, C., Martuscelli, E., Ragosta, G., Yin, J.:* Polymer 28 (1987) 1919
32. *D'Orazio, L., Mancarella, C., Martuscelli, E., Polato, F.:* Polymer 32 (1991) 1186
33. *D'Orazio, L., Mancarella, C., Martuscelli, E., Sticotti, G., Massari, P.:* Polymer 34 (1993) 3671
34. *Tinker, A.J.:* Polym. Comm. 25 (1984) 325
35. *Van der Ven, S.:* Polypropylene and Other Polyolefins, 326, Elsevier Science Publishers B.V., 1990
36. *Danesi, S., Porter, R.S.:* Polymer 19 (1978) 448
37. *Karger-Kocsis, J., Kiss, L.:* Polym. Eng. Sci. 27 (1987) 254
38. *Pukanszky, B., Tudos, F., Kallo, A., Bodor, G.:* Polymer 30 (1989) 1399
39. *Fortelny, I., Kovar, J., Sikora, A., Hlavata, D., Krulis, Z., Novakova, Z., Pelzbaver, Z., Cefelin, P.:* Angew. Makromol. Chem. 132 (1985) 111
40. *Kolarik, J., Agrawal, G.L., Krulis, Z., Kovar, J.:* Polymer Composites 7 (1986) 463
41. *Jancar, J., DiAnselmo, A., DiBenedetto, A.T., Kucera, J.:* Polymer 34 (1993) 1684
42. *Karger-Kocsis, J., Csikai, I.:* Polym. Eng. Sci. 27 (1987) 241
43. *Ho, W.-J., Salovey, R.:* Polym. Eng. Sci. 21 (1981) 839
44. *Bartczak, Z., Galeski, A., Martuscelli, E., Janik, H.:* Polymer 26 (1985) 1843
45. *Martuscelli, E., Silvestre, C., Bianchi, L.:* Polymer 24 (983) 1458
46. *Jang, B.Z., Uhlmann, D.R., Vander Sande, J.B.:* J. Appl. Polym. Sci. 29 (1984) 4377
47. *Kalfoglou, N.K.:* Angew. Makromol. Chem. 129 (1985) 103
48. *Pukanszky, B., Tudos, F.:* Makromol. Chem. Macromol. Symp. 38 (1990) 221
49. *Pukanszky, B., Tudos, F., Kallo, A., Bodor, G.:* Polymer 30 (1989) 1407
50. *Chiang, W.-Y., Yang, W.-D., Pukanszky, B.:* Polym. Eng. Sci. 32 (1992) 641
51. *Nielsen, L.E.:* Mechanical Properties of Polymers and Composites, Marcel Dekker Inc., New York, 1974
52. *Nicolais, L., Narkis, M.:* Polym. Eng. Sci. 11 (1971) 174
53. *Fernando, P.L., Williams, J.G.:* Polym. Eng. Sci. 21 (1981) 1003
54. *Karger-Kocsis, J., Kuleznev, V.N.:* Polymer 23 (1982) 699
55. *D'Orazio, L., Greco, R., Mancarella, C., Martuscelli, E., Ragosta, G., Silvestre, C.:* Polym. Eng. Sci. 22 (1982) 536
56. *D'Orazio, L., Greco, R., Martuscelli, E., Ragosta, G.:* Polym. Eng. Sci. 23 (1983) 489
57. *D'Orazio, L., Greco, R., Mancarella, C., Martuscelli, E., Ragosta, G., Silvestre, C.:* Polymer Blends: Processing, Morphology and Properties, Kryszewski, M., Gateski, A., Martuscelli, E., Eds., Plenum, New York, Vol. II, 1984, p. 111
58. *D'Orazio, L., Greco, R., Martuscelli, E., Ragosta, G.:* Polymer Blends: Processing, Morphology and Properties, Kryszewski, M., Gateski, A., Martuscelli, E., Eds., Plenum, New York, Vol. II, 1984, p. 127
59. *Kesari, J., Salovey, R.:* Polymer Blends and Composites in Multiphase Systems, Han, C.D., Ed., ACS, Washington, D.C., 1984, p. 211
60. *Tervoort-Engelen, Y., Van Gisbergen, J.:* Polym. Comm. 32 (1991) 261
61. *Stehling, F.C., Huff, T., Speed, C.S.:* J. Appl. Polym. Sci. 26 (1981) 2693
62. *Kolarik, J., Vele, G., Agrawal, G.L., Fortelny, I.:* Polymer Composites 7 (1986) 472
63. *Galli, P., Simonazzi, T., Del Duca, D.:* Acta Polym. 39 (1988) 81
64. *Cecchin, G.:* Macromol. Symp. 78 (1994) 213
65. *Galli, P., Haylock, J.C., Simonazzi, T.:* Polypropylene: Structure, Blends and Composites, Karger-Kocsis, J., Ed., Chapman & Hall, New York, Vol. II, 1995, p. 1
66. *Legge, N.R., Holden, G.:* Thermoplastics Elastomer - A comprehensive Review, Hanser, New York, 1987
67. *Day, S.K., Bowmick, A.:* Thermoplastic Elastomers from Rubber-Plastic Blends, Ellis Horwood, New York, 1990
68. *Coran, A.Y., Patel, R.P.:* Polypropylene: Structure, Blends and Composites, Karger-Kocsis, J., Ed., Chapman & Hall, New York, Vol. II, 1995, p. 162
69. *O'Connor, G.E., Fath, M.A.:* Rubber World (1981) Dec., 25
70. *O'Connor, G.E., Fath, M.A.:* Rubber World (1982) Jan., 26
71. *Gessler, A.M.:* U.S. Patent 3 037 954 (1962)
72. *Fischer, W.K.:* U.S. Patent 3 758 643 (1973)
73. *Coran, A.Y., Das, B., Ptel, R.P.:* U.S. Patent 4 130 535 (1978)
74. *Coran, A.Y., Patel, R.:* Rubber Chem. Technol. 53 (1980) 141
75. *Braga, V., Manica, M., Martini, E., Milani, F.:* U.S. Patent 4 963 612 (1990)

76. *Coran, A.Y., Patel, R.:* Rubber Chem. Technol. 53 (1980) 781
77. *Coran, A.Y., Patel, R.:* Rubber Chem. Technol. 54 (1981) 892
78. *Coran, A.Y., Patel, R., Williams, D.:* Rubber Chem. Technol. 55 (1982) 116
79. *Abdou-Sabet, S., Fath, M.A.:* U.S. Patent 4 311 628 (1982)
80. *Abdou-Sabet, S., Patel, R.P.:* Rubber Chem. Technol. 64 (1991) 769
81. *Coran, A.Y., Patel, R.:* Rubber Chem. Technol. 56 (1983) 1045
82. *Katz, H.S., Milewski, J.V.:* Handbook of Fillers and Reinforcements of Plastics, Van Nostrand Reinhold Co., New York, 1987
83. *Pluddeman, E.P.:* Silane Coupling Agents, Plenum Press, New York, 1982
84. *Ulrich, A.D.:* ANTEC 91 Conference Proceedings, 1876 (1991)
85. *Katz, H.S., Milewski, J.V.:* Handbook of Fillers and Reinforcements of Plastics, Van Nostrand Reinhold Co., New York, 1987
86. *Herzig, R., Baker, W.E.:* J. Mater Sci, 28 (1993) 6531
87. *Callais, P.A., Kazmierczak, R.T.:* ANTEC 89 Conference Proceedings, 1368 (1989)
88. *Hogt, A.:* ANTEC 88 Conference Proceedings, 1478 (1988)
89. *Kozel, T.H., Kazmierczak, R.T.:* ANTEC 91 Conference Proceedings, 1570 (1991)
90. *Katz, H.S., Milewski, J.V.:* Handbook of Fillers and Reinforcements of Plastics, Van Nostrand Reinhold Co., New York, 1987
91. *Canova, L.A.:* Effect of Surface Treatments in Mica-Filled Polypropylene; 45th Annual SPI Composite Conference, 1990
92. *Balow, M.J.:* ANTEC 83 Conference Proceedings, 56 (1983)
93. *Pluddeman, E.P.:* Additives for Plastics; Vol. I, R.B. Seymour, Ed., Academic Press, New York, 1978, p. 123
94. *Shorthall, J.B., Pennington, D.:* Plastics and Rubber Processing and Applications 2 (1982) 33
95. *Gupta, V.B., Mittal, R.K., Sharma, P.K.:* Polymer Composites 10 (1989) 16
96. *Kelly, A., Tyson, W.R.:* J. Mech. Phys. Solids 13 (1965) 329
97. *Bertelli, G. et al.:* Polymer Degradation and Stability 20 (1988) 295–314
98. *Calewarts, S.E. et al.:* New Applications for Saytex at HBCD-SF Flame Retardant In Styrenic Polymers and Polyolefins; International Conference on Fire Safety, The Fire Retardant Chemicals Association, 1990
99. *Ilardo, C.S., Markezich, R.L.:* Fire Retardant Chemical Association (1989) March, 101
100. *Van Krevelen, D.W.:* Chimia 40 (1974) 504
101. *Van Krevelen, D.W.:* Polymer 16 (1975) 615
102. *Scharf D., Nalepa, R., Heflin, R., Wusu, T.:* Proceedings of the International Conference on Fire Safety 15 (1990) 306

6   End-Use Properties

Dario Del Duca, Edward P. Moore, Jr.

6.1   Introduction

In this chapter we focus on the PP properties of interest to the manufacturer of the finished part. It is in these properties that the accomplishments of molecular and morphological architecture come to fruition; the fabricator finds the properties useful, and thus valuable, but is not concerned with the causes. However, for the producer, an understanding of the factors leading to the attractive end-use properties is essential to the ability to achieve unusual combinations of properties in PP. Further, achieving them in the polymerization reactor, the most economical means, provides a particularly attractive cost-performance profile for PP. We describe the property range in PP, and explore the molecular, morphological, and other factors that give PP its versatility in end-use properties. This discussion relates primarily to molded or nonoriented parts; intentionally oriented parts, such as fibers and films, are represented as a special case. Also, while significant property improvements, particularly in stiffness and use temperature, may be achieved by the addition of fillers or reinforcing fibers to PP, that subject is covered in Chapter 5.

6.2   Typical End-Use Properties of Unoriented PP

Each of the three principal types of PP, homopolymers, random copolymers, and impact (or heterophasic) copolymers, have evolved their own set of characteristic properties to serve their associated markets. The homopolymers represent the simplest structures and narrowest range of properties, while the impact copolymers exhibit a rapidly growing range of structures, properties, and complexities of manufacture.

Just a few key properties define the major characteristics for the designer of a functional part:

- Modulus,
- tensile strength,
- impact strength,
- maximum use temperature, and
- hardness.

With these properties, and the melt flow rate to determine processability, the vast majority of mechanical parts may be designed and fabricated. It is in just these areas that PP is extremely versatile, providing a wide selection. The key properties of typical PP grades appear in Table 6.1 [1]. The polymers listed represent the ranges of properties achievable in the different commercial types of PP, including the high alloy copolymers [2]. The modulus range,

Table 6.1 Properties of Typical Polypropylenes

Polypropylene type	Flexural modulus, MPa	Melt flow rate, g/10 min	Notched Izod impact, J/m	Heat defl. temp. at 66 psi, °C	Hardness, Rockwell R
Homopolymer	2400	20			
	2000	20	32	124	104
	1895	40	32	121	100
	1895	12	32	118	105
	1790	2	140	110	100
	1720	4	43	97	99
	1720	20	32	100	104
	1655	12	27	99	97
	1585	100			
	1585	0.5	160	93	95
	1515	70		90	
	1480	1.5	70	87	
	1310	35	32	90	98
Random copolymer	1515	3	37	102	95
	1135	25		98	94
	1135	35	43	87	80
	1135	10	54	91	88
	965	1	80	90	80
	895	25	37	85	80
	860	10	37	85	80
	825	6	48	85	80
	690	2.5	85	70	65
	585	7	80	65	65
	495	6			
Impact copolymer	1310	35	70	90	85
	1310	4	135	81	82
	1240	0.5	540	90	75
	1170	50	55	117	90
	1035	4	540	75	65
	1000	11	135	77	72
	965	2	650	72	61
	965	20	185	77	67
	965	30	55	80	80
	930	6	650	90	70
	860	16	650	80	40
	860	1	650	79	55
	790	20	540	85	65
High alloy copolymer	550	0.8			
	540	10			
	390	10			
	380	0.9			
	150	0.8			
	130	10			
	90	0.8			

Sources: D.A.T.A. Business Publishing [1]; Montell Polyolefins [2]

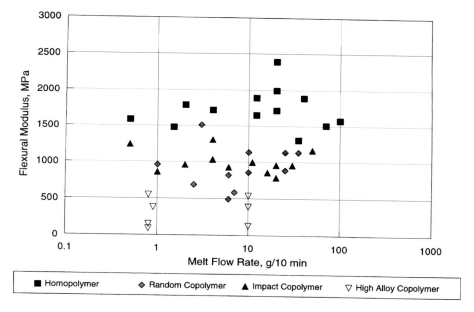

Figure 6.1   Stiffness of commercial PPs listed in Table 6.1. Sources: D.A.T.A. Business Publishing [1], Montell Polyolefins [2]

illustrated in Fig. 6.1, clearly shows the differences among the PP polymer types. Modulus values lower than homopolymers are observed in random and impact copolymers. Although high modulus values would be desirable in those types, the lower values result from a need to compromise on stiffness to enhance other properties, namely clarity and low temperature impact strength, respectively. In Fig. 6.2, the improved toughness of the impact polymers is evident. The extremely low modulus levels achieved with the recently developed high alloy copolymers are described further in Section 6.3.4.

Because the melting point of PP is well above the boiling point of water, as indicated by the heat deflection temperature (HDT) values, it is widely used in applications requiring exposure to hot aqueous liquids, including steam- sterilized medical goods. It is also apparent from these data that grades providing these capabilities are available in a wide range of MFRs, giving PP users a broad range of processing alternatives. Highly substituted random copolymers were developed primarily to improve the optical properties of PP and to lower the melting point.

The resistance of PP to chemicals is legendary, and is well documented elsewhere [3]. It is one of the principal reasons automobile batteries are now constructed of PP. This property has also translated into exceptional stain resistance, of great value in household goods, particularly carpeting, upholstery, food storage containers, and lawn furniture.

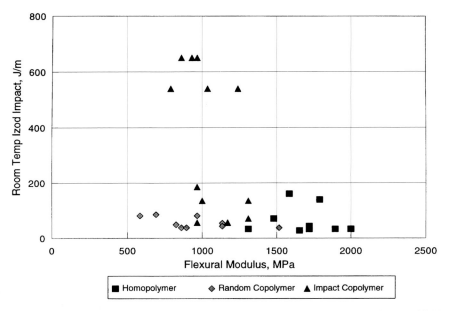

Figure 6.2   Impact strengths of commercial PPs, from Table 6.1. Sources: D.A.T.A. Business Publishing [1], Montell Polyolefins

6.3   Influences on End-Use Properties

The factors influencing the end-use properties of PP are those we have been discussing in the last several chapters: after the catalyst, the primary contributing factors are the polymer structure and morphology. These overall relationships are presented schematically in Fig. 6.3. The relationship between polymer structure and morphology is discussed in Chapter 3 in some detail; here we focus more on the factors determining the end-use properties. In addition to the polymer structure and morphology, the process conditions and additives have roles, as well. For example, cooling rate and nucleation can influence crystallinity substantially. The properties of essentially unoriented items are determined by these factors. Of course, the orientation process has a major effect on the properties of oriented items, which are discussed in Section 6.4. Similarly, the properties of filled products are largely determined by the modifiers, as described in Chapter 5.

6.3.1   Homopolymers

The principal end-use properties of PP homopolymers are good rigidity and high thermal resistance, with limited impact resistance at low temperature. The main structural factors affecting these properties are isotacticity, molecular weight, and MW distribution, mostly through their influence on crystallinity.

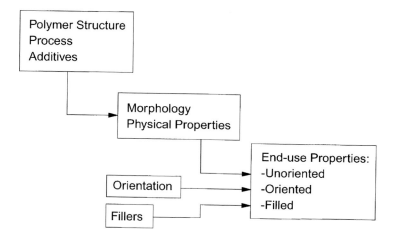

Figure 6.3   Factors influencing end-use properties

The effects of the isotactic level are very strong, as it dictates the basic tendency for, and capability of, the polymer to crystallize. This is the simplest and most fundamental of the morphology-end use property relationships [4]. Figure 6.4 illustrates the effects of tacticity on modulus and impact, at constant MFR. The property changes are primarily due to changes in crystallinity. Higher crystallinity raises the values of a group of related properties: modulus, upper use temperature, hardness, barrier, and chemical resistance, while lowering impact strength and elongation. Any of the variables that increase crystallinity can be expected to

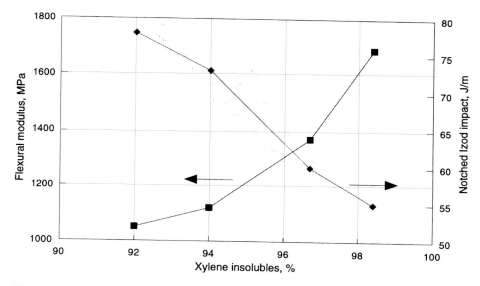

Figure 6.4   Effects of tacticity (xylene insolubles) on stiffness and impact. Homopolymer, MFR = 2. Source: Montell Polyolefins

influence the end-use properties in a similar manner. Thus, lower MW, broader MWD, or high crystallization temperature, either from slower cooling rates or nucleation, can all increase the crystallinity and the values of modulus and related properties.

Molecular weight is also a strong contributor to the definition of properties. While low MW has a positive effect on crystallinity, by allowing the chains to rearrange more rapidly and thus create more perfect crystals, that is not a major response. The change in flexural modulus with MFR, the inverse of MW, in Fig. 6.1 is minimal. More significant than the crystallinity effect, lower MW inserts more chain ends into the structure, resulting in fewer chains completely integrated into the crystal to sustain stress during tensile loading, causing failure at lower elongation in both tensile and impact tests. Table 6.2 illustrates the drop in impact strength with increasing MFR (decreasing MW) for homopolymers and impact copolymers. The result is quite dramatic; just a sixfold increase in MFR can bring the impact strength of a good impact copolymer down to that of a homopolymer. This relationship illustrates the difficulty in reaching one of the most challenging goals with PP (as well as other plastics): maintaining good toughness while increasing the output rate in the fabrication process. A minor increase in MFR quickly results in a significant loss in impact, tensile strength, tensile elongation, or puncture resistance, particularly when one of those properties is already near the limit of acceptability.

To the degree that (unintentional) orientation is involved in the property of interest, as in injection molded parts, higher MW polymers cause significant increases in the amount of orientation that results from normal melt processing. The increase in impact strength with MW has been partly attributed to the orientation molded into the notch of the test bar. Both suppliers and users of PP must remain aware of the degree to which orientation contributes to the increased modulus or other properties in the test specimen, and, perhaps more important, whether orientation is present or desired in the fabricated part. As the orientation from flow is usually unidirectional, weakness in the direction across the flow can easily result under some conditions. In any event, the translation from laboratory measurements to commercial products requires considerable understanding of the factors active in each.

Molecular weight distribution (MWD) also affects crystallinity and the modulus-related properties. Broad MWD PP displays higher crystallinity than normal MWD samples, and gives higher orientation as well. Consequently, injection molded samples are higher in

Table 6.2 Molecular Weight Effect on Impact Strength

Melt flow rate	Izod impact strength, J/m	
	Homopolymer	Impact copolymer (15% rubber)
0.3	150	800
1	110	600
2.5	55	180
6	45	110
12	35	75
35	25	35

Source: Montell Polyolefins

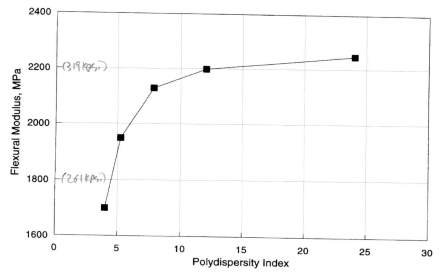

Figure 6.5   Effect of MWD on stiffness. Homopolymer, MFR = 25, xylene insolubles = 98%. Source: Montell Polyolefins

modulus from both causes [5]. An illustration of the effect of MWD on modulus, which is quite strong at the low end of the polydispersity range, appears in Fig. 6.5. Polydispersity Index (PI), a useful measure of MWD based on rheology, is described in Section 6.5.3.

It is possible to obtain some variation in the MWD with the different catalysts, but the change in MWD within one catalyst system is rather small, usually less than one unit of PI. Considerable broadening of MW may be obtained by polymerizing widely different MWs in separate reactor stages, but even that approach is limited by the degree to which the different viscosities may be homogenized in later extrusion or molding operations.

It is possible to achieve narrow MWD outside of the reactor by degrading with peroxide. This technique has been used for many years to provide narrow MWD materials, also known as "controlled rheology" (CR) polymers, principally for the fibers business, and is described in Section 4.5.3.

Nucleation can increase crystallinity several percent. Nucleators cause the crystallization to begin at a higher temperature (lower undercooling), with more initiation sites, leading to both more rapid development and higher levels of crystallinity in more numerous and, therefore, smaller, spherulites. Such spherulites will be more crystalline and higher melting.

Consequently, nucleators are particularly useful when an increase in stiffness, upper use temperature, or improved optical properties are desired for the final applications. A major effect on optical properties is to reduce the dimensions of the surface irregularities caused by the spherulitic growth at the free surface, such as the inside of a blow molded bottle. Reduction in the internal irregularities between and within spherulites also contributes to improved opticals, mostly by creating one type of spherulite instead of mixed types. In particular, the elimination of the highly birefringent β-type spherulites can reduce the internally scattered light.

6.3.2   Random Copolymers

Random copolymers are controlled by the same three factors as homopolymers: tacticity, MW, and MWD. However, the introduction of a comonomer presents an additional variable for determining the usual end-use properties and gives new importance to optical properties. The principal reason for making random copolymer is improved optics.

The introduction of a comonomer into the polymeric chain creates a discontinuity that sharply reduces the crystallization tendency, comparable to a reduction in stereoregularity in homopolymers. The results are a reduction in the rate of crystallization, a lower level of crystallinity, and a reduction in the melting point, all related to the less perfect structure of the chains. The resulting less perfect crystals have a lower density than homopolymer, and thus exhibit a lower refractive index. The difference in refractive index between the crystal and amorphous phases is, therefore, lower, and light is not refracted as readily. The result is lower haze and higher clarity.

Perhaps more important is that the rate of cooling at which the mesomorphic (smectic) phase may be generated is lower for the random copolymers than for homopolymers. Well-quenched films of random copolymers are distinctly clearer than those of homopolymers.

The optical properties of these copolymers may be enhanced further with the use of nucleating agents known as clarifiers. These special organic compounds, besides nucleating the small spherulites desired for improved clarity, also are free of inorganic residues that would contribute to the diffraction that shows up as haze. Thus, they provide the best combination of features for the optical improvement of PP and are widely used in moldings for household applications. The improved optical performance achieved with clarifiers is shown in Table 6.3 [6]. However, clarifiers are somewhat expensive, and some are temperature sensitive.

The second reason for producing random copolymers is to provide a lower melting point, usually for the heat-sealable layer on a film. The reduction in melting point is mainly related to the comonomer content, as illustrated in Fig. 6.6 for ethylene and butene, the most common comonomers with propylene.

Unfortunately, the comonomer behavior is somewhat less ideal than the term "random" suggests. In typical random copolymerizations, the chains exhibit distributions of comonomer content and degree of randomness. Depending on the comonomer reactivity ratio relative to propylene, the polymerization conditions, and the catalytic system used, the distribution of comonomer units along the chains can vary from purely random to alternating segments of homopolymer "blocks," and everything in between. In addition to the desired material (moderate comonomer content, low melting, but crystalline and, therefore, not

Table 6.3 Optical Effects of Clarifiers

Polypropylene type	Haze of 1.2 mm (50 mil) plaque, %	
	No clarifier	Clarified
Homopolymer	60–65	10–15
Random copolymer	40–45	8–12

Source: Milliken & Co. [6]

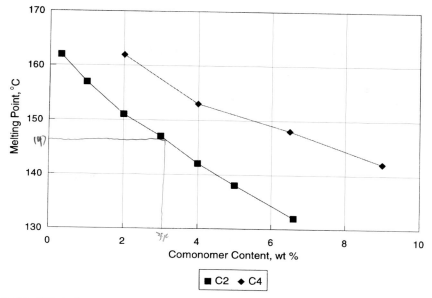

Figure 6.6   Effect of comonomer on random copolymer melting point. Source: Montell Polyolefins

soluble in hot solvent), some high comonomer content, highly random molecules would be made which would have very low melting points and which would be soluble in hot solvent. The fraction exhibiting high comonomer content but low randomness is also highly soluble, but this does not contribute to a lower melting temperature. This becomes a concern because the amount of extractables is a critical factor for regulatory acceptance in food contact applications.

The behavior of the most common comonomers, ethylene and butene, are quite different in this respect. Ethylene, while very effective at melting point depression, also generates a higher level of extractables than does butene. A better balance between the lower melting temperature and a reduction of the extractables is found with an appropriate comonomer combination, where the key advantages of each comonomer can be retained and attractive modification is achieved, as indicated in Fig. 6.7.

It is also worth noting that metallocene catalysts are outstanding in their ability to produce copolymers with very narrow ranges of MW and composition. The difficulties above would be negligible with the use of metallocenes, which are discussed in Section 12.2.

6.3.3   Impact (Heterophasic) Copolymers

The main reason for the development of PP heterophasic copolymers is the improvement in the low-temperature impact strength; thus, the term "impact" copolymers. This is achieved with a polymer structure where an elastomeric phase, usually ethylene-propylene copolymer rubber (EPR), is dispersed uniformly within the PP homopolymer matrix. Although prepared

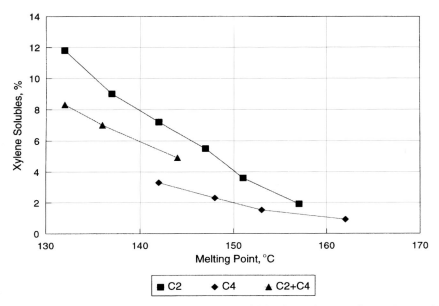

Figure 6.7   Use of combined termonomers to control solubles in random copolymer. Source: Montell Polyolefins

initially by external compounding, reactor-generated impact copolymers were rapidly commercialized in the 1960s. The introduction of the elastomeric component, characterized by a very low modulus, while increasing the impact strength, causes a lowering of the product stiffness, hardness, and tensile strength, as illustrated in Fig. 6.8. As the improvement in the impact strength is related to both the amount and the particle size of the rubbery component, the best compromise between stiffness and impact turns out to be strictly related to the degree of dispersion.

The impact, or heterophasic, copolymers are rather complex; the second phase introduces numerous new factors and limitations in determining the end-use properties. The rubbery phase may vary in amount, size, and composition, in addition to having isotacticity, MW, and MWD affect its properties, as in homopolymers. However, in the dispersed phase, there are some changes: the tacticity is no longer a variable in that the rubber remains essentially amorphous. Further, outside of a desired dispersed/matrix viscosity ratio range, there would be difficulties with the particle size of the rubber, which is discussed below. Thus, while the MW is a "variable," commercial practice dictates that it fall within a range of acceptable values for any given type. Also, MW distribution of the dispersed phase has little influence on the overall resin behavior, so it becomes less important. Comonomer content, however, is an important variable regarding end-use properties.

In impact copolymers (or compounded rubber-toughened PP), the toughening mechanism is related to the generation of many small crazes and the interruption of a propagating fracture in the matrix. When the rubber particles are of the proper size, about 0.4 μm in PP, they initiate many subcritical crazes that absorb significant energy during the stressing of PP and also act to interrupt the crazes before fracture occurs.

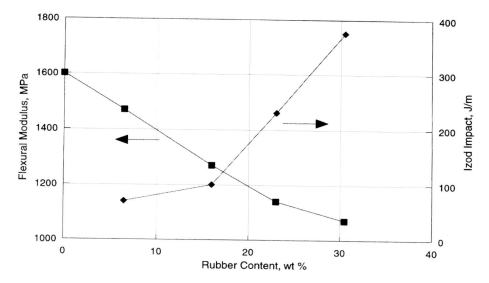

Figure 6.8   Effect of EPR dispersed in homopolymer matrix on stiffness and impact. Source: Montell Polyolefins

This mechanism operates above the glass transition temperature of the dispersed phase, and its effectiveness is determined by the nature of the rubbery phase, as well as by its amount, size, and distribution within the matrix. Section 5.3 describes the particulars of this mechanism in more detail, and Section 3.5 describes morphological details.

The nature of the rubber determines the deformation behavior of the dispersed particles and their ability to absorb and redistribute the energy, while the concentration and particle size (and thus the number of particles) define the probability of both initiating crazes and intercepting the fracture line.

The MW of the EPR phase is crucial to controlling the size of the rubber particles in the matrix. The right ratio between the viscosities of the two phases is essential to transferring the shearing force through the continuous phase for dispersing the rubber during compounding or for preventing the reactor-based rubber particles from agglomerating during downstream processing. Figure 6.9 shows the sharp effect of the rubber phase viscosity on impact at constant matrix viscosity for reactor compositions. Note that the Izod and drop weight impact results respond differently. Thus, the intended application for the part must be considered to determine which test to apply. In general, parts with large unsupported panels relate better to the drop weight method, while complex structural parts will reflect more the behavior of the Izod test.

The composition of the EPR phase plays three important roles in the development of good impact strength:

1.   Glass transition temperature of the rubber,
2.   adhesion between rubber and matrix, and
3.   amount of crystalline polyethylene and shrinkage of the rubber phase during cooling.

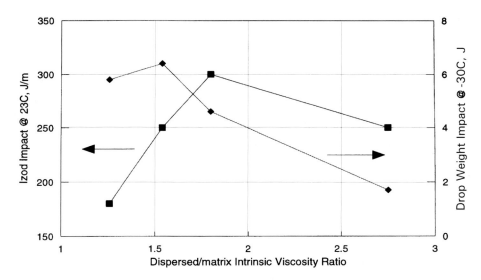

Figure 6.9   Effect of EPR viscosity on impact. Homopolymer, I.V. $= 1.9$, EPR content $= 15\%$. Source: Montell Polyolefins

At high propylene content, the T_g of the EPR is high, and the impact improvement is limited. As the ethylene content increases, the T_g drops, and impact improves. At fairly high ethylene levels, PE crystallinity begins to appear within the rubber phase. As a consequence, the rubber particle shrinks more during cooling. This effect reduces stress that otherwise would build up in the matrix, and the tendency to give a stress-whitening effect is reduced, as described in more detail below. The adhesion and impact values reach a maximum. At still higher ethylene content, the rubber becomes stiffer, the dissimilarity between the high-ethylene EPR and the PP matrix increases, adhesion is lost, and impact falls. The maximum in impact occurs at about 50% to 60% C_2 in the EPR rubber, and falls off rapidly on either side [7].

6.3.3.1   Blush Resistance

One advantage of a highly ethylene-rich elastomeric component is the reduction of the stress-whitening phenomenon, or blushing, that results from a small deformation of the part. The blushing is caused by the formation of crazes or voids during deformation, and by the consequent light diffraction. When a heterophasic copolymer melt is cooled, the crystallization of the matrix and the associated volume contraction, which is substantially greater than that of the amorphous rubber, creates a compressive stress on the dispersed phase and a comparable tensile stress in the matrix. Consequently, relatively minor deformations raise the tensile stress to the point where crazes form in the matrix.

If an ethylene-rich rubber is used with sufficient ethylene to cause some PE crystallization, the volume contraction of the rubbery particles during cooling increases and approaches that of the matrix. This reduces the level of frozen-in stresses and retards the generation of crazes; greater deformation of the part without blushing is then possible. The PE has sufficiently low T_g that impact is not compromised. As the PE tends to gather in the center of the rubber particles, relatively high concentrations are possible without affecting adhesion. The specific morphologies are illustrated in Section 3.5.5.

The addition of a crystalline PE phase has been widely used to eliminate the stress-whitening behavior in impact copolymers through a third phase PE polymerization or via addition of HDPE during compounding. In either case, the structure of the two-component dispersed phase, and the relative amounts of PE and EPR, must be accurately defined to achieve appropriate distribution during downstream operations. It is also important to avoid reaching a composition that would cause a complete detensioning or even development of tensile stress in the rubber, which would result in a reduction of adhesion at the matrix–elastomer interface, with a dramatic decrease in impact resistance.

6.3.4 High Alloy Copolymers

The amount of rubber that may be included in a reactor-generated impact copolymer is strongly dependent on the catalyst and process used. While conventional processes may reach about 50% rubber, later fourth generation catalysts and processes have made possible far higher rubber contents. Catalysts with long-lived activity and the capability of providing PP particles with significantly higher porosities permit the polymerization of much higher rubber content, contained within the particle, without encountering the usual difficulties with reactor fouling and plugging. This containment of the reaction within the protective matrix shell is referred to as the "reactor granule" technology [8]. Rubber content of 70% has been achieved commercially in these materials, which we have called "high alloy copolymers," described further in Section 7.1.8.2. It has been possible to generate cocontinuous phases with the high alloy copolymers, which results in flexural modulus values below 100 MPa and extreme levels of toughness. The toughness of these materials is so high that normal impact measurements are no longer informative. Puncture and tear resistance, and other application-related measures of the toughness, are more appropriate.

The crystallization behavior and toughness of the high alloy copolymers allow processing into films using the air-quenched bubble process [9], or calendering [10], previously impossible with PP. The same control of phase viscosities and interfacial adhesion are necessary to obtain a finely divided rubber phase, in this case cocontinuous layers, as described in Section 3.5.6.

Although conventional PP is not suitable, high alloy copolymers appear well suited for use in biohazard bags, diaper backing films, industrial bags, sheet for roofing and geomembranes, and medical tubing and bags because of the new combinations and exceptional levels of properties offered.

6.4 Properties of Oriented PP

While the variations in the properties of unoriented PP depend strongly on the molecular and morphological characteristics, which has led to the variety of copolymers offered, oriented PP is usually manufactured from homopolymer, and properties depend more on the orientation process than the polymer. Modifications in polymers are most often aimed at improvements in

Table 6.4 Properties of Oriented Fibers

Property	Units	PP	Nylon	Polyester
Melting point	°C	165	260	240
Specific gravity		0.9	1.14	1.4
Tenacity	gpd	6–7.5[a]	6.8–8.6	6–7
Elongation	%	21–28	18–28	9–11
Modulus	gpd	27[a]	38	84
Shrinkage, 100 °C	%	5.5	9.7	8.4
Moisture absorption	%	0.03	4.5	0.4

[a] 1 gpd (gram per denier) = 11.7 kpsi or 81 MPa for PP
Source: Montell Polyolefins [12]

processability, the primary example being the narrow MWD polymers for fine denier fiber spinning. Some properties of oriented items are presented below to provide a general view of the magnitude of the orientation effects; any investigation into specific properties should be preceded by a thorough study of the processes involved.

Some typical property ranges for oriented fibers appear in Table 6.4, as compared to nylon and polyester. The low melting point and inability to dye PP are the major differences that have kept it out of traditional apparel and other high-style fabric applications. Conversely, where PP is suitable, its low cost causes immediate dominance of the application.

The properties of biaxially oriented PP film (BOPP) appear in Table 6.5, along with those of other pertinent films. The balance of properties in the machine and cross directions in BOPP films are somewhat different between the bubble and tenter processes. The tenter process uses higher orientation in the cross direction, and properties in that direction are at the high end of the range indicated, while the MD properties will lie at the lower end. The properties from the bubble films are more balanced and will be closer to the center.

In addition to providing excellent levels of strength and stiffness, the BOPP moisture barrier is outstanding and has been particularly attractive to the food packaging industry. On the other hand, oxygen barrier is virtually nonexistent, so it is provided by coating the film with poly(vinylidene chloride) or metallizing the film, which can reduce the transmission rate about 100-fold.

6.5   Property Measurements and Relationships

Brief descriptions of the methods for determining the some of the more important properties of PP follow. For more detailed information, ref. 7 is recommended. Procedure is not mentioned in these descriptions, but it is critical to obtaining reliable results.

6.5.1   Tacticity

The simplest means of estimating the tacticity of homopolymer PP is hot solvent extraction, usually with heptane or xylene. The insoluble portion is essentially isotactic PP. The original work by Natta used fractionation to differentiate among isotactic, "stereoblock," and atactic

Table 6.5 Properties of Films

Property	ASTM	Units	LDPE	HDPE	Unoriented PP	Biaxially oriented PP	Polyester	EVOH
Tensile strength	D-822	MPa (kpsi)	17–24 (2.5–3.5)	34–69 (5–10)	40–60 (6–9)	140–240 (20–35)	170–210 (25–30)	—
Modulus	D-822	MPa (kpsi)	140–210 (20–30)	550–1250 (80–180)	690–960 (100–140)	1720–3100 (250–450)	3600–4000 (520–580)	—
Elongation	D-822	%	300–600	—	400–800	50–130	120–140	—
Tear strength	D-1922	N/mm (g/mil)	80–160 (200–400)	—	16–160 (40–400)	1.5–2 (4–6)	200[a] (550)[a]	—
Haze	D-1003	%	5–8	High	1–4	1–4	—	—
MVTR	E-96	$\frac{g \cdot mil}{100\ in^2 \cdot d}$	1.2	0.3	0.7	0.3	1–3	2.3
O_2 trans. rate	D-1434	$\frac{cc \cdot mil}{100\ in^2 \cdot d \cdot atm}$	450	150	240	160	5–7	0.08

[a] Graves Tear, ASTM D-1004

Source: TAPPI Press [13]

portions. The Isotactic Index (II), a term widely used in the industry, is the insoluble fraction after extraction with boiling heptane.

The most direct measure of tacticity is made with ^{13}C NMR, wherein the number of meso (same side, isotactic) and racemic (opposite side, syndiotactic) placements of the methyl groups may be measured. Also, NMR is very effective at determining the distributions of comonomers in copolymers.

6.5.2   Molecular Weight

Molecular weight is reflected inversely in the melt flow rate (MFR), a simple and widely used measure of melt viscosity, which is sharply dependent on MW. A more fundamental measurements is intrinsic viscosity (IV, or η), based on solution viscosity; IV is also called the limiting viscosity number (LVN).

6.5.3   Molecular Weight Distribution

A fundamental measure of MWD is gel permeation chromatography, currently known as size exclusion chromatography, which responds to the physical size of the different molecules in dilute solution. In this technique, the polymer solution is passed over a porous medium from which the different sized molecules elute at different times. Assuming the column was properly calibrated, not a simple task, the curve of eluted material versus time becomes the molecular weight distribution. From that curve, it is possible to calculate the weight-average MW, M_w, and the number-average MW, M_n. The ratio of these two, M_w/M_n, the polydispersity, is a widely used term to describe MWD, although it is sometimes called Q.

Because the rheology of PP responds strongly to the MWD, a correlation between the polydispersity from gel permeation and a rheological parameter, called the polydispersity index (PI), has been established [11]. The PI is considerably easier to determine and is consequently growing in use.

6.5.4   Crystallinity

Crystallinity may be determined directly from wide angle X-ray scattering (WAXS) patterns, provided a good amorphous baseline has been established. The baseline for PP has been accepted for years, and X-ray determinations of PP crystallinity are relatively routine.

An alternative method is density, best measured in a density gradient column. This allows the measurement of density to the fourth decimal place, equivalent to 0.1% crystallinity, but requires some assumptions about the densities of crystalline and amorphous PP, as agreement on those values is not universal. These columns require careful setup and maintenance for accurate determinations.

Although differential scanning calorimetry (DSC) measurements are frequently used to measure crystallinity, the accuracy of the determination depends on the value used for heat of fusion, and freedom from odd behavior like multiple melting peaks. The discussion in Section 3.2.4.1 should indicate that caution is advised when using this technique.

Infrared and Raman spectroscopy are also useful for measuring PP crystallinity.

6.5.5   Impact Strength

Among the mechanical properties of PP, impact strength is a special case. In any tensile deformation of a plastic, it elongates to some degree, depending on the conditions. With PP, elongations of several hundred percent are normal at room temperature and slow extension rates, and much of the deformation is irreversible. As the temperature is lowered, or the extension rate is increased, the glass transition temperature is approached, where the chains are incapable of accommodating the deformation and fail in a brittle break. In that case, there is very little extension of the PP, and it is all elastic in nature; it recovers completely after failure. More important, because there is little extension, the energy is about a magnitude less than that absorbed in a ductile failure.

The impact strength of PP can be measured several ways. In the Izod test, a notched or unnotched bar is struck with a weighted pendulum, indicating the energy absorbed in the test. The Charpy test uses a similar device, but the geometry of the sample and striker are different. The limitation of these procedures is the lack of control over the striking velocity, and a maximum energy value. Consequently, relatively tough materials register at the top energy level, often without breaking the sample, which provides no discrimination among materials.

Drop weight tests may be used in a manner to overcome these objections. By varying the drop height of the weighted tup, both the amount of energy and the striking velocity may be raised to quite high levels. However, the simpler systems have no provision for measuring the energy absorbed during the fracture. Therefore, procedures to increase or decrease the drop height are employed to determine the 50% fail height. While not a direct measure of break energy, this procedure is quite effective at discriminating among materials up to high toughness levels.

Regardless of the method, there is a tendency for impact strength of PP, expressed as energy per unit thickness, to lie in one of two areas: high (ductile failure, 600 J/m Izod) or low (brittle failure, 30 J/m Izod), with an intermediate transition region where the scatter of results is high. Note this pattern in Fig. 6.1. Thus, a single test often gives only a fair indication of how close the test material might be to failing in the brittle mode. For this reason, impact tests are often run at several temperatures to locate the ductile–brittle transition temperature, with, of course, a greater expense. The ductile–brittle transition temperature is more informative than conventional impact testing because it indicates how far the sample is from brittle failure; the lower transition temperature indicates a tougher material.

6.5.6   Optical Properties

The unexciting optical properties of moderately thick sections of PP, low clarity, low gloss, and high haze, are due to multiple sources of light scattering:

- Surface irregularities,
- optical differences among spherulite types,
- optical variations within spherulites,
- difference in refractive index of crystalline and amorphous phases,
- catalyst residues,

- dispersed phases in heterophasic copolymers, and
- voids and crazes (occasionally).

In most of these instances, high crystallinity and large spherulites are the principal contributors to the scattering. Two material and two process approaches improve the optical properties of PP:

1. Reduce the perfection (density) of the crystals; make random copolymers.
2. Reduce the size and inconsistencies among spherulites; nucleate the crystals.
3. Reduce the spherulite size to a dimension below the wavelength of light, and prevent the distinct organization of spherulites; quench the polymer rapidly into polymorphic or smectic state.
4. Deform the refracting bodies into a shape that places virtually all the refracting surfaces in the same plane; biaxially orient film.

Because of the refractive index difference between the crystalline and amorphous phases, it is not reasonable to expect that the sparkling clarity of amorphous polymers like PET and PS would ever be approached by PP, but refinements in heterophasic copolymer compositions and catalyst supports offer the potential of continued improvements. Also, considering that syndiotactic PP is already showing major improvements in optical properties, further significant progress in the optical properties of PP, at least in the syndiotactic form, is likely.

References

1. International Plastics Selector, Plastics Digest, D.A.T.A. Business Publishing, 1994
2. Development Data Sheets, KS Series, Himont Inc. (Now Montell Polyolefins), 1993, Experimental Analysis Reports, KM Series, KS Series, KT Series, Himont Inc. (Now Montell Polyolefins), 1993
3. Technical brochure TL-007, "Pro-fax® Polypropylene Chemical Resistance," Himont U.S.A., Inc. (Now Montell Polyolefins), 1993
4. *Paukkeri, R., Lehtinin, A.:* Polymer 34 (1993) 4075
5. *Phillips, R.A., Hebert, G., News, J., Wolkowicz, M.:* Poly. Eng. & Sci. 34 (1994) 1731
6. Technical Brochure, "Millad® Clarifying Agents," Milliken & Co., May 1993
7. *Van der Ven, S.:* Polypropylene and Other Polyolefins, Elsevier Science Publishing Co., New York, 1990
8. *Galli, P., Haylock, J.C.:* The Reactor Granule, Polyolefins VII, SPE, Houston, 1991
9. *Giacobbe, J.:* SPE ANTEC, Detroit, MI (1992)
10. *Shah, A.:* SPE ANTEC, Montreal, Canada (1991)
11. *Zeichner, G.R., Patel, P.D.:* 2nd World Congr. of Chem. Eng., Montreal, Can., 1981
12. Private communication, L.V. Robeson, Montell Polyolefins
13. *Butler, T.I., Veazey, E.W., Eds.:* Film Extrusion Manual, TAPPI Press, Atlanta, GA 1992

Part II

Polypropylene: The Business

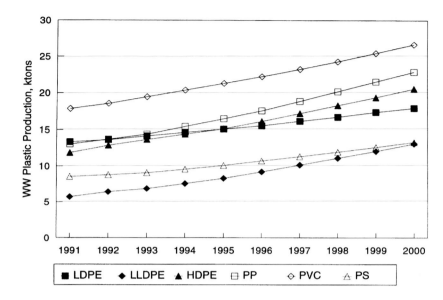

Figure 7.2   Worldwide plastics production. Source: Modern Plastics Encyclopedia [1]

Table 7.1 Worldwide Plastic Production Growth Rates, 1993–2000 (Growth Rates Compounded, %/yr)[a]

World region	PP	LDPE	LLDPE	HDPE	PS	PVC
N. America	3.8	2.2	4.1	3.4	2.9	2.2
W. Europe	5.2	1.5	5.5	4.6	3.3	2.2
Japan	3.1	2.8	7.8	3.8	3.3	2.6
Rest of Asia	11.2	5.9	11.2	12.2	9.8	8
Rest of world	16.1	7.3	20.4	10.9	11.8	8.3
Total	6.9	3.5	9.7	6.1	5.6	4.6

[a] Compound rates derived from the arithmetic rates in the source
Source: Mod. Plast. Encycl. [1]

the low starting point; those areas are consuming very little of any plastic at this time. The per capita consumption of PP follows the same pattern as all plastics, seen in Table 7.2; the developing areas consume about one-tenth that of the three major regions. In spite of the rapid growth in the consumption, the developing areas are expected to move to only about 20% of the major three in per capita consumption by the year 2000. While that does not appear to be too impressive, the effect on the distribution of production capacity is.

The expected increase in worldwide PP capacity, shown in Table 7.3, anticipates continued vigorous growth for PP [2]. However, the growth in the developing regions is even more dramatic, as shown in Fig. 7.3. From virtually nothing in 1985, capacity in the "Rest of Asia" region (excluding Japan) is expected to become the largest producing region in the world around 1998. The "Rest of the World" shows a similar growth pattern, although at a lower volume level. Significant competition can be expected from these new installations.

Table 7.2 Plastic Production, kg per Capita, 1993

World region	PP	LDPE	LLDPE	HDPE	PS	PVC	Total
N. America	10.2	9.8	7.5	13.6	7.2	12.6	61.3
W. Europe	9.7	11.2	1.87	7.8	5.3	12.1	47.7
Japan	15.7	7	5.03	8.1	10.9	16.7	63.2
Rest of Asia	1.07	0.65	0.62	0.81	0.54	1.7	5.4
Rest of world	0.94	1.95	0.87	1.15	0.92	2.63	8.2
Total	3.25	3.19	1.55	3.08	2.04	4.39	17.5

Source: Mod. Plast. Encycl. [1]

Table 7.3 Worldwide Polypropylene Capacity

World region	1994		1998		Growth rate %/yr
	Capacity ktons	% of total	Capacity ktons	% of total	
N. America	5334	26	6313	23	4.3
W. Europe	5568	27	6618	24	4.4
Japan	2649	13	2979	11	3
Rest of Asia	4250	21	7310	27	14.5
Rest of world	2691	13	4321	15	12.6
Total	20492		27541		7.7

Source: Montell USA Inc.

Although the simplification of the PP process in the mid 1980s, with the lower investment costs (Section 7.1.2.1), helped promote this proliferation of capacity, the increased availability of monomer (Section 7.1.4) was also critical to allowing this relocation to occur.

In addition to the PP capacity itself moving overseas, and the consequent loss of export business, increasing numbers of fabricated items are being manufactured in the developing countries using the newly available PP from the local producers [3]. Because of the lower labor costs in the developing nations, those fabricated goods provide even more effective competition than would unprocessed resin. Such items are being exported to the developed countries, reducing the PP demand for local manufacture. Thus, these changing patterns in world production can be expected to provide increasingly strong competition for PP producers in North America, Western Europe, and Japan.

7.1.2   Process

The early PP slurry processes used catalysts with relatively low activity and low stereo-specificity, requiring the removal of the catalyst residues and atactic PP. The complex processes also consumed considerable energy and generated numerous waste streams. Early process improvements were relatively minor and resulted in no significant changes in the process layout. The first major process change occurred when Solvay developed the "second

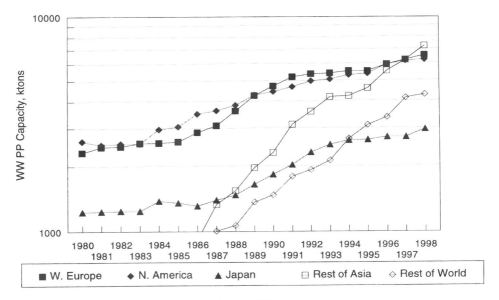

Figure 7.3   Worldwide PP capacity. Source: Montell USA Inc.

generation" catalysts in the 1970s [4]. With a fivefold increase in activity and better stereospecificity, it was then possible to eliminate the atactic removal section. However, even this was not sufficient incentive for the widespread replacement of existing plants.

With the sudden arrival of the energy crisis in the early 1970s, the costs of the monomer raw material and process energy increased dramatically. These difficulties were compounded by growing environmental concerns. A more efficient, cleaner process was urgently needed.

7.1.2.1   Third and Fourth Generation Catalysts

Ed. note: We are adopting the catalyst generation names recommended in Chapter 2, based on the major catalyst advances. The stage we call the fourth generation here has sometimes been called the "super-active third generation" in the past. See Section 2.2.4 for more details on the catalyst differences among generations.

The third generation supported catalysts of the late 1970s, quickly followed by the fourth generation, provided the answer [5]. By replacing, in the third generation, the bulk of the catalyst with an activated $MgCl_2$ support, the quantity of catalyst needed was reduced by several magnitudes. This obviated the need for removal of the catalyst residues, simplifying the plant design and operation. However, removal of atactic polymer was still necessary. The fourth generation catalysts quickly followed, providing higher activity and tacticity, and eliminating the need for atactic removal, in addition to giving better control of particle size, shape, size distribution, and porosity. This reduced catalyst consumption and cost, and considerably widened the produceable range of products. New processes were designed to take full advantage of these improved catalysts, with high productivity, low investment and operating costs, and flexible, cleaner operations.

The attractive economics and versatility of the processes using these high yield, high specificity (HYHS) catalysts led to wholesale replacement of existing plants and a worldwide expansion in production capacity in the late 1980s. Chapter 8 contains further details on PP manufacturing processes.

7.1.3   Producers

Approximately 117 producers, listed in Appendix 7.1, were manufacturing PP at about 155 locations around the world as of the end of 1994 [2]. The producers include a number of new companies, often allied with local governments. This is the result of the investment requirements being lower than a decade ago, the processes being simple enough for organizations with limited chemical experience to operate reliably, and monomer availability.

The government participation in PP manufacturing presents a special set of competitive forces. Often, the government objectives are significantly different from the economic ones we usually associate with a manufacturing venture. Export quotas, local jobs, and trade balances often take priority over the usual profit-related business approaches. In such situations, attempts to compete with price, service, and quality can have negligible effect on business success. Virtually all of the producers in Eastern Europe and China, and many in the Asian and Latin countries, have significant government participation. However, that can be expected to decrease gradually as centrally controlled economies are replaced with market-driven ones.

7.1.3.1   Specialization

Polypropylene can be treated as either a commodity or a specialty business. The commodity approach is more common among the petroleum and government-owned producing companies, which typically prefer operating at high volume and low profit margin, with low technical content and service, and low production cost. This approach has succeeded for a large part of the business, especially in the simpler injection moldings and the coarser fiber products, and is the predominant attitude in the overseas expansions. The low cost of PP relative to the other plastics has served the commodity business well (See Section 7.1.5).

The specialty approach requires that the supplier make a commitment to more research and development, more flexible production capabilities, and more complex customer relationships. The supplier's profit potential depends on the value of the benefits to the customer relative to the supplier's cost of producing and developing the product, plus the degree to which the supplier can create and maintain an exclusive position. Consequently, a supplier's commitment to a particular specialty can often be measured by the number of patents obtained in that area.

The development of new specialty PP products requires trade-offs among processability, product properties, and cost. The more complex the application, the more difficult the balance. For example, in oriented fine fibers, increased molecular weight (MW) favors high strength and few breaks in orientation, while lower MW favors extrusion at higher rates. Since the 1970s, narrow MW distribution (MWD) polymers have been providing an improved balance of these competing limitations, with significant benefits to the fiber manufacturers, and, at least initially, commanding a premium price. In this instance, the manufacturing step was a simple peroxide-assisted extrusion degradation process.

Similar premium-priced products have been developed with, for example, good low-temperature impact strength, high clarity, and special types and levels of oxidative, UV, and radiation stability. The first two examples required changes in the polymerization processes.

While the specialty concept is sound, its application to specific customer situations often had to be tailored to the particular operating conditions and processes used by the customer, the economics of the improvements in these processes, and the comparative value of the downstream product properties. Consequently, progress in these complex and often competing factors requires substantial exchange of information between the PP supplier and the customer. Thus, the establishment of dependable long-term relationships that serve the development goals without jeopardizing the independent positions of the individuals is an essential part of success. It is probably in this regard that the specialty approach differs most from the commodity approach.

Either the commodity or specialty approach can be profitable, but the continued vigorous expansion of the PP business is expected to result more from the latter approach. More details about the developing PP products can be found in Section 7.1.8 and in Chapter 12.

7.1.4   Monomer Supply

A major factor in the profitability of the PP business is the availability of low-cost propylene monomer. Many PP producers are petroleum companies, who usually have sufficient monomer to supply their PP operations internally, providing economic and logistical advantages. The ownership of PP production capacity by petroleum companies, a reasonable approximation of monomer self sufficiency, is about 70% in the U.S., 30% in Europe, and 22% in the rest of the world [3]. Although these figures are approximations, they tell us that the procurement and price of monomer is a much more important factor outside of North America.

There are two main sources of propylene: co-production with ethylene, and separation from gasoline cracker streams in petroleum refineries. The quantity of propylene co-produced with the ethylene depends sharply on the cracker feed; the heavier feeds give about 0.5 lb propylene per lb ethylene, while ethane, the lightest feed, gives virtually no propylene. In the U.S., the average propylene/ethylene ratio has gradually moved from about 0.2 twenty years ago to near 0.3 today, making propylene slightly more readily available [6]. Meanwhile, the price advantage of propylene over ethylene has moved from zero to about 6 cents/lb, as seen in Fig. 7.4.

Ethylene crackers are built to satisfy the ethylene demand, and the resulting co-production provides most of the propylene needed; the remainder comes from refinery streams. The refinery represents about one-half of the source of propylene in the U.S., and about 20% in the rest of the world [7, 2]. As part of the processes for producing gasoline, large quantities of propylene are produced. Much of this remains in the refinery stream and is consumed for its fuel value, either within the refinery operation or as a component of gasoline. However, about half of it is removed and purified by distillation to supplement the ethylene co-product source. Thus, unlike ethylene, there is a substantial pool of crude propylene available for the cost of separating it from the refinery stream, and a low-value fuel alternative use, both of which tend to keep the price lower than ethylene. The only alternative use for ethylene is in chemicals, primarily for plastics. However, the pool of readily available

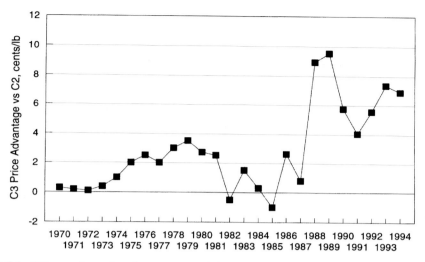

Figure 7.4   U.S. propylene price advantage over ethylene. Source: Chemical Economics Handbook [6]

refinery propylene in the Gulf coast area had dropped to the point in 1995 where the price advantage over ethylene mentioned in the previous paragraph could easily begin to diminish instead of continuing its rise [2].

A third source of propylene is the dehydrogenation of propane. In 1994, "dehy" accounted for about 1.5% of the world capacity for propylene, and significant expansions are expected during this decade [2]. Although the economics of dehy cannot compete directly with propylene co-produced with ethylene, it is attractive in special situations. Because propylene is costly to ship, especially over land, very different economics can exist in adjacent regions. Where there is a surplus of propane, with little alternative fuel use, dehy can provide added value to the propane. Also, because the co-production of propylene is dominated in supply and price by ethylene production, a dehy plant provides some insulation from the fluctuations from the ethylene market. This is especially true when a large captive propylene consumption exists, as with major PP producers. Because of the lower availability of refinery propylene and the supply cushion it provides, dehy installations are found to be more attractive outside of the U.S. The first units were started up in 1990. As more experience is gained, the economics are likely to improve, but dehy is not expected to become a major source of propylene. Commercial dehydrogenation technologies are offered by ABB Lummus (Catofin process) and UOP (Oleflex process), and Mobil is considering licensing their Maxofin process, in development at press time.

Propylene is consumed in three grades: refinery, chemical, and polymerization. Each higher grade requires more careful distillation to achieve higher propylene concentration and to remove compounds harmful to the polymerization. Propane is usually the major inert component. More details on monomer specifications are discussed in Chapter 8.

Following the installation of major oil refineries in the Asian and Latin sections of the world, the expansion of capacity for ethylene, and consequently propylene, has allowed the installation of PE and PP plants in those areas. Table 7.4 shows the expected growth of propylene capacities in the world, with the most rapid expansion occurring in the developing areas [6].

Table 7.4 Worldwide Polypropylene Capacity

World region	1992		1997		Growth rate %/yr
	Capacity ktons	% of total	Capacity ktons	% of total	
N. America	13910	34	15340	31	2
W. Europe	12207	29	13163	26	1.5
Japan	4860	12	5800	12	3.6
Rest of Asia	4670	11	6705	14	7.5
Rest of world	5864	14	8359	17	7.3
Total	41511		49367		3.5

Source: Chem. Econ. Hbk. [3]

Both ethylene and propylene demands are driven by the equivalent polymers, which consume about one-half of the monomer. Beyond PP, merchant propylene is used for several chemicals, as shown in Table 7.5.

7.1.5   Economics

The profitability of PP manufacture has varied greatly over the years. Polypropylene is one of the cyclic businesses where good profits lead to overbuilding of capacity, followed by fierce competition and lower profits, eventual reduction in capacity buildup, and, thus, a return to better profitability. Figure 7.5 traces the homopolymer PP price and monomer cost in the United States since 1970 [3]. Prior to the first energy crisis in 1973, monomer cost was a very small part of PP selling price. Since 1973, energy costs have risen substantially, and with it, propylene cost. Roughly half of the current propylene cost is due to the cost of the energy contained in it, or its equivalent fuel value. It is evident from this graph how dramatically the oil crisis, and the resulting increase in energy costs, affected the economics of PP production.
   The U.S. PP profit margin (homopolymer PP price less propylene price) appears in Fig. 7.6, which shows how profitability has varied over the last 25 years. Except for the major

Table 7.5 Worldwide Propylene Uses

Use	1992 Consumption, million tons	% of total
PP	16.7	48
Acrylonitrile	4.5	13
Oxo chemicals	3.1	9
Propylene oxide	2.8	8
Cumene	2.4	7
Isopropyl alcohol	1.5	4
Polygas chemicals	1.4	4
Other	2.5	7
Total	34.9	

Source: Chem. Econ. Hbk. [3]

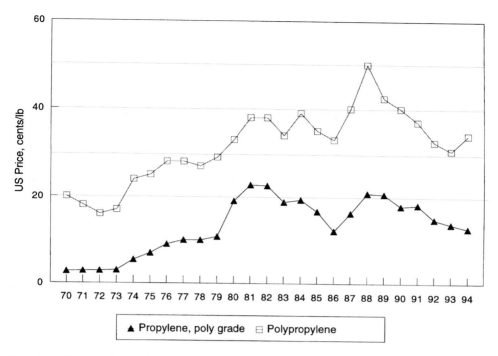

Figure 7.5   U.S. propylene and PP prices. Sources: Chemical Economics Handbook [6], Montell USA Inc.

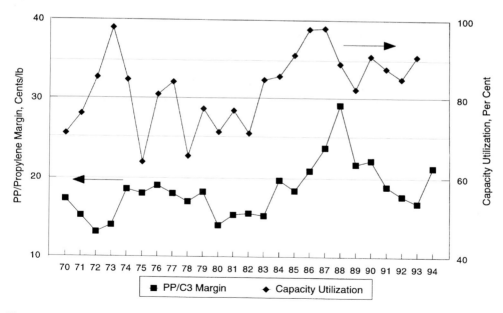

Figure 7.6   Polypropylene margin and capacity utilization. Sources: Chemical Economics Handbook [6], Montell USA Inc., SPI

Table 7.6 U.S. PP Price Advantage

Competitive resin	PP Volumetric price advantage, cents/cu. in.	
	1983 to 1986	1990 to 1993
HDPE	− 0.1 to + 0.2	+ 0.15 to + 0.3
PS	− 0.1 to + 0.5	+ 0.15 to + 0.5
PVC	+ 0.05 to + 0.4	+ 0.5 to + 0.8
Average	0.14	0.4

Source: Phillip Townsend Associates, Inc. [8]

spike around 1988, when PP was in very short supply, the margin has generally been in the 15 cents/lb to 20 cents/lb range, with no clear long-term trend. In 1994 and 1995, higher margins were experienced, but are expected to recede as the market enters the next phase of the cycle.

The profit margin is driven, as basic economics suggest, by the demand/supply balance, which also appears in Fig. 7.6. The profit margin roughly tracks the capacity utilization from its low point in the early 1980s, up to the very short supply in the late 1980s, and drops back when the supply crunch is relieved in the 1990s. The very tight supply of the early 1970s did not result in a profit increase because price controls were in effect at that time. Although we have only shown the experience in the U.S., the margins in Europe have followed a very similar pattern [8].

In competition with the other major plastics, PP has usually been the least expensive on a volume basis (cents/cu. in.), although the differences have varied considerably over time and among different regions. In the United States, as seen in Table 7.6, PP has had an advantage of 0.2 cents/cu. in. to 0.7 cents/cu. in. over HDPE, PS, and PVC during the 1990s, which is higher than that of the early 1980s by about 0.3 cents/cu. in. [8]. Considering that the average volumetric price for these commodities has been around 1.5 cents/cu. in. to 2 cents/cu. in., PP has been sold at a 15% to 20% more competitive price during this decade. The 6-cent propylene monomer advantage over ethylene mentioned in Section 7.1.4 would account for 0.2 cents/cu. in. of the PP advantage over HDPE. This illustrates the importance of monomer price to the PP business. In this case, it helps sustain the growth by providing a resin that is more competitive.

7.1.6   Conventional PP Products

7.1.6.1   *Properties*

As described in Chapter 1, the PP products include homopolymers, random copolymers, and impact copolymers. The property range of PP was established early in its history, and only evolved gradually until the 1980s. For example, good molding PPs were established in the late 1950s; the formulations and properties have remained essentially the same since. Early developments also provided resistance to whitening (blush resistance), clarity, oxidative and UV stability, and a wide range of desirable properties in filled PPs.

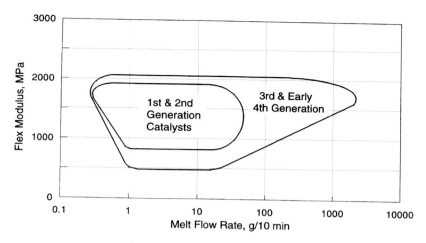

Figure 7.7   Growth of PP property envelope. Source: Montell Polyolefins

Low temperature impact strength was provided initially through physical mixtures with rubber, and some of the more demanding applications are still provided that way today. It wasn't until the late 1960s that producers learned how to polymerize the rubber phase in impact copolymers, and the effectiveness of that technique has varied among suppliers. Those able to produce the product reliably generated valuable properties at a low cost.

When the third and fourth generation high activity, high stereospecificity supported catalysts arrived after 1980, a significant expansion in the PP property envelope occurred, illustrated in Fig. 7.7 [9]. Higher stereospecificity allowed stiffness to increase, or the inclusion of higher levels of rubber allowed stiffness to decrease. Of course, the object of the higher rubber content was ductility at a lower temperature, not just lower stiffness. The increase in melt flow rate was possible due to greater flexibility in polymerization and because the spherical product could by-pass the extrusion into pellets, which was very difficult at melt flow rates above 35.

7.1.6.2   *Applications*

Over its lifetime, PP uses have grown more by replacing natural products than by displacing other plastics. Table 7.7 lists some of the significant applications captured by PP from its inception, in approximately chronological order. The vast majority of those applications remain in PP today. Once PP was found suitable for an application, it was seldom replaced.

The process of injection molding PP was immediately found to be relatively straightforward; no new techniques were needed, and the easy molding characteristics and high strength quickly placed PP in numerous applications. The development of low temperature impact PP expanded those applications, and that property still determines the boundary between PP and HDPE in most situations. One unique characteristic of PP, a very durable molded-in hinge, was employed early, but often primarily for sales promotion. More recently, it is a valuable feature of reclosable bottle caps, an expanding market for PP.

Table 7.7 Forty Years of New PP Applications

Application	Material replaced	Still in PP?
Auto fan shroud	Steel	Some
Rope, baler twine	Hemp	Yes
Chair webbing	Cotton fabric	Yes
Luggage	Leather, pressed board	Some
Interior auto trim	Natural fiber fabrics	Some
Film for overwrap	Waxed paper, cellophane	Yes
Carpet face yarn	Wool, nylon	Some
Wire coating	Rubber, PVC	Some
Molded chairs	Wood and fabric	Some
TV backs	Phenolic, FR PS	No
Film for textile bags	Cellophane, LDPE	Yes
Closures	Phenolics, aluminium	Some
Medical ware	Glass	Some
Bread wrap	Waxed paper, glassine	Some
Washing machine agitator	Porcelainized steel	Some
Ball point ink reservoir	Rubber	Yes
Medical gowns	Cotton	Yes
Drinking straws	Waxed paper	Yes
Capacitor insulation film	Paper	Some
Strapping tape	Steel	Some
Hard candy wrap	Waxed paper, Cellophane	Yes
Carpet backing	Jute	Yes
Sportswear	Cotton, polyesters	Some
Sandbags	Jute	Yes
Wheel well liners	Steel	No
Battery cases	Hard rubber	Yes
Food containers	Glass	Some
Decorative ribbon	Rayon	Yes
Dishwasher liners	Coated steel	Some
Upholstery fabric	Wool, nylon, cotton	Some
Small appliance housings	Steel	Some
Mattress covers	Cotton	Yes
Diaper liners	Cotton	Yes
Snack bags	Cellophane, glassine	Yes
Auto bumpers	Steel	Some
Candy bar wrap	Glassine, waxed paper	Some
Lawn chairs	Wood	Yes
Adhesive tape	Paper	Some
Structural foam trash containers	Steel	Yes
Molded plumbing fixtures	Brass	Some
Labels	Paper	Some
Australian currency	High grade paper	Some

Compared to the other major plastics, an added bonus for PP was the ability to orient it to form a strong fiber or thin film, a result of its crystalline nature. The technology of orientation, and the equipment and processes to achieve it, are all part of a major science within the PP business and are described in more detail in Chapter 9. A comparison of the applications for PP and the other major plastics, in Fig. 7.8, shows that oriented fibers and films currently contribute to about one-half the consumption of PP, and are unique to PP. With the exception of a small amount of oriented PS film, the other films in Fig. 7.8 are unoriented (although a minor amount of melt orientation is normally present).

Biaxially oriented PP (BOPP) films exhibit excellent moisture barrier properties due to the oriented crystal structure, and, with high clarity, it has largely replaced cellophane. The gradual replacement of cellophane with BOPP film has been a classic case of the economical material winning out in spite of significant user difficulties, which were eventually overcome.

Oriented PP fibers provide excellent strength in rope, twine, and strapping. In these areas, PP soon took firm hold. During the Vietnam War, PP slit tape replaced jute as the material for sandbags, partly due to the unreliable jute supply from Bangladesh. Soon PP slit tape had replaced jute in other major applications, such as carpet backing and other bags.

However, some difficulties arose due to the inertness of PP. The usual techniques of dying or printing fabrics to provide high style and value were not effective with fine PP fibers, and prevented early penetration of conventional fabric applications. Fibers were pigmented for color, but the fiber production process became rather complex as a result. Regardless, substantial business was enjoyed, especially when tastes for bold plaids were more fashionable in upholstery. While success was experienced in low pile commercial carpet face yarns, PP yarns did not compete well with nylon in residential carpets. However, during the 1990s,

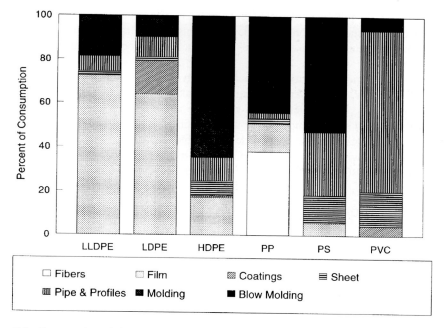

Figure 7.8   Consumption of plastics by process. Source: Modern Plastics Encyclopedia [1]

PP has regained about a 10% market share in carpet face yarn [3]. Recently, PP fiber use in apparel markets has increased due to the ability of PP fabrics to transmit moisture without absorbing it. This gives greater comfort in athletic wear, underwear, and diapers. Thus, PP fiber has found a strong position where it provides a function, but has seen less success where colors and design are important.

An application ideally suited to PP's strengths is nonwoven fabrics in medical gowns and drapes, mattress covers, and diaper liners. In these areas, PP usage grew with the nonwoven industry, especially the spunbonded and melt-blown webs, which required major investments in spinning and bonding equipment, process development, and application development over a period of many years. Aiding the process were the development of PPs with specific process and property characteristics tailored to customers' needs. Today, PP is a major component of nonwoven fabrics.

Chapters 9 and 10 cover, in more detail, current practice in the processing and applications of PP.

7.1.7   Downstream Integration

Worldwide, approximately 15% of PP capacity, excluding compounding, is consumed by in-house downstream operations, typically in oriented fibers or films [7]. Although the lure of captive use appears compelling at first, many PP producers have found the complexities of the next step so different from their normal chemical businesses that management difficulties have often occurred. In spite of those problems, the high levels of technology required for production favored the chemical companies for a while. Early producers used highly proprietary processes kept under tight secrecy, such as the bubble processes for BOPP film production used by ICI, Hercules, DuPont, and Cryovac. Few independent fabricating companies could sustain the continuing developments needed to design and operate a PP fiber or film plant, and develop the improved products and processes that were needed to remain competitive.

As the technologies of downstream operations have became simpler, less expensive, and more widely available, independent companies have taken the lead in expanding this business [10]. In recent years, the proliferation of very wide tenter frames for producing biaxially oriented PP film, and smaller and simpler units for fiber production, are good examples of downstream operations based on more widely available technology. Today, a broad range of smaller companies, without major development efforts, can purchase an economical tenter frame and enter the BOPP film business, or a smaller fiber line and produce PP fibers.

7.1.8   Recent Developments

7.1.8.1   Later Fourth Generation Catalysts

As exciting as they were, the process and product improvements from the third and early fourth generation catalysts were eclipsed by the results from the later fourth generation catalysts. To be effective, these catalysts had to exhibit several specific attributes:

- High surface area,
- high, uniform porosity,

- uniform distribution of active centers,
- adequate mechanical strength to prevent attrition, but to allow expansion during polymerization,
- high monomer diffusion rates throughout polymerization, and
- tolerance to numerous comonomers.

As a result of these attributes, it has been possible to have significantly greater control of MW, MWD, stereospecificity, particle shape and size, size distribution, porosity, and reactivity and distribution of comonomers in both the continuous and dispersed phases, as well as the amount of dispersed phase. A whole new process was designed around these capabilities [11, 12, 13], fostering another major expansion in the range of properties achievable in propylene-based polymers. With proper application of these factors, it is possible, for example, to maintain a particle surface that prevents agglomeration and sticking, while conducting a reaction within the particle involving high levels of rubbery and amorphous compositions that are normally quite sticky. Thus, it became possible to create a wider range of copolymers and heterophasic copolymers with extremely high levels of the rubbery phase. As this technology encases the later reaction within the protection of the growing polymer granule outer shell, it has been referred to as the "reactor granule" technology [11].

7.1.8.2   High Alloy Copolymers

7.1.8.2.1   Properties   The improvements in fourth generation catalysts, combined with a flexible multistage multi-monomer process, termed the "Catalloy" process by Montell, has allowed the property envelope to be expanded further, as shown in Fig. 7.9, and to other properties advantages, listed in Table 7.8. The advantages are often the achievement of a better balance of two competing properties, rather than any individual result. Properties of some molding and extrusion types of polymers from the Catalloy process appear in Table 7.9, and film and sheet resins appear in Table 7.10 [14].

One property in particular, extreme softness, now in the range of LDPE flexural modulus values, reveals the magnitude of the progress that has been achieved with this technology. The

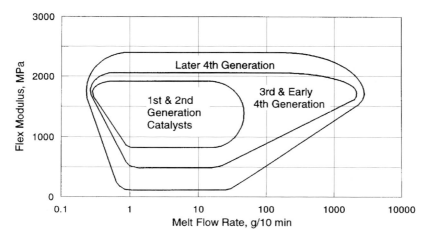

Figure 7.9   Growth of PP property envelope. Source: Montell Polyolefins

Table 7.8 Property Advantages of High Alloy Polymers

Type	Property advantages	Application
Heterophasic	V. high impact/stiffness balance	General injection molding
Heterophasic	High impact with high flow	Auto bumpers
Heterophasic	Puncture resistant, good heat seal	Roofing, pond liners
Heterophasic	Flexible, autoclavable	Medical
Random	Low melting, nonsticking	Heat seal film
Random + rubber	High impact, high clarity	Housewares
Homopolymer	Very high stiffness and heat defl. temp.	High temp. applications

Source: Montell Polyolefins

Table 7.9 Properties of Propylene-Based Molding and Extrusion Polymers from the Catalloy Process

Type	Application	Melt flow rate g/10 min (ASTM D1238)	Flex modulus 1% sec, 0.05 in/min MPa (kpsi) (ASTM D790A)	Hardness 15 sec Shore D (ASTM D2240)	Heat defl. temp. at 66 psi °C (ASTM D648)
7052XOP	Inj. molding	20	2400 (350)	114[c]	120
KM-111P	Extrusion	0.5	1900 (270)	104[c]	115
KS-011P	Inj. molding	11	540 (80)	45	62
KS-035P	Inj. molding	9	395 (57)[a]	39	57
KS-021P	Impact modif'n	0.9	380 (55)[b]	38	49
KS-059P	Inj. molding	10	130 (19)[b]	37	45

[a] 55 mm/min, D790B
[b] 0.5 in/min, D790B
[c] R scale
Source: Montell USA Inc. [14]

Table 7.10 Properties of Propylene-Based Film and Sheet Polymers from the Catalloy Process

Type	Application	Melt flow rate g/10 min (ASTM D1238)	Film thickness microns	Elongation at break MD/CD[a], % (ASTM D882)	Elemendorf tear strength MD/CD[a], g (ASTM D1922)	Dart drop impact grams (ASTM D1709)
KS-027P	Blown film	0.8	50	570/575	130/465	330
KS-063P	Blown film	1.1	50	400	530/800	710
KS-089P	Blown film	0.6	50	460/350	61/860	410

[a] Machine direction/Cross direction
Source: Montell USA Inc. [14]

soft materials are so different from conventional PPs that they can be processed into tough and clear films on air-cooled film lines [15]. No conventional PP could survive that slow cooling process without becoming brittle and hazy. In addition, sheet and film of these materials can be prepared by calendering, previously impossible with PP [16].

The polymerization and production technologies have been well established, as evidenced by operation of commercial-scale plants [17]. This business development is in the process of defining new applications, often in markets not normally served by PP but with substantial business already established.

7.1.8.2.2 Applications   Some of the products listed in Tables 7.9 and 7.10 simply extend the properties beyond those available from conventional PPs and are aimed at providing extra benefits in the normal applications, such as auto bumpers, film heat seal layers, or clear molded housewares. However, the more unusual grades provide such different properties that the markets are entirely new to PP. The soft films and sheets, in particular, are opening up new opportunities for PP:

- Biohazard bags require a combination of extreme toughness and the ability to be autoclaved.
- Diaper backing films need puncture resistance and strength, without giving a "crackling" sound when wrinkled.
- Industrial bags call for toughness and strength, with high temperature durability.
- Sheet for roofing and geomembranes must be very tough, with high puncture resistance, be easily heat sealed for large installations, and have adequate UV, chemical, and heat resistance.
- Medical tubing and bags require toughness, autoclavability, and clarity.

The information presented here is just a small sample of the types available, and the list of types, properties, and applications is expected to grow in the coming years.

7.1.8.3   High Melt Strength PP

7.1.8.3.1 Definition   Linear polymers, such as HDPE or PP, are known to be deficient in a characteristic known as melt strength. There are two regions where melt strength is important: at very high shear rates, and at virtually zero shear rates.

High melt strength (HMS) at high shear rates refers to a melt that becomes stiffer and stronger, rather than one that thins and breaks when stretched or drawn. This stiffening upon drawing is commonly called "strain- hardening." Polymers with long-chain branches, such as LDPE, exhibit good melt strength, or strain-hardening behavior. The effect of good melt strength is very evident in extrusion coating operations, where the melt is pulled down from the die opening to a very thin web at a high speed. Higher melt strength allows higher speed, with uniform coating and less narrowing of the melt web, all important to the economics of the process. Other high drawdown processes that are sensitive to melt strength are fiber spinning, thin film extrusion, and extrusion of low density foams.

In some processes, HMS is desirable at very low shear or extension rates. Extrusion of pipe, for example, is a process where the extrudate must retain its shape until it reaches the quench bath, while virtually no deformation of the melt is occurring. Similarly, the extruded

parison for blow molding and the sheet being reheated for thermoforming are examples
where resistance of the melt to deformation, or sagging under the influence of gravity, is
favored by HMS, while the shear rate is essentially zero. Both broad MWD and long-chain
branching favor HMS at low shear rates.

7.1.8.3.2   Properties   Both the high shear and low shear melt strength behaviors are
improved with long-chain branching. Montell Polyolefins has developed a post-reactor
process for creating long-chain branches in PP [18].

High melt strength PP also exhibits strong nucleating behavior. Thus, the physical
properties of HMS versions of PP are those of nucleated versions of the corresponding
starting PPs.

High melt strength PP has required the refinement of test methods for measuring the melt
strength. Beyond extensional viscosity measurements, which may be conducted on conventional extensional rheometers [19], Montell has developed a relationship for describing the
degree of branching, called a branching index [20].

7.1.8.3.3   Applications   Several types of HMS PP are being produced and sold on a
commercial scale, and numerous publications have described the behavior of this material in
extrusion coating [21], thermoforming [22], blow molding [23], and foamed articles [24].
Historically, these applications have not been large PP-consuming applications.

7.2   Patent Rights

Clearly, the patent rights to a composition-of-matter patent on crystalline PP would be of
major economic importance, and the U.S. rights were intensely contested for 29 years. We
described in Chapter 1 the patent contest in Europe between Natta and Ziegler, which Natta
won. Both men recognized the chemical and economic potential, although neither could have
imagined the scope of the business that would result. Natta prepared PP in March 1954, and
applied for his first patent, in Italy, on June 8, 1954. Ziegler also prepared PP, in June 1954,
and applied for his patent on August 3, 1954 [25]. Both men pursued their goals with
comparable determination and moved quickly to characterize the materials and mechanisms
in their work, file patent applications, and publish. In contrast, those who encountered PP
independently of Ziegler and Natta seldom conducted more than a cursory study of the PP
they produced, and their weak patent positions and sparse publications reflected that lack.

At Standard Oil of Indiana, in 1950, A. Zletz was polymerizing ethylene over molybdena
on alumina. Although initial attempts to polymerize propylene were unsuccessful, D.R.
Carmody was later able to obtain some solid polymer from propylene, but the composition
was intermediate between PE and PP. It was later determined that metathesis of propylene to
ethylene and butene was occurring. By altering the conditions to minimize metathesis, E.F.
Peters was able to obtain, in May 1953, a solid polymer more characteristic of PP. Limited
analyses were conducted, and a patent application was filed on October 15, 1954.

In June 1951, J.P. Hogan and R.L. Banks at Phillips Petroleum Co. were trying to prepare
low MW polymers of ethylene and propylene over a nickel oxide on silica-alumina catalyst to

obtain high octane gasoline fractions. In one run, in addition to the usual liquid products, they observed the presence of a white solid. Their notes recorded at the time gave no indication that they were aware of the crystalline nature of their PP. Phillips filed an initial patent application covering PP on January 27, 1953, and several related ones, including one on January 11, 1956. It was studies conducted by Natta, after 1954, testing the examples of the January 1953 application, that showed that the solid contained crystalline PP. Following the applications, work at Phillips led to the preparation and evaluation of multi-kilo quantities of PP, high-density PE, and poly(4-methyl-1-pentene). Phillips went on to dominate the HDPE production technology for many years. However, the company published little and did not lead the world into PP technology or production. That came essentially from Natta.

At DuPont, N.G. Merckling was following up the work of Fischer at BASF, described in a 1953 German patent. W.N. Baxter, with a $TiCl_4$/Grignard reagent catalyst, made a polymer containing some crystalline PP in May 1954. The X-ray diffraction pattern proving the crystalline content was included in the patent application, filed August 19, 1954.

Hercules Powder Company had an excellent opportunity to be the first to prepare crystalline PP, but hesitated a little too long. Although they had a chemist in Ziegler's lab during the summer of 1953, Hercules allowed their option on Ziegler's chemistry to lapse in late 1953, then renewed it in mid-1954. In October 1954, within a week of renewing work, E.J. Vandenberg prepared crystalline PP and went on to discover the use of hydrogen to control the MW of PP, the method generally used even today. Hercules applied for a PP patent on April 7, 1955. Hoechst and PCL Ltd., other Ziegler licensees, also prepared PP in late 1954, but did not apply for patents [26].

The above claims came together in the U.S. Patent Office, where an interference proceeding was declared in 1958, among Standard of Indiana, Phillips, DuPont, Montecatini (Natta), and Hercules. The subject of the interference was reduced to a single count: "Normally solid polypropylene, consisting essentially of recurring propylene units, having a substantial crystalline polypropylene content."

Early in the proceedings, Hercules was dropped due to their late priority date. After hearing over 18,000 pages of testimony, the Board of Patent Interferences, after finding that the Phillips priority date was determined by the January 1956, application, awarded the June 1954 priority to Natta and Montecatini (by then changed to Montedison), and U.S. Patent 3,715,344 was issued to Montedison in 1972. The three remaining claimants appealed, and the appeals were consolidated in the Federal District Court in Delaware.

At this point, with the PP industry almost 15 years old and thriving, the stakes involved were clearly higher than originally anticipated. The subsequent legal maneuvering has become known for its intensity, expense, and longevity, but not for bringing about a cessation of the disagreement and debate surrounding this invention and the patent awarded. The court found the Standard of Indiana product failed the "recurring propylene units" definition. The DuPont product, while meeting the requirements of the court, carried a later priority date than Natta (Montedison). In the most controversial and bitterly fought decision in the case, the initial Phillips patent application was found to inherently meet the requirements of the court, and Phillips received the earlier priority date of January 27, 1953. After final appeals, Phillips was awarded, on March 15, 1983, the composition-of-matter patent on PP, U.S. Patent 4,376,851 [27].

Considerable discussion and continuing disagreement have followed this decision. The questions raised enter the area of U.S. patent law and are beyond the scope of this publication.

How frustrating it must have been, first for Zeigler, then Natta and Montedison, to believe the PP rights were theirs, only to find them going, unexpectedly, to someone else. Curiously, the U.S. patent as originally issued to Phillips contained a typographical error in that single claim: "Normally solid polypropylene, consisting essentially of recurring *poly*propylene units, having a substantial crystalline polypropylene content." Considering the broad interest and intensity of the PP patent proceedings, it is ironic that the final product, the patent itself, was far less perfect than isotactic PP must be to crystallize.

7.3   Environmental Concerns

The more densely populated areas of the world are searching for better ways of disposing of solid waste than burying it in landfills. While composting and incineration are feasible possibilities, recovery of the materials or the energy contained in them are more attractive long-term solutions. With thermoplastics, their inherent recyclability suggests that recycling might be the best approach.

Considerable recycling occurs during the production of plastic items, where off-grade products are remelted and extruded or molded into acceptable parts. This takes place simply because it is economical for the processor; no special incentive is necessary. Recycling post-consumer parts presents greater difficulties, principally the economical identification and separation of the different materials for reclaiming.

7.3.1   Recycling

According to Environmental Protection Agency (EPA) statistics, plastics make up 21% of the volume of all solid waste but only 9% of the weight [28]. Accordingly, the discussion of plastic recycling is only meaningful within the context of recycling all solid waste.

Where communities have committed to a recycling program, the materials most easily identified and separated are usually selected first for recycle. They are:

1. Ferrous metals,
2. glass,
3. aluminum,
4. paper products,
5. cardboard,
6. lead (batteries),
7. PET (soft drink bottles), and
8. HDPE (milk bottles).

Takoma Park, MD, began community separation, collection, and processing of news-papers in 1985, then expanded the program to include community separation of the items on the above list by 1991 (with the exception of lead, which is recycled through its own return stream). Although 90% of the public participated, only 19% of these products were being recycled in 1991, with most of the remainder still going to landfill [29]. Thus, although a mandated situation, the ineffectiveness of the separation process did not permit high levels of recycling, even among the most easily identified materials. Thus, the prognosis for the materials more difficult to separate from the consumer waste stream, such as thin films, is not very good.

By the time we reach the bottom of the list, the capabilities and economics of recycling have diminished sharply. The main reason why people use plastics in the first place now becomes a problem: they are inexpensive. Consequently, virgin material is often about the same cost as the recycled material. Limiting ourselves to products which, as described above, are easily identified and separated, such as the soda or milk bottles, the cost of recycled plastic comes to about 30 ¢/lb to 45 ¢/lb, most of which is labor [30]. Thus, for materials like HDPE, which only cost about 40 ¢/lb much of the time, the incentive to recycle is not an economic one. In comparison, PET costs around 65 ¢/lb, and 40-cent recycled material is quite attractive. Largely as a result of these economics, the amount of any plastic post-consumer recycling is quite low; none recycles more than 15% [31].

There have been numerous attempts to pave the way for plastics recycling, most notably the identifying numbers organized by the SPI that are molded into many plastic items, enclosed in the three-arrow recycling logo. The intent was to make separation of the different plastics easier. However, this well-intentioned plan has had little effect, mostly because it does not measurably reduce the cost of manually separating plastics. Worse, it has also generated some friction, as much of the public believed that the symbol indicated that the item was made from already recycled material and, thus, felt that the symbol was misleading.

Perhaps the most significant attempt to recycle plastics was the Plastics Recycling Alliance, the joint venture between DuPont and Waste Management, Inc. formed in 1989, with plans for several regional plants to recycle PET from soda bottles and HDPE from milk bottles. The venture failed a few years later [31].

7.3.1.1   Recycling PP

PP is highly recycled in one product, not because of the value of PP involved, but because of the value of the lead in it: storage batteries. Batteries were recycled initially to recover the value of the lead in them, to properly dispose of the acid contained, and to prevent the lead from entering the landfill. It is a relatively simple task to simultaneously recover the PP in the battery cases as part of the process, so PP is recovered at high percentages from returned storage batteries.

Businesses have been established to recover PP from major industrial streams of off-grade products, such as nonwovens (used in diapers) and slit tape fabrics (used in carpets), and those businesses continue to operate profitably. However, they benefit from a single source of relatively clean PP, eliminating the expense of manually separating their starting materials, an economy not available to post-consumer waste processors.

The diversity of applications and uses for PP is a problem in collection, as no single large identifiable application exists, such as the milk jug in HDPE, or the soft drink bottle made from PET. Numerous efforts by PP producers and end users have been made to identify sources and create applications, and progress is being made. A pilot program in Canada demonstrated that the PP gathered from post-consumer waste exhibited satisfactory properties [32]. Murphy's Oil Soap was packaged in a bottle containing 25% post-consumer recycled PP. In spite of the identification and separation difficulties, the amount of post-consumer PP collected continues to increase, but the 220 million pounds processed in the USA in 1993 still represents only 2.5% of the amount of virgin PP sold annually.

7.3.2   Other Approaches

7.3.2.1   Life Cycle Analysis

Life cycle analysis (LCA) involves examining all of the steps in the life of an article from its initial creation to its final disposal, and considers the total effect on the environment. The use of LCA, though not standardized or fully quantitative, has shown plastics in a favorable light versus paper, metal, and glass with respect to energy use, pollution generation, and resource consumption over the life of a given product [33]. The LCA of PP, the lightest of all common plastics, has been shown to have among the lowest environmental impact of any plastic [34].

7.3.2.2   Source Reduction

Source reduction aims at providing a particular function with less material. Plastics in general are popular precisely because of that advantage. Polypropylene's unique combination of properties makes it an ideal material to select when searching for lighter, thinner, and tougher articles. Its ability to provide exceptional strength through orientation, a major factor in the success of PP, embodies all of the source reduction benefits to the environment, although having been pursued originally for economic reasons.

Once source reduction and recycling have been optimized, then landfill and incineration become the remaining approaches to disposal.

7.3.2.3   Landfill

While landfill is unsightly and unpopular, it remains one of the most economical methods for disposal of most municipal solid waste, and it can be expected to continue playing a major role in waste disposal for some time. Since one of the principal concerns regarding landfill is the effect of leached contaminants on the soil and groundwater, PP once again scores well. Being inert under the fill conditions, PP has no adverse effect on the surroundings.

Much discussion has centered around the need for degradable plastics, and many technical solutions have been developed to make polyolefins more readily degradable in the presence of moisture, bacteria, sunlight, or heat. Were the desired behavior available without any reduction in other properties, the end would be clearly worthwhile. However, the degradability is usually accompanied by the loss of, or serious compromise in, one of the desirable properties of PP, such as melt stability. Consequently, the gain in a small but visible and annoying problem (roadside litter) requires forfeiting a property that is important to virtually all PP used. In addition, the products of degradation now become more soluble in water, and the potential for leaching by-products from landfills into the water table increases. For these reasons, degradable PP, and plastics in general, are not expected to provide lasting answers to the environmental questions being addressed today.

7.3.2.4   Incineration and Energy Recovery

When it comes time for disposal through incineration, polyolefin waste streams are clean burning, with the highest energy content of all municipal solid waste components. Paper, wood, and other plastics deliver about 40% to 70% of the energy of PP, yard and food waste about 10%, and metals and glass, none [35]. Thus, PP presents an excellent material for disposal by incineration, particularly if designed for energy recovery.

7.3.3   Summary

Due to the complexities of recovering post-consumer waste and varying local community requirements, the successful solution to maintaining a low environmental impact for PP is most likely to be an integrated solid waste management program consisting of:

1.   Reducing article weight through product development and property enhancement,
2.   reusing containers and articles where possible,
3.   recycling easily identified, major volume products back into similar applications,
4.   incineration to produce energy, and
5.   landfill.

While none of these provides a major improvement in the environmental impact, it is largely because PP is already an environmentally friendly material.

Appendix 7.1 Worldwide PP Producers

Worldwide PP Producers as of Year-End, 1994

Country/Company	Location	Producers	Locations
Europe			
Western Europe			
Belgium		5	5
North Sea Petro	Antwerp		
Borealis A.S.	Beringen		
Amoco Chemicals	Geel		
Montefina	Feluy		
Solvay & CIE	Antwerp, Lillo		
France		6	7
Appryl	Lavera		
Appryl	Gonfreville		
Polychim	Dunkerque		
Exxon	N de Gravenchon		
Hoechst France	Lillebonne		
Montell Polyolefins	Berre l'etang		
Solvay & CIE	Sarralbe		
United Germany		7	8
OMV Deutschland	Burghausen		
Farbwerke-Hoechst	Knapsack		
Vestolen GMBH	Gelsenkirchen, Marl		
BASF	Ludwigshafen		
ROW	Wesseling		
Montell Polyolefins	Köln		
Veb Chemische Buna	Schkopau		
Italy		1	3
Montell Polyolefins	Brindisi		
Montell Polyolefins	Ferrara		
Montell Polyolefins	Terni		
Netherlands		3	3
DSM	Geleen		
BASF	Rozenburg		
Montell Polyolefins	Pernis		
United Kingdom		2	2
BASF	Wilton		
Montell Polyolefins	Carrington		
Austria		1	1
PCD Polymers	Schwechat		
Finland		1	1
Borealis	Porvoo		
Norway		1	1
Borealis A.S.	Bamble		
Spain		4	4
Repsol quimica	Puertollano		
Transformdora De Propileno	Tarragona		
Hoechst Iberica	Tarragona		
BASF Espanola	Tarragona		
Western Europe Subtotal		31	35

Worldwide PP Producers as of Year-End, 1994 (*continued*)

Country/Company	Location	Producers	Locations
Central & Eastern Europe			
Bulgaria		1	1
Neftochim	Burgas		
Czech Republic		1	1
Chemepetrol	Livinov		
Slovak Republic		1	1
Slovchemia	Bratislava		
Hungary		1	1
Tiszai Vegyi Komb	Tiszaujvaros		
Poland		1	1
Pol Cekop/MZRip	Plock		
Romania		1	2
Romchim	Midia, Romania		
Romchim	Ploiesti, Romania		
Serbia		1	1
Hemijska Ind	Odzaci		
Former USSR			
Russia		3	3
Kazakhstan		1	1
Ukraine		1	1
Eastern & Central Europe Subtotal		12	13
Europe Total		43	48
North America			
Canada		1	2
Montell Polyolefins	Varennes, Quebec		
Montell Polyolefins	Sarnia, Ontario		
United States		16	20
Amoco Chemical	Chocolate Bayou, TX		
Amoco Chemical	Cedar Bayou, TX		
Aristech	Neal, WV		
Aristech	Laporte, TX		
Fina Oil & Chemical	La Porte, TX		
Rexene	Odessa, TX		
Lyondell Petrochm	Bayport, TX		
Epsilon Products	Marcus Hook, PA		
Exxon Chemical	Baytown, TX		
Formosa Plastics	Point Comfort, TX		
Novacor Chemicals	Marysville, MI		
Montell Polyolefins	Bayport, TX		
Montell Polyolefins	Lake Charles, LA		
Huntsman Chemical	Woodbury, NJ		
Huntsman Chemical	Longview, TX		
Phillips Sumika PP Co.	Pasadena, TX		
Quantum Chemical	Morris, IL		
Shell Chemical Co.	Norco, LA		

(*continued*)

Worldwide PP Producers as of Year-End, 1994 (*continued*)

Country/Company	Location	Producers	Locations
Seadrift Polypro Co.	Seadrift, TX		
Solvay America	Deer Park, TX		
Mexico		2	2
Pemex	Morelos		
Indelpro	Tampico		
North America Total		19	24
Asia			
Japan		16	20
Chiba PP	Chiba		
Chisso Petro	Chiba, Goi		
DPP Inc.	Kashima		
DPP Inc.	Mizushima		
Idemitsu Petro	Anegasaki, Chiba		
Mitsubishi Kagaku	Mizushima		
Mitsubishi Kagaku	Kashima, Ibaraki		
Mitsubishi Kagaku	Yokkaichi		
Mitsui Petrochem	Ichihara, Chiba		
Mitsui Toatsu	Hiroshima		
Makoto Murata	Tsurusaki, Oita		
Makoto Murata	Mizushima		
Senboku Poly	Takasago		
Sumitomo Chem.	Ichihara, Chiba		
Tokuyama	Tokuyama City		
Tonen Chem.	Kawasaki		
Ube Industries	Sakai, Osaka		
Ube Polypropylene	Ube City		
Ukishima Polypro	Kawasaki		
Yokkaichi Polypro	Yokkaichi		
Rest of Asia			
China (PRC)	Various Prefectures	23	23
India		2	4
India Petrochem Corp.	Baroda, Koyali		
India Petrdochem Corp.	Nagothane, Mahar.		
India Petrochem Corp.	Vadodara		
PP India Ltd.	Mathora, Uttar		
Indonesia		2	2
P.T. Tri Polyta	Cilegon		
Pertamina	Palembang		
Korea		8	8
Daelim	Yeochon Complex		
Honam Petro	Yeochon		
Honam Oil	Yeochon		
Hyundai	Daesan		
Korea Petrochem Inds	Ulsan		
Samsung Gen Chem	Daesan		
Tonyang Nylon	Ulsan		
Yukong	Ulsan		

Worldwide PP Producers as of Year-End, 1994 (*continued*)

Country/Company	Location	Producers	Locations
Malaysia		2	2
Polypropylene Malaysia	Kuantan		
Titan Himont	Pasir Gudang, Johor		
Singapore		1	1
Polyolefin Co. Singapore	Pulau Ayer, Merbau Is.		
Taiwan		2	2
Taiwan Polypro Co.	Kaohsiung		
Yung Chia Chem.	Linyuan		
Thailand		3	3
HMC Polymers	Map Ta Phut		
Thai Polypropylene	Map Ta Phut		
Thai Petchem Ind Co.	Rayong		
Rest of Asia Subtotal		43	45
Asia Total		59	65
Rest of World			
Australia		3	4
Hoechst Australia	Altona, Victoria		
Montell Polyolefins	Clyde, N.S.W.		
Montell Polyolefins	Geelong, Victoria		
ICI Australia	Botany Bay, N.S.W.		
Latin America			
Argentina		2	2
Petroquimica Cuyo	Lujon deCuyo		
Petroken	Ensenada		
Brazil		3	4
Braspol	Duque De Caxias, RJ		
Polibrasil S.A.	Maua, Sao Paulo		
Polibrasil S.A.	Camacari, Bahia		
PPH	Rio Grande Do Sul		
Colombia		1	1
PQ Colombiana	Cartagena		
Venezuela		1	1
Polipro De Venez	El Tablazo		
Latin America Subtotal		7	8
Mid East & Arabian Peninsula			
Iran		1	1
Arak Petrochemical	Sandor Khomeni		
Saudi Arabia		1	1
Saudi European PC	Ibn Zahr		
Turkey		1	1
Petkim-Petrok	Aliaga-Izmir		
Mid East & Arabian Peninsula Subtotal		3	3
Africa			
Nigeria		1	1
Warri Ref & PC	Ekpan		

(*continued*)

Worldwide PP Producers as of Year-End, 1994 (*continued*)

Republic Of South Africa		2	2
Sasol	Secunda		
South Africans Polys	Sasolburg (Safripol)		
Africa Subtotal		3	3
Rest Of World Total		16	18
World Total		137	155
Producers Repeated In Different Regions	20		
Net Producers	117		

Source: Himont U.S.A. Inc. (Now Montell USA Inc.)

References

1. Mod. Plast. Encycl., 1994
2. Montell Polyolefins estimates
3. Chem. Econ. Hbk., Polypropylene 580.1430, SRI International, 1994
4. Ger. Offen. 2 213 086 (1972) Solvay & Cie SA
5. *Galli, P., Lucciani, L., Cecchin, G.:* Angew. Makromol. Chem. 94 (1981) 63; *Galli, P., Barbe', C., Noristi, L.:* Angew. Makromol. Chem. 120 (1984) 73–90; *Galli, P., Cecchin, I., Simonazzi, T.:* Advanced Polymer Properties: The New Frontiers of the Ideal Ziegler–Natta Catalysts, 32nd International Symposium on Macromolecules, IUPAC, Kyoto, Japan (1988)
6. Chem. Econ. Hbk., Propylene 436.0000, SRI International, 1993
7. Polyolefins in the 1980s—The Continuing Revolution, SRI International, 1988
8. Polypropylene 1994, Phillip Townsend Associates Inc., 1993
9. *Galli, P.:* Polypropylene: A Quarter Century of Increasingly Successful Development, In Structural order in Polymers, Ciardelli, F., and Giusti, P., Eds., 63–69, Pergamon Press, Oxford, UK, 1981
10. Chem. Mktg. Rep. (Aug 12, 1991) 5
11. *Galli, P., Haylock, J.C.:* The Reactor Granule, Polyolefins VII, SPE Houston, TX, 1991
12. *Lieberman, R.L., DelDuca, D.D.:* Advanced Olefin Polymerization Technologies, Polyolefins VIII, Houston, TX, 1993
13. *Galli, P., Haylock, J.C., Albizzatti, E., DeNicola, A.J.:* High Performance Polyolefins, 35th Int'l Symp. on Macromolecules, IUPAC, Akron, OH, 1994
14. Development Data Sheets, "A Catalloy Process Polymer," KS Series, Himont USA, Inc. (now Montell), 1993; Experimental Analysis Reports, KM Series, KS Series, KT Series, Himont USA, Inc. (now Montell), 1993
15. *Giacobbe, J.:* Evaluation of Air-Quenched Blown Film Made with Low Modulus Polyolefins. SPE ANTEC, Detroit, MI, 1992
16. *Shah, A.:* Low Flexural Modulus Calenderable Polypropylenes, SPE ANTEC, Montreal, Canada, 1991
17. Euro. Chem. News (June 20, 1994) 19
18. *Yoo, H.J., Done, D.:* Rheology of High Melt Strength Polypropylene, SPE ANTEC, Detroit, MI, 1992
19. *Munstedt, H.:* J. Rheol 23 (1979) 421
20. *Yoo, H.J.:* Performance of High Melt Strength Polypropylene Resins in Extrusion Coating Process, SPE ANTEC, San Francisco, CA, 1994
21. *Phillips, E.M., McHugh, K.E., Bradley, M.B.:* High Performance Polypropylene Extrusion Coating Resins, TAPPI Polymers, Lamination, and Coatings Conference, Orlando, FL, 1989

22. *McHugh, K.E., Ogale, K.:* High Melt Strength Polypropylene for Melt Phase Thermoforming, SPE ANTEC, Dallas, TX, 1990
23. *Beren, J.R., Cappellman, C.:* Advances in Polypropylene for Automotive Blow Molding, SAE International Congress and Exposition, Detroit, MI, 1994
24. *Bradley, M., Phillips, E.M.:* Novel Foamable PP Polymers, SPE ANTEC, Dallas, TX, 1990
25. *Pino, P., Moretti, G.:* Polymer 28 (April 1987) 683–692
26. *Seymour, R.B. and Cheng, T.:* History of Polyolefins, D. Reidel Publishing Company, Dordrecht, Holland, 1986
27. U.S. Patent Quarterly 206 (1980) 676
28. Characterization of Municipal Solid Waste, EPA/530-SW-90-042, 1990
29. Plastic Waste Primer, League of Women Voters Education Fund, Lyons and Burford, New York, NY, 1993
30. Plastics Reclamation and Recycling, SRI International, Menlo Park, CA, 1992
31. Garbage (Spring 1994) 44
32. *Ehrig, R.J.,* Ed.: Plastic Recycling—Products & Processes, Hanser Publishers, 1992, p. 96
33. *Begley, R.:* Chem. Week (Dec 9 1992) 45
34. Himont (now Montell) brochure, Maintaining the Eco-Balance Profitably (June 1991)
35. Shell Canada Ltd (now Montell) brochure, Polypropylene and the Environment, Making the Right Choice, 1993

8   Manufacturing

Richard B. Lieberman, Richard T. LeNoir

8.1   Early Processes

Processes initially used for the manufacture of polypropylene (PP) were designed to accommodate the limitations of the early Ziegler–Natta catalyst systems. Removal of the catalyst from the polymer and separation of the nonstereoregular atactic fraction were required to produce a salable product. The first processes, commercialized at Ferrara, Italy, by Montecatini and then at Parlin, New Jersey, in the United States by Hercules, were based on the use of a hydrocarbon diluent to suspend the crystalline polymer particles and dissolve the amorphous polymer fraction. Residual catalyst components were deactivated and solubilized by treatment with alcohol. The titanium and aluminum alkoxides thus formed were separated from the diluent by treatment with water. The crystalline polymer product was separated from the diluent by filtration or centrifugation and then dried. Amorphous polymer, soluble in the diluent, was separated from it by evaporation. These first plants employed semi-batch polymerization technology, first adding diluent, catalyst and aluminum alkyl, then continuously feeding propylene monomer and hydrogen, which is used to control molecular weight [1].

As the demand for PP increased, continuous polymerization processes were employed. As shown in Fig. 8.1, the batch polymerization vessels were replaced by a series of stirred vessels. The first polymerization plants usually included facilities for the manufacture of the first generation $TiCl_3$ catalyst, reducing $TiCl_4$ with an aluminum alkyl chloride. Catalyst was then prepared for polymerization by suspension in the diluent and contact with the aluminum alkyl used as cocatalyst (usually diethyl aluminum chloride). This premix of catalyst and diluent was then continuously fed to the first polymerizer. Monomer and hydrogen were continuously fed to each polymerizer as required to produce the desired polymer. Polymerization temperatures were usually in the range of 60 °C to 80 °C, and pressures as high as 14 bar (200 psi) were used, depending on the process and diluent. For example, the early Hercules process shown in Fig. 8.1 employed relatively low pressures of less than 5 bar (70 psi) because of the use of kerosene as diluent and the lack of monomer recycle. The last reactors in the series provided residence time for the reaction of small amounts of residual monomer. Other processes, such as the early Montecatini process, operated at higher pressures, using hexane or heptane as diluent, and contained equipment for the degassing of the slurry and recycle of unreacted monomer [2]. After polymerization and degassing, the polymer slurry was treated with alcohol and then with aqueous caustic to neutralize the HCl formed in the alcohol treatment. The aqueous phase containing the alcohol, water, and the products of the catalyst neutralization was separated from the hydrocarbon phase. Polymer, suspended in the hydrocarbon phase, was separated from the diluent and amorphous polymer by filtration or centrifugation. In the original Hercules process, the diluent–wet polymer was then steam distilled to remove residual kerosene, then dried in air. In the Montecatini process

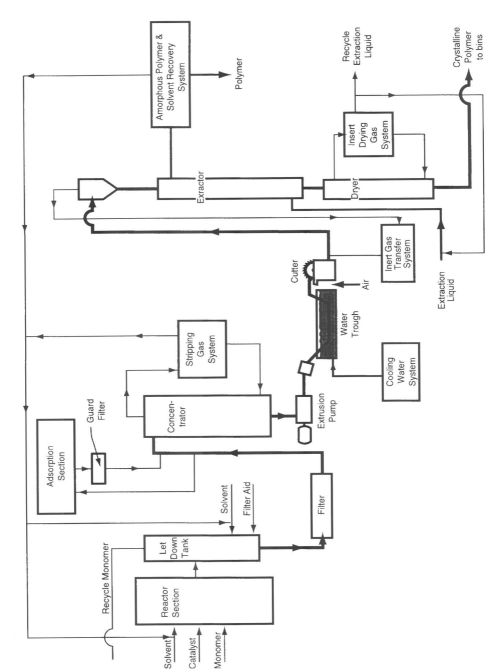

Figure 8.2 Eastman solution polymerization process [5]

and solid polymer is formed by passage through a devolatilizing extruder. Additional purification is obtained by extraction of the solid polymer with heptane or similar hydrocarbon, which also removes amorphous PP. The use of alcohol, and the multiple distillations required for its recycle, is avoided. This process was used for the production of a number of unique, specialty grades of polymers having lower modulus and greater toughness than those produced by the slurry process.

Use of liquid monomer as the polymerization medium has two advantages when compared to a hydrocarbon solvent or diluent: higher polymerization rates as a result of the higher monomer concentration; and process simplification which reduces cost by eliminating a component that must be purified and recycled [6]. Operating pressures in excess of 30 bar (440 psi) are required to maintain propylene in the liquid phase at polymerization temperatures of 60 °C to 80 °C. The earliest examples of polymerization processes of this type are the Rexall (Rexene, El Paso) process [7], and the Phillips process [8]. Initially, both processes used first generation TiCl$_3$ catalysts; consequently, catalyst residues were a substantial problem, and removal by alcohol treatment and neutralization was required. Removal of atactic polymer was also required to obtain product with commercially acceptable properties. These process requirements effectively eliminated any process simplification and cost advantages that may have resulted from the use of liquid monomer. The later use of second generation (Solvay) TiCl$_3$ catalysts [4], eliminating the need to remove atactic polymer, provided significant advantage in these processes. In the Rexall process (Fig. 8.3), a continuous stirred tank reactor is used for polymerization. Removal of the heat of polymerization through the jacketed walls of the reactor and internal cooling coils can be augmented by the refluxing of monomer. This use of the latent heat of the monomer minimizes heat removal problems in large reactors. In the Phillips process (Fig. 8.4), the polymerization vessel is a jacketed loop reactor with a high ratio of cooling area to reactor volume. The velocities required to maintain a uniform polymerization slurry also increase the cooling efficiency. The loop reactors are operated in a manner in which most of the slurry is

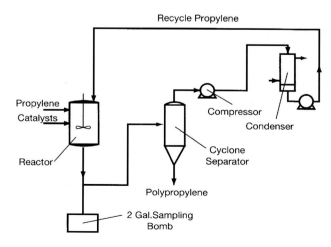

Figure 8.3 Rexall process [7]

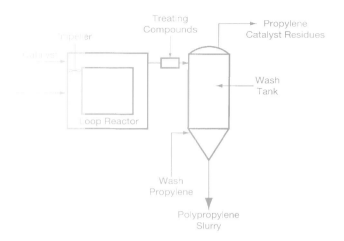

Treating
Compounds

Propylene
Catalyst Residues

Wash
Tank

Loop Reactor

Wash
Propylene

Polypropylene
Slurry

consequently, these loops are the chemical equivalent of stirred
more efficient plug flow type.

phase propylene polymerization process was developed by
Novolen process (Fig. 8.5) uses stirred bed polymerizers
20 bar (300 psi) and temperatures of 70 °C to 90 °C [9].
tained in the polymer bed by mechanical mixing using helical,
reacted monomer is condensed and recycled to remove the heat
mechanical agitation rather than fluidization to provide mixing,
zed. Initially, plants contained only one polymerizer, for the
however, technology for the production of impact copolymers,
was developed in the late 1970s. This process does not contain
the atactic polymer or for catalyst removal. When first generation

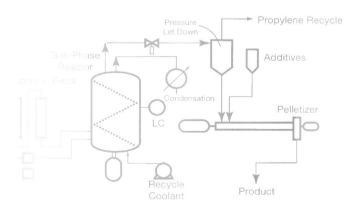

Pressure
Let Down

Propylene Recycle

Gas Phase
Reactor

Additives

Condensation

Pelletizer

LC

Recycle
Coolant

Product

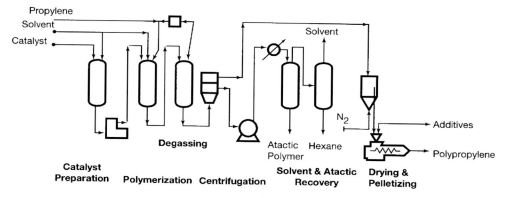

Figure 8.6 High yield Montedison PP process [10]. Reprinted with permission from Hydrocarbon Processing, May 1981, Copyright by Gulf Publishing Co., all rights reserved

catalysts were used, the polymer product contained more of the noncrystalline fractions than products from most other processes and, as a consequence, had lower modulus (stiffness). Catalyst residues are neutralized, and chlorides removed, by reaction with propylene oxide in the extruder.

The introduction of high yield magnesium chloride-supported third generation catalysts by Montedison and Mitsui in 1975 enabled PP producers to use processes in which the removal of catalyst residues was not required [10]. Removal of atactic polymer was still required to obtain a product with satisfactory physical properties. The high yield Montedison slurry process (Fig. 8.6) illustrates the process simplification and operating cost savings achieved by elimination of alcohol treatment. Obviously, equipment for alcohol treatment and neutralization of catalyst residues was not required. However, the largest savings were obtained in the solvent recovery sections, since the separations of alcohol and water and alcohol and hydrocarbon were no longer required. Significant energy savings were also achieved by using high yield catalysts in previously existing slurry process facilities by merely by-passing the deashing and neutralization sections. The El Paso (Rexene) liquid monomer process was also improved in a similar manner [11]. This was of great importance in the late 1970s and early 1980s, when energy costs were at historically high levels and the low capacity utilization limited polymer price increases.

8.2   Current Processes

Commercialization of high yield, high stereospecificity fourth generation catalysts by Montedison and Mitsui enabled the development of processes in which removal of catalyst and atactic polymer are unnecessary. These processes also eliminate the use of hydrocarbon diluent by using either liquid or gaseous monomer as the polymerization medium. The reduction in capital and operating costs achieved by these new processes has both promoted the expansion of PP production and established the high yield process products as the

such as ultra high melt flow rate homopolymers and high
can only be produced using these advanced catalysts and
PP capacity installed since the mid 1980s has utilized high yield
Technology provided by the major process licensors,
Carbide (Unipol), BASF (Novolen), and Mitsui (Hypol), is
facilities. Recently constructed facilities often consist of one
capacity of over 100 ktons/yr to take advantage of the economy of

monomer as the polymerization medium are often divided into
continuous stirred reactors, and those using loop reactors. In
monomer as the polymerization medium maximizes the rate of
providing high monomer concentration. Processes using
used to produce homopolymer PP and random copolymers with
phase processes are not well suited for the production of the
copolymers due to the solubility of the rubber in the liquid
or producers of impact copolymers often use a hybrid process,
in the liquid phase followed by copolymerization in the

the production of copolymers (Fig. 8.7) [12] is the most widely
process. In this process, catalyst components and monomer are
homopolymerization. The high heat removal capability of the loop
turbulent mixing of the slurry and the large surface-to-volume
specific outputs in excess of 400 kg/hr-m^3 of PP. The use of
a narrow particle size distribution, coupled with the high liquid
fouling. Operating conditions are typically in the range of 60 °C
1500 psi to 700 psi) [13].
diameter of the loop reactors, these operating pressures do not
special fabrication techniques. Consequently, the use of
economically favorable, and capacities over 180 ktons/yr

the PP/propylene slurry is depressurized and flashed at a
the vaporized monomer by condensation using cooling
gas phase copolymerization. Impact copolymers are produced by
phase reactor to produce ethylene-propylene rubber in the
first reactor. Operating temperatures in the gas phase reactors
operating pressures of 15 bar (220 psi). Polymer exiting the
through a low pressure separator, in which the remaining
a steam treatment vessel for deactivation of the residual
bed dryer. In addition to the Spheripol process, loop reactors
a number of producers including Phillips, Fina, and Solvay.
agitated (liquid pool) reactors, as pioneered by Rexene (El
the new high yield catalyst systems [11]. The Lippshac process
catalysts (SHAC) in such a process for the production of
copolymers [14]. Exxon (under license from Sumitomo) can
with low levels of low molecular weight polymers and
the reactor product with fresh monomer (Fig. 8.8) [15]. In each

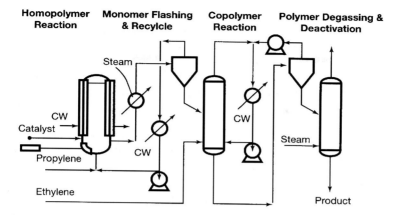

Figure 8.7 Spheripol process [12]. Reprinted with permission from Hydrocarbon Processing, March 1995, Copyright by Gulf Publishing Co., all rights reserved

of these processes, condensation of boiling monomer is the primary method of heat removal, allowing the use of large single-line plants. Mitsui Petrochemical's Hypol process (Fig. 8.9) utilizes Montedison/Mitsui high yield, high stereospecificity catalysts in a series of continuous stirred reactors, followed by gas phase polymerization in a fluidized bed reactor for the production of impact-modified copolymers [16].

The gas phase process pioneered by BASF has become more competitive by the use of high yield, high stereospecificity catalysts [17]. This has eliminated major product deficiencies by reducing the quantities of atactic polymer and residual catalyst. In addition, the higher polymerization rates made possible through the use of these catalysts has facilitated an increase in the maximum capacity of a single-line plant. The incorporation

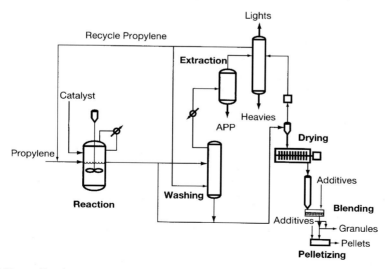

Figure 8.8 Exxon (Sumitomo) process [15]

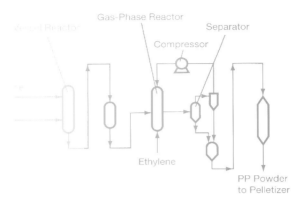

Gas-Phase Reactor

Separator

Compressor

Ethylene

PP Powder
to Pelletizer

series for the production of homopolymer and random copolymers has improved product flexibility. Although this process is believed to be offer facilities, capacities of over 130 ktons/yr have been demonstrated. Gas fluidized bed reactors for olefin polymerization was pioneered by development of the Unipol process for polyethylene in the late 1960s. This for the production of PP in 1985 by incorporating Shell high activity [ ]. The most recognizable feature of this process (Fig. 8.10) [19] is the reactor a wider upper section that serves to separate the fluidized polymer gas. One reactor is required for the production of homopolymer or a second smaller reactor is used in series for the production of the rubber component of impact-modified copolymers. Polymer circulation

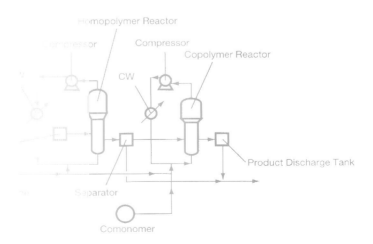

Homopolymer Reactor

Compressor

Copolymer Reactor

CW

Product Discharge Tank

Separator

Comonomer

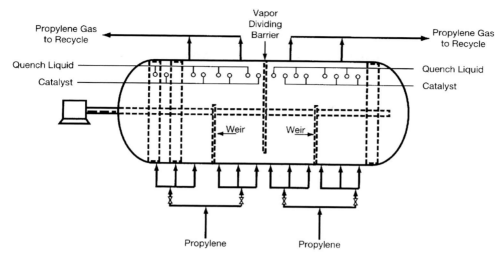

Figure 8.11 Amoco reactor [20]

resulting from the fluidization maintains product uniformity and promotes heat transfer in the large polymer bed. The heat of reaction is removed by cooling the recycle gas by heat exchange with cooling water. Recycled propylene can thus be cooled below its dew point, allowing some liquid monomer to be fed in homopolymer production. Union Carbide refers to this technique as the "condensed mode" of operation. As in other processes, vaporization of the liquid monomer enhances heat removal in the reactor. The polymerization temperature is typically 65 °C with operating pressures of 30 bar (440 psi) in the homopolymer reactor and 20 bar (300 psi) in the copolymer reactor. Plant capacities of Unipol PP plants are often in the range of 100 kton/yr to 140 kton/yr, although larger plants are feasible.

The Amoco/Chisso process makes use of a patented, horizontal, mechanically agitated, multistage gas phase reactor (Fig. 8.11) [20]. This reactor design, where the polymer passes from one baffled zone to another, behaves as a series of stirred reactors providing a narrow overall residence time distribution. Polymer particle size and copolymer composition distributions can be significantly narrowed as compared to those from single-stage stirred reactors. In addition, homopolymer molecular weight distributions can be broadened, when desired, by varying the hydrogen fed to each section to provide different molecular weights. As in other gas phase processes, some liquid monomer is fed to the polymer bed to facilitate heat removal. Operating conditions are also similar to the other gas phase processes. Amoco commercialized this reactor design in 1979 for the production of homopolymer using $TiCl_3$ catalyst. The impact copolymer process, using two separate reactors in series (Fig. 12) [21], was developed in cooperation with Chisso and uses controlled-morphology, high yield, high stereospecificity catalysts. Copolymer production started in Japan in 1987, in a small plant. A world scale, 135 kton/yr copolymer plant started up in Texas in 1992.

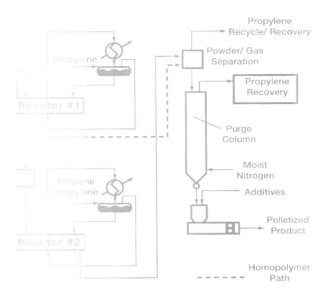

...systems require propylene of significantly higher quality than that ...catalyzed systems. Compounds that will bind strongly to the ...as carbon monoxide and arsine, can only be tolerated at ppb ...affecting performance. Maximum recommended levels of impurities ...high yield polymerizations are shown in Table 8.1 [22]. Propane, ...acts as a diluent to reduce polymerization rate but has no other ...likely inert components are nitrogen, methane, ethane, and other ...grade propylene, which contains approximately 5% propane, can ...polymerization in processes that can tolerate the presence of these ...catalyst poisoning components are at the target levels shown in the table. ...such as water and alcohols, which react with the aluminum alkyl co- ...mitigated by using high concentrations of the cocatalyst. Many ...propylene purification facilities to insure against upsets from ...sieves are commonly used as adsorbents to remove water and CO_2. ...available to remove H_2S, COS, arsine, and carbon monoxide from

er Finishing

...used directly as reactor product, fully stabilized pellets are the most ...stabilization is discussed in Chapter 4. In the most modern facilities,

Table 8.1 Propylene Quality Requirements

Type of component	Component	Recommended concentration
Monomer	Propylene	95 vol % minimum
Inert	Propane	5 vol % maximum
	Butane	900 vol ppm max
	Noncondensables	200 vol ppm max
Copolymerizing monomer	Ethylene	100 vol ppm max
	Butene	100 vol ppm max
Poison	Acetylene	5 vol ppm max
	Methyl acetylene	5 vol ppm max
	Propadiene	5 vol ppm max
	Methanol	5 vol ppm max
	Carbon dioxide	5 vol ppm max
	Water	2 vol ppm max
	Oxygen	2 vol ppm max
	Total sulfur	1 wt ppm max
	Arsine	0.03 vol ppm max
	Phosphine	0.03 vol ppm max
	Carbon monoxide	0.03 vol ppm max
	COS	0.02 vol ppm max

Source: Montell Polyolefins

one high capacity twin screw extruder can process the product from a high capacity polymerization line. Extruders with capacities as high as 240 kton/yr have been operated commercially [25]. Werner and Pfleiderer, Japan Steel Works, Kobe Steel, and Berstoff are manufacturers of these large machines.

Typically, PP and the desired additives are mixed prior to being fed to the extruder. Usually, the additives are in solid form, either as powder or in high concentration in PP pellets. Additive concentrates adsorbed on PP spheres, sold as Xantrix concentrates, can be used to deliver liquid additives to a solids mixing system [26]. The solids are metered into the extruder, which serves to melt the polymer, mix the additives, and deliver the molten polymer to the pelletizing system. Typical extrusion temperatures are above 200 °C to reduce melt viscosity and below 250 °C to minimize degradation. Low melt flow rate grades are extruded at the higher temperatures, while higher melt flow rate grades can be extruded at the lower temperatures and still maintain production rates.

The molecular weight of molten PP can be reduced by degradation initiated by organic peroxides, such as 2,5 di(tert-butylperoxy)-2,5 dimethyl hexane [27]. In this visbreaking reaction, the peroxide forms peroxy radicals which attack the tertiary carbon atoms on the polymer backbone to form radicals. Under extrusion conditions, the radicals undergo chain scission reactions. Since each tertiary carbon in the melt is equally likely to be attacked, large molecules, which contain more carbon atoms, are more likely to undergo chain scission. Consequently, visbreaking reduces the weight-average molecular weight, M_w, more dramatically than the number-average, M_n. As a result, the molecular weight distribution, as described by the polydispersity, M_w/M_n, is narrowed. These narrow molecular weight distribution resins have desirable properties in some fiber manufacturing processes.

...can be stabilized, without extrusion, by using the Addipol ...ggll. In ...ddition to avoiding the high capital cost associated with ...shing process provides product advantages by eliminating one ...on process, and can employ melt flow rates outside of the range ...economically [28].

...shipment, usually by rail, is common in the United States. Railcars ...pounds of product, while bulk trucks usually contain 40,000 lbs. ...PP is most commonly sold in bags, each containing 25 kg polymer. ...nds each, are also commonly used by small volume consumers.

Environmental Issues

...ocesses presented many environmental concerns. There were many ...of hydrocarbons into the atmosphere from the slurry process ...were vented from process equipment in the drying area, as well ...area. This led to relatively high emission of volatile organic ...ll as significant costs due to the loss of solvent.

...ocesses used alcohol and water for catalyst deashing. This presented ...ranging from disposal of the extracted catalyst residue solids ...complexes) to malfunctioning of the alcohol recovery systems, ...gh concentrations of alcohol going out with the supposedly clean ...dues were allowed to settle in on-site ponds, many of which are ...use has been found for these titanium and aluminum compounds. ...missions in solvent recovery, there was also a need to remove solids ...bed in atactic PP being removed and collected and, in some cases, ...the large volumes of solvents and alcohol being stored on-site, ...opportunity for these materials to be spilled, thereby causing ...ater and soil contamination.

...propylene evolved and the use of propylene as the polymerization ...acturing processes have become more environmentally friendly. ...Technipol is a good example of the new technology that reduces ...associated with previous slurry processes. Point source emissions ...cling of propylene in the operation. With the advent of fugitive ...es (for valves, flanges, etc.), overall air emissions from the ...reduced, thus lowering the amounts of VOCs that are released ...deashing in the new technology, and, therefore, the use of water ...quent recovery of these materials is not an issue. There is a ...spills of lubricating oil from the various pieces of equipment ...the process has been designed to capture these small amounts of oil ...out of the process. With propylene being used as the reaction ...PP recovery necessary.

...have not been eliminated with the new technologies; however, the ...and have been greatly reduced with their use.

References

1. *Vandenberg, E.J., Repka, B.C.:* Polymerization Processes, Shildknecht, C.E., and Skeist, I., Eds., John Wiley, New York, 1977, p. 337
   Kresser, T.O.J.: Polypropylene, Reinhold Publishing, New York, 1960
2. Hydrocarbon Processing, 48(11)(1969) 230
3. Chemical Week 139 (Dec. 3, 1986) 33
4. *Hermans, J.P.:* Ger. Offen. 2 213 086(1972) Solvay & Cie. SA
5. *Hagemeyer, H.J., Park, V.K.:* U.S. Patent 3 423 384 (1969) Eastman Kodak Co.
   Hagemeyer, H. J., Hull, D.C., Park, S.J.: U. S. Patent 3 600 463 (1971) Eastman Kodak Co.
   Hagemeyer, H.J., Park, V.K.: U.S. Patent 3 679 775 (1972) Eastman Kodak Co.
6. *Kirschner, H.G., Gumbolt, A.G.M., Bier, B.:* U.S. Patent 3 002 961 (1961) Farbenwerke Hoechst Aktiengesellschaft
7. *Stryker, A.B.:* U.S. Patent 3 639 374 (1972) Rexall Drug and Chemical Co.
   British Patent 1 044 811 (1966) Rexall Drug and Chemical Co.
8. *Smith, D.E., Keeler, R.M., Guenther, E.:* U.S. Patent 3 476 729 (1969) Phillips Petroleum Co.
9. *Ross, J.F., Bowles, W.A.:* Ind. Eng. Chem. Prod. Res. Dev. 24 (1985) 149
10. *DiDrusco, G., Rinaldi, R.:* Hydrocarbon Processing 60(5) (1981) 153
11. *Cipriani, C., Trischman Jr., C.A.:* Chem. Eng. (April 20, 1981) 80
12. Hydrocarbon Processing 74(3) (1995) 140
13. *DiDrusco, G., Rinaldi, R.:* Hydrocarbon Processing 63(11) (1984) 113
14. European Plastics News, 16 (July, 1988) 4
15. *Jones, A.M.:* Products from a new High Yield Polypropylene Catalyst, Polyolefins V International Conference, SPE RETEC, Houston, TX, 1987, p. 33
16. Hydrocarbon Processing 74(3) (1995) 140
17. Eur. Chem. News 31 (July 1989) 15
18. *Burdett, I.D.:* Chemtech 22(10) (1992) 616
    Goodenbour, J.W., Burstain, I.G., Cummings, W.C.: Unipol Polypropylene Process: A Progress Report, Polyolefins VI International Conference, SPE RETEC, Houston, TX, 1989, p. 37
    Sawin, S.P., Powers, G.W.: New Catalysts for Propylene Polymerization, Advances in Polyolefins, Plenum, New York, 1987, p. 355
19. Hydrocarbon Processing 74(3) (1995) 142
20. *Shepard, J.W., Jezl, J.L., Peters, E.F., Hall, R.D.:* U.S. Patent 3 957 448 (1976) Standard Oil Company
21. *Brockmeier, N.F.:* The Amoco/Chisso Gas Pase Polypropylene Copolymer Technology, Polyolefins VI International Conference, SPE RETEC, Houston, TX, 1991, p. 68
22. Montell Polyolefins, internal correspondence
23. ALCOA Adsorbents and Catalyst Materials: Product Data Selexsorb COS, Warrendale, PA, May 1988
24. Oil & Gas J. (Oct. 10, 1994) 50
    Hydrocarbon Processing 64(5) (1985)
25. *Anderson, P.G., Kenney, M.J.:* Trends in Large Scale Polymer Conversion, Polyolefins VI International Conference, SPE RETEC, Houston, TX, 1989, p. 155
    Munz, R., Wobbe, H., Ferguson, J.G.: New Generation of Twin Screw Extruder For Processing Polyolefins Without the Need of a Melt Pump Discharge, Polyolefins VIII International Conference, SPE RETEC, Houston, TX, 1993, p. 94
26. *Amos, S. Goldin, M.:* Performance Characteristics of a Novel Concentrate System for Liquid and Low Melting Additives, Technical Papers, Vol XXXIX, SPE, New Orleans, LA, 1993, p. 2534
27. *Henman, T.J.:* Degradation and Stabilization of Polyolefins, Allen, N.S., Ed., Applied Science Publishers, London, 1983
    Tzoganakis, C., Vlachopoulos, J., Hamielec, A.E.: Intern. Polymer Processing III 3 (1988) 141
    Xanthos, M.: Reactive Extrusion Principles and Practice. Xanthos, M., Ed., Hanser Publishers, New York (1992)
28. *Galli, P.:* The Introduction of the New Super Active Spherical Form Catalysts are Driving a Revolution in the Polyolefins World, Polyolefins VI International Conference, SPE RETEC, Houston, TX, 1989

9   Fabrication Processes

Edward P. Moore, Jr.

9.1   Introduction

Polypropylene (PP) is transformed into useful products by a wide variety of processes, which has been a major factor in its commercial success. Figure 9.1 shows the breakdown of sales in North America among the major processes. The ease of molding and the attractive strength, stiffness, and high use temperatures of articles molded of PP have made injection molding the largest consumer of PP among the processes used. A unique aspect of the PP processes compared to the other major plastics is the use of orientation to develop enhanced properties, principally in fibers and films, constituting nearly one-half of the consumption. None of the other major plastics uses orientation to any appreciable extent, unless PET is considered a major plastic, where orientation is used in fibers, biaxially oriented films, and soda bottles, or nylon, which is oriented into fibers. Lesser but significant quantities of PP are used in unoriented film, sheet, and blow molding.

9.1.1   Introduction to Extrusion Processes

Extrusion-based processes may consist of the following steps:

- Extrusion,
- forming of the extrudate within and outside of a die,
- quenching the extrudate and crystallizing it,

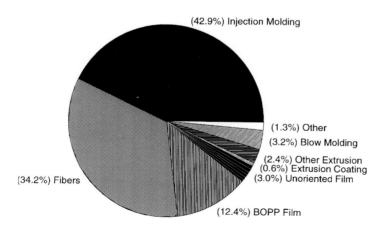

Figure 9.1 Polypropylene consumption in North America, 1993, by process. Source: Phillip Townsend Associates Inc. [4]

for forming, or
extrudate.

in every extrusion-based PP process, but they are basic to the
shows the variety of products that use these process steps. All use
and some use one or more of the downstream processes in forming

to deliver a molten polymer, uniform in temperature, molecular
and free of contaminants or faults such as bubbles or unmelted
A whole separate science has been built around the process of
stated aims, and rather than attempt to present that science, we will
important points that govern the selection, design, and operation of
the consequences to the products.
of the PP products are considered, along with the fineness of
such as fibers, the requirements for cleanliness and uniformity of
melt (whether from temperature or MW variations) are extremely
on a regular basis. The processor must know the limitations of
the above needs, as well as the appropriate polymer grade, to
The supplier, in turn, must recognize the sensitivity of the
each of the polymer variables under his control. With any given
the equipment can be exceeded, leading to quality fluctuations. It is

Processes and **Products**

	Oriented product	Melt formed product
	SPPF* items	Thermoformed items
	Slit tape	
	Biaxially oriented film (tentered)	
	Decorative ribbon	
blown film	Biaxially oriented film (bubble)	Blow molded items
blown film	Twine	
	Strapping	
	Slit tape	
	Continuous multifilaments	
	Staple multifilaments	
	Spun-bonded nonwovens	
	Melt blown nonwovens	

Profiles

the task of the processor, with the assistance of the polymer supplier, to reach the best balance of polymer, equipment, operating conditions, and end-use properties for the intended application. For this reason, the large volume, critical PP processing operations usually require close cooperation between supplier and processor to achieve the best balance of these factors. Of course, cost is always part of the equation, as well.

To aid in producing the most uniform output rate and melt quality, metering pumps are often used in extruding PP, and melt filters are almost universally employed. Although continuous filters are often used, most filters are batch operated, and a shutdown is needed to replace or renew them. This results in gradually changing conditions as the filter plugs and the back-pressure increases. While this can be mitigated to some degree by using larger filters, the size can quickly become cumbersome. In spite of attempts to improve the filter designs and operation, filtration remains an problematic but essential step for reliable extrusion operations.

The designs of extrusion dies are highly varied; they are often custom designed for the particular process or customer. Fortunately, PP is far less prone to disastrous thermal breakdown in the die than, for example, PVC, where minor hang-up points can lead to major degradation of the polymer, with the release of toxic and corrosive gases. In such a situation, PP merely degrades to a somewhat lower MW, and proceeds on through the die. Consequently, the design of dies for extrusion of PP is simpler than for the more sensitive polymers.

In general, where the extrudates are thin, high melt flow rates are used to reduce the pressure drop through the die. This normally results in some compromise in toughness properties, which is less of a problem in oriented items. Where the melt must retain its shape for some time before crystallization occurs, or where high toughness is crucial, low melt flow rates are used. Enhancement of the melt shape retention can be provided with a special type known as "high melt strength PP," described in Section 7.1.8.3.

For thin extrudates, a large drawdown from the die is usually employed to allow a larger die opening and lower pressure drop through the die, and, in the case of slot and annular dies, more practical die opening adjustments for controlling thickness distribution across the extrudate. The smallest die openings are in thin films, extrusion coating, and fibers, where 0.3 mm to 0.5 mm (10 mil to 20 mil) are typical openings, although the final extrudate is often a small fraction of that.

If the drawdown ratio is high, it is possible to encounter a phenomenon known as drawdown surge. This is a rheological response to the drawing stress that can give a large periodic variation in the thickness of the drawn item. It is most commonly found in fiber processing but may also occur in thin film or extrusion coating operations. It is alleviated by lowering melt viscosity, reducing the draw stress, or more rapid cooling during the draw, which solidifies the drawn item more quickly, stabilizing it. Depending on the particular process, changes in the rheology of the polymer can also help.

9.1.1.2   Quenching

The cooling, or quenching, of the PP extrudate is easily separated into two categories: slow and rapid. With thick extrudates, greater than about 2 mm (80 mil), no amount of rapid outside cooling can speed up the removal of heat held inside the PP section, and at least the center of the extrudate will be slowly cooled, with the high crystallinities and large spherulites

crystallization temperatures. In water-cooled thick sections, such as
necessary to provide enough heat transfer on the water side, through
prevent the stagnation of the water movement and the occasional
the causing bubbles and visual faults on the surface of the extrudate.
less than about 0.3 mm (12 mil), the heat transfer from the inside of the
part is tough that the external cooling rates control the PP form obtained.
exceeds 80° C/second, lower crystallinities and the clearer, tougher
to form is obtained. This usually means being sure that the melt is
by the cooling device, such as a chill roll. In the case of chill roll cast
must used to insure that the melted web is in contact with the metal roll,
thin layer of air between the film and roll. A layer of air even 25 μm
is in may reduce the cooling rate. The most rapid cooling results, of
the cooling device. However, practical considerations usually limit the
they, i.e., in the case of a chill roll, the condensation of moisture from
exposed section of the roll would lead to difficulties in obtaining
to the film.

cooling, as with a bundle of fibers, the uniform flow of the air over
usually the factor limiting the rate and the uniformity of the cooling.
the attention is given to the design of air distribution systems. Air
enough to achieve the smectic form of PP in conventional grades.
conventionally appeared in air-cooled films, while this has been a
known as well, the development of more rubbery, less crystalline forms of
the polymers, air-cooled films have become a reality with PP. Further
more 6.2.3.3.

in a thermoforming operation, a new set of questions arise. While
heating comes from the highest temperature source, such as radiating
the uniformity of heat becomes a problem with PP. Because PP does
not well, variations in the temperature reached can be quite high,
differences in thickness, crystallinity, composition, or proximity to the
sharp melting point of PP usually means that the behavior of the partially
crumble as the temperature rises, requiring a quite precise temperature to
the process step. It is for this reason that, for processes such as
forming, PP has been regarded to have a narrow processing window. That
dealt with the development of high melt strength PP (Section 7.1.8.3).
provides more precise temperature control, but larger installations
investments are needed. This approach is taken in the tenter frames
oriented films.
others, some advantage can be realized by conducting the down-
the extrusion. In that instance, the quenching operation need
to establish the dimensional stability of the extrudate, and reheating
considerable sensible heat remains. While this reduces the amount of
condition of the form entering the final operation now depends on the

Even at room temperature, the oriented item will shrink slowly, which can cause considerable distortion of inside layers of film or fiber on a wound package. In addition, the onset of shrinkage limits the temperatures at which heat-based processes such as coating, printing, or heat-sealing can occur. To eliminate the room temperature shrinkage, and to raise the temperature at which significant shrinkage begins to occur, the fiber or film is usually "heat set." In this procedure, the oriented item is brought to a temperature somewhat above the orientation temperature, commonly in line with the orientation step, and allowed to shrink a controlled amount, typically about 5%. With a proper balance of conditions, a room temperature shrinkage of zero can be achieved for the practical life of the wound package with only minor sacrifices in the desired properties of high strength and stiffness. In addition, the temperature at which shrinkage becomes a problem can be raised substantially.

While heat-setting fibers is relatively straightforward, heat-stetting biaxially oriented film presents more problems with the control of allowed shrinkage in the two directions. As a consequence, heat-setting of BOPP film is often predominantly in one direction, as evidenced by unbalanced shrinkage retained in the film. Besides heat-setting, shrinkage is also reduced by using high orientation temperatures.

Another method widely used for achieving orientation in fibers is to rapidly draw molten strands from the extrusion die while simultaneously cooling them with high velocity air. The resulting fiber bundle may be gathered on a moving screen and heat-bonded into a nonwoven web. This product is thus referred to as "spunbonded." In a somewhat similar process, "melt-blown" fibers are also oriented, but to a lower degree, by air exiting the die with the polymer. In the melt-blown operation, finer fibers are sought, and the web is not bonded. In both cases, the orientation developed is about one-third to one-half that of fully oriented fibers. The lower level of orientation is an acceptable compromise to realize the economies of these processes.

Even articles intended to be unoriented may show some orientation if there is sufficient drawdown or shear during cooling. Typically, thin films, spun fibers, and injection molded items from low melt flow resins display orientation. Often, such orientation is a problem in later operations, causing splitting, warping, shrinking, or variations in processing behavior.

9.1.2.3   Properties of Oriented Articles

Most important to the user is the effect of orientation on the end-use properties. The most evident and most valuable properties are the increases in strength and modulus, which rise essentially in proportion to the draw ratio. Figure 9.3 illustrates the increase in strength with draw ratio for fibers and films [5], and more detailed properties appear in Chapter 6, Tables 6.4 and 6.5. The increases in strength and stiffness are essentially because a larger number of chains are aligned in the stressed direction, so a smaller cross section can carry the same load. Consequently, the most economical means of delivering high strength PP is to achieve the maximum draw ratio consistent with processing continuity and other properties negatively affected by orientation. Most slit tape and monofilament processes are operated at the high end of the operable range of draw ratios. As the stiffness increases with higher orientation, the elongation to break decreases.

Orientation also markedly improves the low temperature impact behavior of PP. While unoriented homopolymer films and fibers are brittle at $0\,°C$, oriented films and fibers are tough at temperatures well below zero. Consequently, impact failures during shipping or use of oriented PP at low temperatures are of no concern.

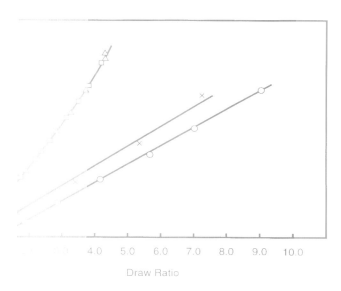

Draw Ratio

other valuable properties are enhanced by orientation: moisture strength. The reduction in moisture vapor permeability that of PP is quite dramatic, and represents one of the most valuable [6, 7]. It results from the increase in crystallinity and the more tortuous path for migrating molecules to pass through crystalline regions are essentially impervious to the passage of

morphology during biaxial orientation from spherulitic, with amorphous interfaces aligned in all directions, to the planar interfaces in the plane of the film, and at mostly submicron opportunity for light to be refracted while passing through the "cobblestone" surface associated with spherulitic growth, which reflected light, is reduced to virtually zero vertical dimension, As a result of these surface and internal changes, BOPP film has gloss levels.

moisture barrier, biaxial orientation increases the resistance to current. The voltage required to break down the insulating roughly three times that of unoriented film [8]. This property insulating layers and has helped the entry of BOPP films into

increased stiffness of BOPP films causes a significant reduction film is punctured, the opening will propagate with very little force.

Another curious but not entirely academic weakness in BOPP film is the strength through the film thickness. When BOPP film is heat-sealed with a tough coating, the weak point in the seal can be the internal film strength in the direction normal to the surface. This is because so few chains remain oriented in that direction; they have all been pulled into the plane of the film.

9.1.2.4   Measurement of Orientation

The degree of orientation of the polymer chains in a uniaxially drawn fiber is described with the Hermans orientation function:

$$f = \frac{3\cos^2 \Phi - 1}{2} \tag{7.1}$$

where Φ is the angle between the polymer chain axis and the drawing direction. The orientation function, f, has a value of zero for no orientation (random arrangement), 1.0 for 100% uniaxial orientation, and -0.5 when all chains are normal to the drawing direction. While this relationship applies to all chains in amorphous materials, crystalline polymers require consideration of the orientation in the amorphous and crystalline phases separately, which develop differently during drawing. The orientation functions of the phases are related to the overall average orientation function in the equation:

$$f_{\text{ave}} = \beta f_{\text{c}} + (1 - \beta) f_{\text{am}} \tag{7.2}$$

where f_{ave} is the overall average orientation function, β is the weight fraction of the crystalline phase, f_{c} is the orientation function for the chains in the crystalline phase, and f_{am} is the orientation function for the chains in the amorphous phase.

Using this concept, studies of PP orientation show that the chains in the crystalline phase orient first, with the chains in the amorphous phase going slightly negative initially (more perpendicular to the stretch direction), then turning positive, always being lower in orientation than the crystalline chains. These results are at odds with a popular perception of semicrystalline materials, that of discrete, isolated crystalline regions connected with a continuous amorphous phase, wherein the amorphous phase would orient first.

Indeed, the studies of orientation reveal much about the nature of the crystalline phase, its melting and recrystallization behavior, and its rearrangements and responses to the stresses or orientation. While we have spoken here about the orientation of the chain, which is the c axis of the PP crystal, the orientations of the a-axis and b-axis directions of the crystal are not random. A phenomenon known as "a-axis orientation," a tendency for the a-axis to have a higher orientation function than the b-axis (or to be less negative) occurs often with PP. High orientation temperature or orientation from the melt favor this behavior, which is related to a phenomenon called cross-hatching in the spherulite originally present (see Section 3.2.2).

The measurement of orientation is a highly developed science that is beyond the scope of this book. A layman's measure would be the modulus of the item; it is virtually proportional to the degree of orientation. Sonic modulus was one of the fundamental measurements used by Samuels in his description of PP orientation [5]. Another would be the refractive index, which can be considered in the three directions. The difference between the refractive index in the MD and the CD is the birefringence, which is used extensively in studying oriented fibers. The measurement of the refractive indexes in the MD and CD in films is a somewhat more

The relationship between the orientations of the individual phases indexes is a useful tool for a more detailed study of orientation. scattering pole figures provides a direct measurement of crystalline phase.

on Processes

processes for producing oriented products, then nonoriented

most demanding of the PP processes, those making the finest requiring the highest quality polymer with characteristics designed used fibers. We include in the fibers category a wide variety of vary considerably also. We will consider them from the finest to fibers are oriented.

melt blown process is that it can make very fine filaments and fabrics with excellent uniformity. The result is a soft fabric with properties, meaning effective filtration characteristics and resistance to This latter property is becoming vital in medical applications diseases increase. The disadvantage of melt-blown fabrics is strength, especially compared to spunbonded fabrics (next section). illustrated in Fig. 9.4, molten polymer moves from the blowing die. As the molten filaments exit the die, they are high velocity air (called process or primary air). This air with the quench air, solidifies the filaments. The entire place within 7 mm (0.25 in.) of the die. Die design is the key efficiently.

blowing the filaments directly onto a forming wire, about 15 in.) from the spinnerets. This distance influences fabric melt speed and throughput determine fabric weight. Although than spunbonded fabrics, because the finer filaments of melt-barrier properties, the optimum fabric is a combination of fabrics: spunbonded for strength, and melt-blown for barrier construction.

important to the formation of a consistent, desirable melt-blown filament breaks, leading to a defect known as "shot." These are the fabric that affect porosity, uniformity, and hand (texture) of the

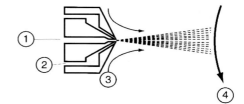

Figure 9.4 Schematic of melt blow fiber process: 1:
Molten polymer. 2: hot air. 3: cooling air. 4: collector
screen

fabric, and are a principal cause of off-quality fabric. Shot can also be caused by excessive
melt or process air temperatures, but too low a melt or process air temperature increases
filament size, adversely affecting fabric uniformity and barrier properties.

Melt blowing requires very high melt flow rate (MFR) (> 200 g/10 min), to obtain the
finest possible fibers. Some melt blowing manufacturers purchase about 35 MFR homopolymer and carry out peroxide-assisted degradation during extrusion to achieve the required
MFR. Degradation can be a source of process and fabric property variation. Commercial
resins with MFR in the 400 g/10 min to 1500 g/10 min range, made available with the
fourth generation catalyst technology, can be used without degradation. Higher MFR resins
allow lower melt and air temperatures, and save energy costs. Melt-blown fibers require
narrow molecular weight distribution (NMWD), ultra clean, low smoke PP resins for good
operations. The need for NMWD is explained further under spunbonded fabrics, where the
effects are more acute.

9.2.1.2   Spunbonded Fabric

The spunbonded process appears in Fig. 9.5. Filament formation can be accomplished with
one large spinneret having several thousand holes or with banks of smaller spinnerets
containing as few as 40 holes. After exiting the spinneret, the molten filaments are quenched
by a cross-flow air quench system, then pulled away from the spinneret and attenuated
(drawn) by high pressure air. There are two methods of air attenuation, both of which use the
venturi effect. The first draws the filament using an aspirator slot (slot draw), which runs the
width of the machine. The second method draws the filaments through a nozzle or aspirator
gun. Multiple guns are used, since orifice size is very important.

Filaments formed in this manner are collected on a screen ("wire") or porous forming
belt to form the fabric. Fabric weight is determined by throughput per spinneret hole, number
of holes, and the speed of the forming belt. A vacuum is maintained on the underside of the
belt. This vacuum is very important to uniform fabric formation and removes air used in
attenuating the filaments.

Air handling and control is critical to the process. The fabric formation area is frequently
sealed off from the rest of the line to improve control. Various methods are used to aid fabric
formation and improve uniformity. Examples include stationary or moving deflectors, and the
use of static electricity or air turbulence to improve the dispersion of the filaments.

To improve fabric integrity, it passes through compression rolls, which can also seal off
the forming chamber. The fabric is then passed between heated calender rolls where the raised
lands on one roll bond the fabric at points covering about 20% to 40% of its area to increase

Figure 9.5 Spunbonded fabric process: A: spinning. B: stretching. C: nap formation. 1: molten polymer. 2: gear pump. 3: die block. 4: filament. 5: stretching nozzle. 6: stretching pipe. 7: deflector. 8: web. 9: suction. 10: receiver mat. 11: air

strength. The choice of resin influences the bonding temperature and affects fabric strength and softness. A wide bonding temperature range is a combination of operability and properties.

... topical finish can be applied to the fabric to make it hydrophobic, ... or anti-static, as desired. Topical finish application is the common fabric attributes, but the use of concentrates added to the PP before or ... The use of concentrates allows the additive to become part of the ... treating, the fabric is slit into rolls of desired widths and lengths. ... quality of fabric produced can vary widely, depending on a ... including equipment choice. While there are several equipment ... Reifenhäuser and STP Impianti, almost every spunbonded line is ... modified by the processor to improve fabric quality or efficiency. Air ... throughput per spinneret hole, fabric weight, and numerous other ... significant impact on fabric quality and process efficiency. These factors ... of proprietary information that has been developed by each ... fabrics, although the spread of such information has increased ... operation.

For example, filament denier (diameter) has a significant effect on fabric quality and process efficiency. Filament denier is determined by melt viscosity, throughput per spinneret hole, and the velocity of the attenuating air. While higher denier filaments give fewer breaks in spinning, finer denier gives desirable fabric properties such as softness, uniform coverage, and strength. These counteracting results constitute a classic trade-off of fabric properties versus efficiency and cost that is part of the processing business.

The ability to draw the filaments is often limited by available air pressure. This can be overcome by reducing throughput per hole, but at a cost penalty. This reduces denier per filament (dpf) but increases melt draw down and the possibility of spin breaks, consequent fabric defects, and waste. Filament diameter is also affected by distance of the draw from the spinnerette, type of drawing device, quench conditions, melt strength, resin rheology, and resin quality.

The typical resin used for spunbonded fabric is a 30 MFR to 40 MFR controlled rheology, NMWD homopolymer resin. The high MFR is to provide a reasonable throughput while attaining reasonable fabric properties. The NMWD is specifically designed for developing higher orientation during the very high drawdown of these fibers. While broad MWD polymer is more viscous and develops more orientation at low drawdown situations, the roles reverse at a high draw rate, and NMWD becomes more effective at retaining the drawdown as orientation; it is more viscous at these conditions. At the spunbonded draw rates, NMWD responds better. For the same reason, NMWD also gives better spinning continuity; the highly drawn fiber "strain hardens" more quickly and is less likely to fail. Instead, the thicker part of the fiber is drawn down more. Ideally, the polymer should also be gel-free, and the additive package should provide good melt stability to maintain process performance and fiber physical properties, and should resist gas fading and thermal discolorations. Additives can also affect the amount of "smoke" (volatiles) released as the filaments are extruded, which can foul spinnerets, guns, or slots and leads to the formation of drips, which can cause filament breaks. The grade of polymer must take into account all of these needs to perform well. Both PP suppliers and fabric processors have made remarkable progress in the development of effective polymer grades in recent decades.

9.2.1.3   Conventional Fine Denier PP Fibers

In the three more conventional PP fiber operations, continuous filament (CF), bulked continuous filament (BCF), and staple, the formation of the molten fiber at the die is crucial. Because the holes in the die, called a spinneret, are quite small, 0.3 mm to 0.8 mm (10 mil to 30 mil) in diameter, low melt viscosity is important. Consequently, high melt temperature (230 °C to 280 °C) and high melt flow rates (15 g/10 min to 40 g/10 min) are used. A relatively large extruder is usually equipped with a manifold to distribute a high output of molten PP to a bank of eight to twenty spinnerets. Each spinhead is usually equipped with a separate gear pump to regulate output through that spinhead; a filter pack, supported by a "breaker plate;" and the spinneret plate within the head. The number of holes in the spinneret plate determines the number of filaments in a yarn and varies considerably with the different yarn constructions, but it is typically in the range of 50 to 250. The holes are typically grouped into round, annular, or rectangular patterns to assist in good distribution of the quench air flow.

que used to enhance the appearance of PP fabrics is to alter the cross
fabrics are more attractive when shiny reflections are observed, so
Consequently, spinnerets are built with hole shapes to provide more
round. A summary of some cross sections used in PP fibers

Filament Fibers

process was originally used to produce continuous filament (CF)
in Fig. 9.7, shows that the spinning and drawing operations are
process, molten polymer is extruded through spinnerets to form
usually with a traditional cross-flow air quench. The product at
"spun yarn." Finish application is usually applied at the bottom of
fiber is cool enough for good pickup. This extends the time before
finish to distribute better over the filaments. This slight
improves drawing efficiency.
use the two-step process, which, like any interrupted process,
difficulties. With PP, the secondary crystallization, which
exacerbates the quality problems. However, the two-step
and higher tenacities if needed.
yarns typically range from 40 denier to 2,000 denier
Filaments can range from 1 to 20 dpf, and the range is growing.
produced filaments finer than 2 dpf. Total denier and dpf are end-

typically 800 m/min to 1500 m/min (2500 ft/min to 5000 ft/min).
draw ratios of 3:1 or more (one- or two-stage draw) and wound
drawing allows higher draw ratios to be achieved. These draw
filaments and slit tape because rather high levels of orientation
step. Winding speeds are 2,000 m/min to 3,500 m/min
The product is known as "flat yarn," meaning it has no
used as-is, or textured and combined with other yarns.
900 m/min (3000 ft/min) require a NMWD to get the best
Filaments. Resins with a MFR of about 35 and a NMWD, with a
under 2.8 are typical. In slower spinning processes, or in heavier
reactor grade product may be more appropriate. Long-term heat
thermal or gas yellowing, and good UV stability are required for
yarn applications. See Section 4.6.1.2 for more details regarding

cross sections and corresponding filament cross sections

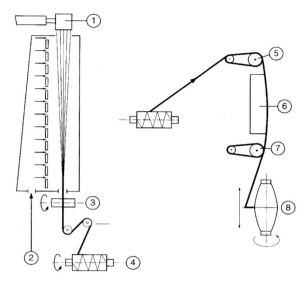

Figure 9.7 Layout for two-step continuous filament (CF) yarn process: 1: Extrusion head, with gear pump. 2: cooling air inlet. 3: finish application roll. 4: takeup for unoriented yarn. 5: slow rolls. 6: heated plate (stretching occurs here). 7: fast rolls. 8: takeup for stretched and twisted yarn

For lower denier, finer dpf yarns, the resin must be gel- and dirt-free to obtain the spinning continuity necessary for an efficient process. As with spunbonded fibers, smoke and volatiles are more critical in the finer filaments, and deposits and drips are less tolerable. Since most CF yarns are fine denier (2 dpf to 5 dpf), a low-smoke resin is required to control broken filaments and loops that cause waste and inefficiency. Slower spinning, heavier dpf products are less critical, but cleaner resins give better process performance.

9.2.1.5   Bulked Continuous Filament

The largest fiber use of PP in the United States is in bulked continuous filament (BCF) yarns. These yarns are used mainly in carpet face yarns and upholstery fabrics.

Like CF yarns, BCF fabrication processes fall into two basic types, one-step and two-step. In the older, two-step process, an undrawn yarn is spun at less than 1,000 m/min (3,300 ft/min), usually about 750 m/min, and placed on a package. The yarn is drawn (usually in two stages) and "bulked" on a machine called a texturizer. Winding and drawing speeds are limited by the bulking or texturizing device to 2,500 m/min (8,200 ft/min) or less. As in the two-step CF process, secondary crystallization requires prompt draw-texturizing.

The most common process today is the one-step spin/draw/text (SDT) process, illustrated in Fig. 9.8. This process provides better economics, efficiency, and quality than the two-step process. It is similar to the one-step CF process, except that the bulking device is in-line.

Bulk or texture changes yarn appearance, separating filaments and adding enough gentle bends and folds to make the yarn appear fatter (bulkier). This gives more coverage in a fabric

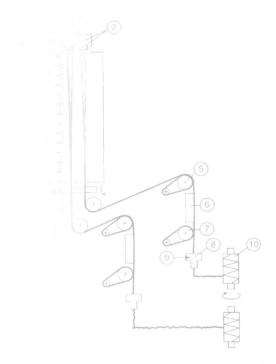

... ... drawn/texturize (SDT) bulked continuous filament (BCF) yarn process.
... ... spinnerets, each with a gear pump to control output. 3: Cooling air inlet. 4:
... ... Heated plate. Stretching occurs here. 7: Fast rolls. 8: Bulker-interlacer.

... ... It also improves hand and softness and gives the yarn a more
... ... Bulking (aka hot air texturing) is achieved by aspirating the yarn
... ... 160°C (285°F to 330°F) compressed air. Expansion of the air
... ... causing the filaments to separate, intermingle, fold, and form
... ... The plug is forced out of the bulking chamber and contacts a
... ... pulled through the relaxed yarn cools it and sets its bulk. Folds
... ... near the softening point become permanent.

... ... filament yarns range from 150 yarn denier to 3,600 yarn denier with
... ... 40 dpf. However, 1,200 denier to 3,000 denier and 15 dpf to 30 dpf
... ... 38,000 denier or more can be made by combining BCF yarns.
... ... BCF resins are 12 MFR to 22 MFR with normal MWD. For finer
... ... process, total denier, and spinning speeds, NMWD resins with MFR
... ... For special situations, broad MWD is desired. For example, a
... ... produces a more resilient yarn than a NMWD, resulting in better
... ... tufted carpet after traffic and wear. Broad MWD resins give low
... ... in the 2.8 gpd to 3.2 gpd range. The high elongation and lower
... ... would provide in this case would cause processing problems on today's
... ... and the resulting carpet or fabric.

Heavier filament BCF is more tolerant of gels and dirt than finer products, but good practice limits impurities to avoid broken filaments and frequent screen pack changes. Higher isotacticity PP (xylene solubles < 4%) fibers are more soil resistant and easier to clean, a benefit in upholstery fabrics and carpets. The additive package should not contribute to gas fading and thermal yellowing. In outdoor carpet or furniture, additional UV and heat stabilizers are usually incorporated for longer service life.

As with spunbonded fibers, volatile components released from molten filaments generate smoke and can cause condensation and dripping, a source of spin breaks and process problems. More frequent spinneret change are also needed with a smoky resin.

9.2.1.6   Staple Fibers

There are two basic staple fiber fabrication processes: traditional and compact spinning. The traditional process involves two steps: 1) producing, applying finish, and winding undrawn tow, followed by 2) drawing, a secondary finish application, crimping, and cutting into staple. In a traditional fiber tower, the spinning operation is essentially the same as continuous filament operations, and drawing may be in-line or two-step, with the same difficulties associated with the interrupted two-step process. The tow may be wound on bobbins or placed in 500-pound containers called cans. If the tow ages for more than three days before the second step, secondary crystallization reduces drawability, causing waste and inefficiency in the final step.

The bobbins or cans are moved to a creel and combined into a large tow band (over a million denier) to be processed on the fiber line. The tow is reheated on heated rolls or in ovens and drawn, usually in two stages, given a second coating of spin finish, and crimped. Some lines dry the tow at this point to remove excess moisture and improve crimp stability. The tow is cut to staple fiber and baled, or air conveyed to a subsequent process. Filaments can range from 1.5 dpf to > 70 dpf, depending on the application. Staple length can be as short as 7 mm or as long as 200 mm (0.25 in. to 8 in.) to suit the application.

Crimping is conducted to give the fiber bulk and cohesion, which are needed if the fibers are to be spun into a yarn or formed into a web. Most applications do not require crimp. Crimping is accomplished by over-feeding the tow into a steam-heated stuffer box with a pair of nip rolls. The tow is still wet with finish solution, which acts as lubricant and aids heat transfer in the stuffer box. The over-feed folds the tow in the box, forming bends or crimps in the filaments. These bends are heat-set by steam injected into the box. When the pressure of the tow being forced into the stuffer box exceeds a set pressure applied by a hydraulic cylinder, the box opens and crimped tow is released. The MW, MWD, and isotactic content of the resin all affect crimp stability, amplitude, and ease of crimping.

The second staple process is known as compact staple spinning and is mostly used to produce finer staple fibers (1.5 dpf to 5.0 dpf). Compact spinning is a one-step process and has a cost advantage over the two-step process. Spinning speed is about 100 m/min (330 ft/min) or less than 10% of the traditional process. To make up for the low spinning speeds, spinnerets with as many as 50,000 holes are used, which require a different quench system. Compact spinning uses a radial outflow, 25 mm to 50 mm (1 in. to 2 in.) quench zone versus the traditional cross-flow, 300 mm to 600 mm (12 in. to 24 in.) quench zone. The short quench zone and the number of holes limit the denier of filament that can be quenched.

...hybrid staple systems representing crosses between traditional and
... and has its own benefits and disadvantages.
...depends on the type of staple fiber being made, its application and
... choice of traditional versus compact process is a consideration.
... aspect, temperatures, and equipment limitations can also limit the
... fibers for spun yarns for secondary carpet backing and industrial
... correctly (> 4.0 grams per denier, gpd) and moderate elongation
... PP with a MFR of 10 g/10 min to 14 g/10 min is required. In
... PP with a MFR of from 18 g/10 min to 30 g/10 min would be used
... to obtain the combination of fabric strength, fabric elongation,
... wide MWD resins give stronger fabric, and high fiber elongation
... The higher MFR gives better spinnability. For needle-punched
... applications, tenacity should not exceed 3.4 gpd with 50% to 70%
... MFR of 14 g/10 min to 22 g/10 min would likely be chosen.
... also require tenacities of 3.4 gpd or less but should have a fiber
... fiber hot air shrinkage under 4%.
... PP fibers, staple resins should have good melt stability,
... oxides and heat, and generate little smoke. Narrow MWD resins
... for staple applications.

... filaments are extruded into a water bath and subsequently drawn
... cpf. Filaments (each also called an "end") are combined to
... Drawing is usually conducted using a set of heated rolls. A bundle of
... one) is collected on cones. Rope or twine is then produced by
... together into strands, and twisting strands, commonly three or
... strands are also braided into lighter duty ropes. Individual
... into straps or fabrics.
... in monofilament is tenacity (strength). Low MFR resins,
... oriented efficiently and provide high tenacities at draw ratios
... MWD polymers allow higher draw ratios, which produce higher
... flow rates, the heat built up during extrusion is greater than
... fibers, and more attention to melt stability and extrusion
...
... comparable to monofilaments, as the individual filaments are
... extrusion process is similar in design and output rate. However,
... processes used are highly varied. They range from lightweight,
... dware and produce bags, based on counter-rotating annular die
... made by perforating and orienting sheet for animal, snow, and
... nets are also produced with complicated dies that add cross-
... extruded MD filaments. The processes in this category
... than those of conventional fibers.

Widths of 600 mm to 2000 mm (24 in. to 80 in.) are common. Extruders from 60 mm to 150 mm (2.5 in. to 6 in.) in diameter are used, with outputs of 260 kg/hr to 600 kg/hr (600 lb/hr to 1300 lb/hr).

The extruder is often equipped with a gear pump to regulate output and control sheet thickness and quality, two crucial aspects of sheet production. The slot die, with the die lip opening set slightly greater than the desired sheet thickness, extrudes the melt at 200 °C to 230 °C (400 °F to 450 °F), horizontally into a nip between two rolls of a three-roll stack. Figure 9.15 illustrates the process. A small bead of melt is usually built up in the first nip so that the surface of the sheet may be "polished" by (in this case) the bottom roll prior to being cooled by the center roll. This action helps provide a uniform thickness across the sheet and gives a smoother surface to the air side of the sheet. Care must be taken not to build up too large a bead, as melt disturbances can occur and cause defects in the sheet.

Except in very thick sheets, crystallization is usually complete through the thickness before leaving the first cooling roll, and the second cooling roll is simply for the removal of additional heat. The sheet passes over a roller conveyor, which sometimes will employ fans to complete the cooling process. After passing through a thickness measuring device (not shown), the sheet is cut and stacked, or wound into rolls.

Considerable attention to melt and roll temperatures is necessary to produce good quality sheet, as small differences can influence the crystallization and shrinkage behavior differently on the opposite sides of the sheet, leading to curling and warping of the sheet.

While quality sheet may be made with a wide range of PP types, preferably at about 1 MFR, the end-use application, often a thermoformed container, usually dictates the polymer used. Thus, random copolymer is often used for the clarity. If a lower temperature impact is needed, then impact copolymer, with the poorer optics, is preferred. In all cases, well-stabilized polymer is needed, not only to provide the best melt uniformity during the sheet operation but to allow for the very high rates of scrap associated with the thermoforming operation. The thermoformer often has an arrangement for the return to the sheet extruder of the 40% to 50% scrap that can easily occur.

9.2.3.4.1 Thermoforming   Thermoforming is the process of forming heated, pliable plastic sheet into a desired shape. Thermoforming has the advantages of relatively low forming pressures, low mold costs, production of multilayer structures, and low cost fabrication of large parts. By using a multicavity tool, small thin-wall parts, such as those used for food packaging, can be made in high volume with relatively low cost. Although PP has not enjoyed wide acceptance in this area, modest business exists, and recent PP developments in melt strength could alter that situation. Critical process issues in thermo-

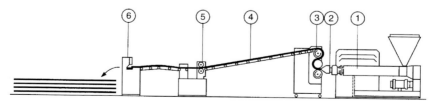

Figure 9.15 Sheet process. 1: Extruder. 2: Slot die. 3: Cooling roll stack. 4: Roller conveyor. 5: Take-off nip rolls. 6: Guillotine and stacker, or winder for thin sheet

forming include sheet quality, formed part thickness uniformity, dimensional stability, part reproducibility, and regrind use.

The typical thermoforming sequence, illustrated in Fig. 9.16, involves heating, clamping, shaping, cooling, and trimming of an extruded plastic sheet. The two methods used for PP are melt phase thermoforming and solid phase pressure forming (SPPF).

Melt phase thermoforming is performed above the melting point of the polymer and uses vacuum or low pressure to achieve the desired form. The low pressures used simplify tool design and extend tool life. The thermoforming process can be sheet fed (intermittent) or roll fed (continuous). Larger or thicker sheet may require a rotary process, with several heating stages. Even in a roll fed process, thicker sheets will require multiple heating stops.

The thermoformability of PP is directly related to the quality of the extruded sheet. Sheet gauge uniformity of less than $\pm 5\%$ is required for acceptable part uniformity. High levels of sheet orientation cause distortion during heating and result in variation in sheet temperature. Orientation can be measured by the amount of shrinkage in the machine or cross-direction of the sheet when heated to a temperature of $170\,°C$ to $185\,°C$ ($340\,°F$ to $365\,°F$). Shrinkage should be below 10%.

Conventional PP grades can be difficult to melt thermoform due to sheet sagging, sheet thinning, and a small operating temperature window. Greater dimensional change takes place in melting PP than in amorphous polymers, due to the crystallinity. This tends to cause more warping, wrinkling, and sagging. Some mechanical measures such as support bands and air pressure have been useful in combating these difficulties.

Thermoforming is accomplished by vacuum, positive air pressure, plug-assisted vacuum forming, or combinations and variations of these, once the sheet reaches thermoforming temperature of $170\,°C$ to $185\,°C$ ($340\,°F$ to $365\,°F$). A prestretched bubble step is used, especially on large parts, to improve material distribution. Plug-assisted forming is generally used for small deep drawn parts. Plug material, design, and timing can be critical to optimization of the process. Plugs made from insulating foam avoid premature quenching of the plastic. The plug shape is usually similar to the mold cavity, but smaller and without part detail. A round plug bottom will usually promote even material distribution and uniform side-wall thickness. For a semicrystalline polymer such as PP, fast plug speeds generally provide the best material distribution in the part.

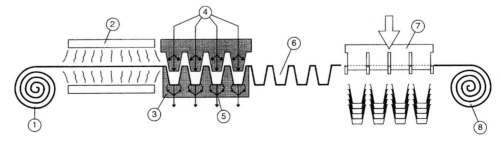

Figure 9.16 Melt phase thermoforming. 1: Sheet unwind. Sheet feeder for thicker sheets. 2: Infrared heating station. 3: Forming mold. 4: Air pressure plug assist. 5: Vacuum. 6: Transport and cooling station. 7: Cutting and stacking station. 8: Scrap winder

The formed part is cooled in the mold. Sufficient cooling to maintain a mold temperature of 30 °C to 65 °C (90 °F to 150 °F) is needed. The part should be below 90 °C to 100 °C (200 °F to 220 °F) before ejection.

Trimming the part from the web depends upon the temperature of the sheet and the type of trimming equipment. Thinner sheet (less than 1 mm or 0.04 in.) is easily trimmed after 1 to 2 minutes cooling time. Thicker sheet may require air or water spray cooling to allow trimming in a continuous process. Thick sheet (over 3 mm or 0.125 in.) and large parts are often trimmed off line after cooling for several minutes, sometimes using a sizing tool. Thin parts (up to 0.75 mm or 0.03 in.) are trimmed using sheet rule dies. Thicker parts are sheared with dies having tool and die clearances less than 0.01 mm (0.0005 in.). Thermoforming typically yields large amounts of trim (50% or more) which economy requires be reused. Excellent polymer melt stability and the use of mild extrusion conditions are essential for reuse of trim.

The PP types for thermoforming are first selected according to the sheet extrusion needs. As mentioned above, these would usually be about 1 MFR, but could vary depending on the sheet thickness. In addition, the application for the thermoformed part also determines resin selection. For a high temperature or high stiffness use, a homopolymer would be chosen. To provide good clarity, a random copolymer would be used. For cold temperature uses, impact copolymers must be chosen.

For the best behavior in thermoforming, the lowest melt flow rate polymers would be preferred. However, they can present problems in extrusion. A PP with higher melt strength has been developed that possesses better resistance to the sagging normally encountered with PP. It holds its shape better during heating and gives better distribution in the formed part, while exhibiting the other properties normally attributed to conventional PPs. Further details may be found in Section 7.1.8.3.

9.2.3.4.2 Solid Phase Pressure Forming

Prior to the development of high melt strength PP, solid phase pressure forming (SPPF) was developed to avoid sag problems with PP and to provide enhanced properties in the formed part. Higher forming pressure (> 5 bars) used in SPPF allows PP to be formed at a temperature just below the melting point (typically 160 °C or 320 °F). At this temperature, the forming process orients PP, increasing part clarity, stiffness (crush resistance), and tensile strength, thus allowing reduction in part thickness and weight. However, the mold and other equipment costs for SPPF are higher than for conventional thermoforming, which has limited the popularity of this approach.

9.2.3.4.3 Melt Forming

Another process for forming PP into shallow shapes is melt forming. In this process, a thin sheet of PP, usually in the 0.1 mm to 0.5 mm (5 mil to 20 mil) range, is extruded over a segmented roll or belt having numerous cooled molds into which the molten sheet is drawn with vacuum. The PP cools and is crystallized quickly, and the formed web is pulled away from the molds and wound for later trimming. The parts made from this process are limited to thin walls (for rapid cooling), shallow shapes, and low uniformity. However, the process can be operated at a low cost and has been used to a limited extent with PP.

9.2.3.5   Extrusion Coating

Polypropylene is useful as a coating resin where easy release for pressure-sensitive labels, liquid-resistant coatings, strength enhancement, or abrasion resistance are desired. Coating thickness on smooth paper can be little as 15 μm (0.6 mil), but is typically about 25 μm (1 mil). Coatings on other substrates such as cloth or woven scrim can be much heavier depending upon the final product requirements. A typical coating process is illustrated in Fig. 9.17.

To promote adhesion, extrusion coating melt temperatures are normally above 260 °C (500 °F), and occasionally exceed 315 °C (600 °F). These temperatures are needed for oxidation of the melt in the short gap between the die and nip to develop adhesion. The minimum gap possible should be used to minimize temperature loss in the gap and, thus, maintain the maximum temperature at the nip. PP exposed to air at high temperatures generates noticeable smoke, especially at 290 °C (550 °F) and above. Therefore, effective fume control measures must be used. Additionally, flash point values for PP are about 330 °C (625 °F), so precautions against overheating and fire must be taken.

In the paper coating operation, the die lip opening is typically 0.4 mm to 0.5 mm (15 mil to 20 mil). The melt falls directly down into the nip between the cooling roll and the rubber-covered pressure roll. Polypropylene requires high roll pressures to promote adhesion, so sometimes higher durometer rubber rolls must be used. An air knife is sometime used to assure that the melt touches the substrate just prior to entering the nip.

Polypropylene resins with melt flows of 30 and higher are utilized. Conventional PP experiences edge-weave and drawdown surge at coating speeds much above 100 m/min (300 ft/min). The use of high melt strength PP, described in Section 7.1.8.3, eliminating these difficulties, raises the coating speed to over 350 m/min (1200 ft/min) in most coating situations.

Special PP grades for extrusion coating on paper, which combine good adhesion, good clarity, low gel count, pinhole resistance, and excellent cleanliness, are available. Other resins are available for other substrates such as carpet backing, cloth woven slit tape, raffia, and woven scrims.

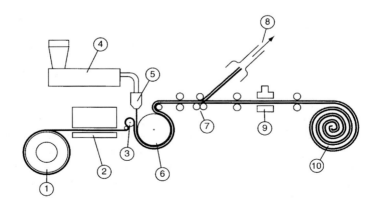

Figure 9.17 Extrusion coating process. 1: Substrate feed. 2: Substrate preheat oven. 3: Rubber pressure roll. 4: Extruder. 5: Slot die. 6: Polished chill roll. 7: Edge trim slitter. 8: Vacuum trim take-off. 9. Thickness profile gauge. 10: Winder

9.2.3.6   Other Extrusions

9.2.3.6.1   Profiles and Pipe   The properties of PP, particularly the toughened grades, make it attractive for profiles such as auto rub strips and body cladding, where it is used in appreciable volumes. While other more complicated profiles may find PP desirable, the process becomes difficult. Limited quantities of small-diameter pipe are extruded from PP. In a normal profile extrusion, the melt, usually at a low temperature to maintain the extrudate shape, is extruded into a shaping mandrel and cooling device and pulled through this assembly with a soft belt caterpillar or rubber rolls. The cooling section can be an open trough or a vacuum-sizing box, depending on the shape. The speed through the unit is usually slow, because the sections to be cooled are relatively thick. For PP, the combination of slow cooling of thick sections, the extra heat of crystallization to be removed, the normal low melt strength, and the changes in dimensions due to crystallization make processing PP into profiles a difficult challenge. However, it is successfully done commercially.

The design of the die to produce a particular profile is a difficult task even for amorphous polymers, and is more severe for crystalline polymers like PP. Attention to die design, heater placement, water circulation, and profile guides are all important.

Well-stabilized fractional (<1) melt flow rate resins and use of high melt strength PP are most effective for profiles of PP. Melt temperatures lower than 200 °C (400 °F) are used.

9.2.3.6.2   Wire and Cable Coating   Most PP used in wire coating has been for insulating outdoor cable singles, usually on solid wire from 19 to 26 gage. Small amounts of resin have been used in foamed or thick-wall constructions. Coating of larger constructions may differ in detail from the following.

Equipment required for wire and cable coating are similar in approach and differ mainly in size. A coating line consists of an extruder with screen pack, crosshead die, wire or cable supply, wire or cable preheater, cooling trough, water stripper, spark tester (checks for pinholes or breaks in the coating), optional capacitance and optical diameter gages, capstan (tractor) unit, accumulator, and wind-up unit or spooler. Depending on coating speed, wire supply can range from in-line drawing, to tandem reel pay-off, to single spool sources. High-speed take-ups provide automatic reel feeding, instantaneous reel changeover, and automatic reel discharge. Automation is rarely needed for the lower speed operations.

Coating crossheads are of two types, pressure and tubing; pressure heads are much more common. They have a wire guider near the exit side of the core tube that provides a tight fit, about 0.06 mm (0.0025 in.) clearance for 22 gage wire to prevent back flow of melt. A contoured flow channel guides melt around the core tube, wire guider tip, and onto the moving wire before it exits the die. Die diameters 5% to 20% larger than the insulated outside diameter give a good compromise between smoothness and insulation elongation. Conductor preheat, typically 120 °C to 150 °C (250 °F to 300 °F), is vital to control insulation elongation and shrink-back. Larger conductors are less sensitive to preheat. Cooling of the PP provides a snug fit to wire without a bond.

For some operations a tube-on type head can be used. The head is a modified tube or pipe die, but instead of inflating the extruded tube, a vacuum draws the extruded tube down onto the wire surface after both exit the crosshead. The wire enters the crosshead through a core tube fitted with a flexible seal that allows the vacuum to be controlled. Shrinkage of PP provides a tight fit to the conductor.

Polypropylene wire coating grades used commercially have MFRs of 0.5 g/10 min to 3 g/10 min and are stabilized to resist copper promoted oxidation. Such resins must be tough at low temperature, free of contamination, and have excellent flow characteristics at high shear. Foaming is achieved with chemical blowing agents and low melt temperatures. Melt temperatures in the range of 200 °C to 270 °C (400 °F to 515 °F) are typical. Insulating speeds up to 2100 m/min (7000 ft/min) have been achieved for telephone wire, while larger constructions may employ rates as low as 30 m/min (100 ft/min). A water tank 6 m (20 ft) long is adequate for low speeds, while a longer cooling trough, 25 m (80 ft), designed with boundary layer removal and drag management features is needed for high-speed telephone wire processes.

9.2.3.6.3   Corrugated Board   Corrugated board is an unusual application for PP; it is a replacement for corrugated paper board, but is substantially more durable. Few polymers have enjoyed use as a corrugated board, but PP has managed to become fairly widely accepted. The "board" cross section is actually parallel (horizontal) walls joined by frequent vertical strips (flutes) that run, of course, in the machine direction. The cross section looks like a ladder.

The corrugated board process, shown schematically in Fig. 9.18a, is an integrated process in four steps: extrusion, forming, annealing, and cutting. In the first step, the molten PP polymer is extruded through a custom-designed die with a ladder cross section, Fig. 9.18b. Forming, the second step, cools the molten extruded board as it passes through a vacuum former where the vacuum applied to the top and bottom platens hold the vertical dimension of the board while the sheet and flutes solidify into the final shape. The vacuum applied to the sheet must be controlled to get acceptable flatness and crush resistance. The optimum crush resistance is obtained when the internal flutes are perfectly perpendicular to the top and bottom surfaces. The third step is annealing the sheet in an oven to release induced stresses and insure flatness. The sheet is cut into its final dimension in the last step.

Commercial corrugated board ranges from 2 mm to 16 mm (0.08 in. to 0.65 in.) in thickness. The difficulty in making corrugated board is directly related to the thickness of the sheet. The line speed and output is limited by the forming step. Polypropylene grades with faster crystallization time or high melt strength (which is also nucleated) can reduce the forming time. At higher line speed, the annealing step becomes the next limitation. Overcoming this bottleneck will require longer ovens.

Low MFR PP grades are suitable for the process. However, if the final product must also have low temperature impact resistance, an impact copolymer would be required. Since this is essentially a profile extrusion process, melt strength is important, so use of low MFR and/or high melt strength PP grade is recommended.

9.2.3.6.4   Foamed Sheet   Although most foamed sheet is prepared from PS, one product has persisted in PP: a low-density, tough sheet for packaging items with delicate surfaces, such as furniture and electronic devices. The process uses a mixture of a PP copolymer and a solvent that causes a rapid, adiabatic expansion when extruded at a relatively low temperature, forming a very low density foam, less than 1 lb/cu ft. The control of this process is very sensitive and operates satisfactorily within a rather narrow temperature range.

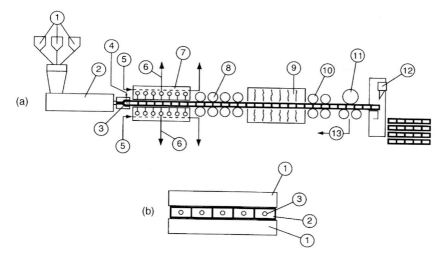

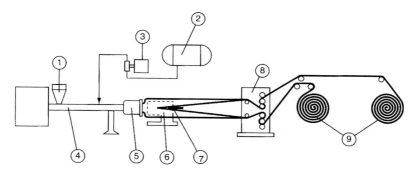

Figure 9.18 (a) Corrugated board process. 1: Polymer, recycle, and pigment feeding hoppers. 2: Extruder. 3: Special "ladder" cross section die. Note that flutes are shown here symbolically in side view, but flutes actually run in the machint direction. 4: Air pressure for inflating channels. 5: Cooling water. 6: Vacuum, pulled at both surfaces of board. 7: Cooling and calibrating platens. 8: Haul-off nip rolls. 9: Stress relief oven. 10: Nip rolls. 11: Edge trim and grind. 12: Guillotine. 13: Trim recycle to extruder. (b) Face "ladder" die detail. 1: Adjustable outer die lips. 2: Fixed center blank. 3: Air outlet

Figure 9.19 Foamed sheet process. 1: Polymer hopper. 2: Blowing agent storage tank. 3: Blowing agent feed pump. 4: Extruder. 5: Annular die. 6: Cooling and calibrating mandrel. 7: Slitting knives. 8: Take-off rolls. 9: Winders

With the development of high melt strength PP, it is now possible to manufacture foamed PP sheet in the normal density range of 3 lb/cu ft to 10 lb/cu ft. The process for foamed sheet is illustrated in Fig. 9.19. The selection of blowing agents, melt temperatures, and aging conditions for PP are different than for PS. Although use of PP in this product has been very limited, the process for manufacturing PP foamed sheet has been defined [9].

9.3   Injection Molding

The injection molding process is a cost-effective means for producing most high-volume, three-dimensional PP parts. Advantages are appearance, performance, cost, and flexibility to respond to changing market needs. Successful injection molding requires adequate product design, mold or tool design and construction, machine design and operation, and resin selection. It is a complex business with much history among almost all the major plastics, in addition to PP. The advantages of PP have been similar for several decades: easy molding and low material cost, combined with a range of PP types to choose from.

9.3.1   Product Design

The product must be designed not only to perform its function but also to facilitate consistent manufacture to acceptable tolerances. The following are normally recommended for PP parts:

- Parts should be designed with 1.5 degree or more of draft angle per side.
- Generous radii should be allowed on internal and external corners to reduce stresses.
- For "living hinge" design, the design guide [10] should be consulted.

9.3.2   Mold Design

- Runners should transfer the molten PP from the nozzle to the cavities via the shortest practical path with little pressure or temperature change. Commercially available, streamlined, hot runner systems with solid state controls are preferred over cold runner, three-plate, or insulated runner designs.
- Gases displaced as the mold fills must be vented to prevent compressed air burn marks (diesel effect) and avoid weak weld lines.
- Cooling line layout must be designed to remove heat controllably and uniformly to prevent warpage and achieve minimum cycle times.
- Mold coolant flow rates and dimensions should provide turbulent flow when possible.
- The ejection system should provide positive mechanical movement of the part with little deformation.

9.3.3   Molding Cycle

In a reciprocating screw machine, the molding cycle, illustrated in Fig. 9.20, consists of the following steps:

1. Mold close,
2. injection mold fill,
3. mold pack,

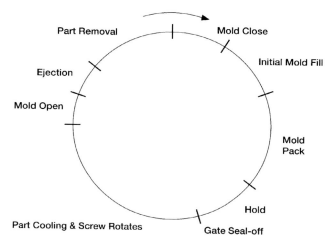

Figure 9.20 Injection molding cycle for reciprocating screw machine

4. hold (mostly in cold runner molds),
5. part cooling,
6. mold open,
7. part ejection, and
8. screw recovery cycle.

After hold, step 8 occurs in parallel with the cooling cycle to melt and mix PP for the next shot. Details of the molding cycle are described in the following sections.

9.3.3.1   Mold Fill

In this step, PP melt is pushed through the runner system into the cavity by the extrusion screw check ring or valve assembly. The fill cycle strongly impacts part quality. Important resin variables are melt viscosity (a function of MFR and temperature) and crystallization rate. Process choices include injection fill rate (programmable), gate and runner design, mold temperature, and transfer point. At the transfer point, the hydraulic pump moving the screw check ring assembly changes from high volume, low pressure to low volume, high pressure. Elapsed time or ram travel (or pressure) data trigger the transfer point, but ram deceleration or travel is the most reliable. High MFR resins are more tolerant of minute differences in runner and mold geometry. Higher freezing rate resin may require higher fill rates or mold temperatures.

9.3.3.2   Mold Pack

This step completes fill of the cavity to a set pressure (and part weight), usually with little screw movement. This is often done by setting a high final fill pressure so that ram momentum packs the cavity.

9.3.3.3   Hold

This step uses the melt pressure transmitted from the screw assembly to maintain the internal cavity pressure until 1) the gate freezes off or 2) the part solidifies. If the cycle is too short, any melt movement will create unwanted stresses.

9.3.3.4   Cooling

Mold cooling efficiency (heat removal rate) and initial melt temperature (heat to be removed) control cycle length. For a high melt flow resin, lower melt temperature may be used, reducing the cycle, lowering differential cooling stresses, and giving more uniform surface temperature.

9.3.3.5   Screw Recovery

Concurrently with the cooling cycle, the screw rotates, melting PP and feeding it through the open check valve, creating melt pressure which pushes the screw back to a preset position (shot size). If screw recovery is slower than the cooling cycle, it lengthens the total cycle. Lower MFR resins often give faster recovery but increase melt temperature and cooling time. Since equipment varies, a MFR choice might require molding trials.

9.3.3.6   Ejection

The ejection goal is to remove the part from the mold quickly, reliably, and without damage to the part. Damage can occur if the part is ejected too hot or too cold. Early ejected parts are hot enough to distort on cooling. Uneven ejection when the part is malleable will also warp a part. Ejection forces for very cold parts are often excessive. Undercuts or high ejection forces can dent or stress-whiten the part.

Molds can be designed with cold runners, which must be cooled and ejected with the desired part, or hot runners, which remain in the mold during ejection. The hot runner approach reduces the cycle time by eliminating the hold step and reduces the closing clamp forces somewhat, at the cost of more expensive molds.

9.3.4   Resin Selection

The selection of PP grade will affect most of the steps in the process. While all materials undergo some shrinkage during cooling, crystalline PP exhibits higher shrinkage than amorphous materials like PS and ABS. As a consequence, PP has a greater tendency to warp in large parts and form sink marks at thick sections. Those tendencies may be counteracted to some degree by adjusting the molding conditions and designing the part properly. Polypropylene also requires more cooling prior to ejection, but can be ejected at higher temperatures than PS or ABS.

Resin selection must consider the performance of the part in its application in combination with the influence of the resin on the molding process. Low MFR resins are less notch sensitive, but they are difficult to mold and have higher molded-in stresses. Higher MFR resins can improve productivity and reduce stresses. In conventional molding, resins from 1 to 20 MFR may be used, but 10 to 20 is most common today. Nucleated resins harden more quickly and are stiffer, but they limit filling length and freeze in more stresses.

9.3.5   Thin Wall Injection Molding

Thin wall injection molding (TWIM) is the pioneering division of injection molding, where both polymer and equipment are pushed to their limits. Thin walls are defined as being thinner than 0.7 mm (30 mil), with a length/thickness ratio over 150. Polypropylene fits TWIM well due to rheology, stiffness, and toughness. Most applications are packaging, such as dairy containers, margarine tubs, and stadium cups.

Molding machines for TWIM require fast injection speed and high platen opening and closing speeds. Melt accumulator systems are used to give high injection rates. Injection times of less than 0.20 seconds are sometimes achieved, and cycles can vary between 7 to 20 per minute. Machine characteristics also include large hydraulic oil capacity, fast acting control valves and systems, and high PP plasticating capacity.

Two main types of TWIM equipment can be found: two-stage machines and recipro-cating-screw machines. Two-stage machines have an extruder and a transfer valve. The extruder delivers molten PP through the valve to an injection cylinder. During the injection step, the valve is closed to prevent back flow to the extruder. Reciprocating-screw machines with high screw speed and fast injection rates are used successfully. Injection rate on some machines is so high that injection programming is no longer possible. A 25:1 L/D ratio plasticating screw is recommended to produce uniform melt. The high pressure in these applications requires a shut-off nozzle for the injection unit. Both types of equipment require high speed platen movement.

Molds usually have multiple cavities, typically ranging from four to thirty-two. Stack molds, with more than one parting line, each with a set of cavities, are commonly used to minimize the clamping force required per cavity, which for TWIM is typically 7 tons/in.^{2} (1 met. ton/cm^2), compared to about half that for conventional molding. In contrast to usual single-face mold designs, melt is injected from a central platen to cavities along each side. Core sections of the mold may be attached to either the fixed or moving platens. Molten PP is delivered through the sprue bar, which links the nozzle to the hot runner system of the mold.

Air ejection devices are used to eject the part, replacing knockout pins and ejector plates of conventional molding. Robot ejection systems are often used to eliminate the time for parts to fall clear of the platens. Robots help reduce mold open time and can stack parts in shipping boxes. Mold surface finish is a determining factor for ease of ejection. Highly polished surfaces, as desired for a clear part, are more difficult to eject than ones with a matte surface.

A major PP resin requirement for TWIM is high fluidity to reduce pressure during the rapid flow through the thin walls. Today a typical MFR for a reactor-based TWIM PP grade is about 35 g/10 min, but 70 g/10 min resins are expected to permit more wall thinning and source reduction. Polypropylene with a MFR above 15 had formerly been achieved by a degradation process, which also provides a narrow molecular weight distribution (NMWD) compared to reactor PP. The NMWD PP has a lower stiffness than regular polymers, and shows less of a tendency to orient and be splitty. The degradation process can also generate color and undesirable odor and taste characteristics. The viscosity of a typical broad MWD, reactor-based resin drops more at high shear rates (shear thins) than a NMWD grade, and will have the advantage of lower viscosity at process conditions. The actual grade used will depend on the end-use.

Food containers for refrigerated applications need to withstand impacts at moderately low temperatures, and frozen applications at even lower temperatures. Impact PP copolymers offer good top load strength and suitable impact resistance. At these high injection rates and in thinner parts, PP has been shown to provide an excellent balance of moldability and part properties compared with HDPE, the conventional molded container material. Antistatic additives are needed in many thin wall applications. Unfortunately, they tend to foul the molds, and frequent cleaning is needed to maintain productivity in molding.

For clear containers, random copolymer would be used. Random copolymers are softer, slower crystallizing, and more difficult to eject from a highly polished molds. Better mold and part designs will be needed to use random copolymers efficiently.

9.3.6   Special Molding Processes

9.3.6.1   Gas Assist Molding

As the name suggests, the process utilizes a gas, usually nitrogen, injected through the melt stream and into a gas channel within the part to assist in filling and pack-out of the mold. Thick-walled structural sections become hollow beams, giving the best stiffness/weight performance, reducing cooling time, and, in some instances, reducing visible faults like sink marks. Depending upon geometry, the result can be parts molded with significantly lower injection pressures, lower residual stresses, and thinner, more uniform wall sections.

A specially designed machine is required. Several firms offer equipment and/or licenses to practice this technology. Little practical information is in the public domain, and the user may have to develop methods for his own needs. Licensing fees for the technology are significant and will impact part cost.

The gas assist process is compatible with a wide range of resins and viscosities.

9.3.6.2   Structural Foam Molding

There are two commonly used types of foam molding, both having been used for many years: the nitrogen injection process, and the chemical blowing agent process. In the nitrogen injection process, nitrogen gas is typically introduced into the vent of a two-stage screw. Under the pressure and mixing of extrusion, the gas dissolves in the PP melt. By controlling the gas level and using a nozzle shut-off valve, sometimes with a melt accumulator, the resulting part density can be adjusted. Depending on wall thickness and MFR of the PP resin, densities as low as 0.55 g/cm^3 can be obtained. Wall thickness less than 5 mm (0.2 in.) cannot usually be foamed. The quickly chilled skin layer has little expansion, but near the centerline, numerous large bubbles are formed.

A significant drawback of this process is that the surface appearance of parts tends to be rough and swirly, similar to wood. Often color does not mix well, giving the surface a somewhat variegated look.

The low clamping forces allow the use of aluminum molds. By regulating nitrogen levels, zero degree draft angle parts can be produced, which reduces tooling costs further. The low pressures required also permit molding of large parts such as storm doors, trash cans, and shipping pallets. This process also lends itself to the use of commingled post-consumer plastics in "plastic lumber" applications.

In the blowing agent process, the blowing agent is mixed with the PP, the mold is partially filled by injection, and the foaming completes the filling of the mold. There are a number of blowing agents available. Two types are often used in PP: azo dicarbonamide-based compounds, and sodium carbonate/citric acid types. The former generates nitrogen, and the latter carbon dioxide. Particularly with nitrogen generating compounds, residual products can be corrosive or can cause plate out on molds.

Blowing agent can be added as a pellet concentrate or by tumbling it onto the resin with mineral oil. Up to 2% of blowing agent may be used depending on the desired density reduction in the part. Sometimes, blowing is used just to reduce sink marks, in which instance a blowing agent level under 0.5% would suffice. Shot weight is adjusted to control the amount of blowing. This process can produce parts having a solid skin and a high gloss. It is important to maintain sufficient pressure in the barrel to prevent preblowing in the machine. Lower temperatures and short residence time often give better part cell structure.

9.4   Blow Molding

Blow molding is separated into three major divisions: extrusion, injection, and injection stretch blow molding. Extrusion blow molding is by far the dominant technique, although many small bottles are made via the injection blow molding route and, recently, by stretch blow molding.

The basic extrusion blow molding concept is to form a hollow cylinder (parison) from the molten plastic, clamp it in a mold, expand the molten parison with air pressure, cool and eject the article, and trim or finish as necessary. There are two categories of extrusion blow molding machines, depending on the method of forming the parison: continuous and intermittent.

9.4.1   Extrusion Blow Molding

Continuous parison equipment trades the simpler parison extrusion for a much more complicated press section necessary for good mold utilization. Continuous extrusion machines have a simple extruder with few heads, but two or more sets of molds must sequentially move into the parison drop area to capture the parison, and away from the drop area while the part is cooling in the mold.

Forming the parison intermittently complicates extrusion but simplifies the press by limiting mold movements to opening and closing on the parison. For increased output, multiple parison and press sections may be used.

Low, uniform melt temperatures around 200 °C (400 °F) are normally used. Because lack of melt homogeneity is the most frequent reason for difficulties in blow molding, mixing devices, good screw design, and adequate extruder size are important to successful operation. The parison must hold its dimension until the mold closes, so a degree of melt strength is needed. In comparison with HDPE, which dominates the blow molding business (see Fig. 7.8), conventional PP has exhibited low melt strength, with excessive parison sag. The use of high melt strength PP has substantially improved the behavior of PP in this process [11]. Polypropylene has been used in blow molding bottles employing a barrier layer, where the moisture barrier property of PP helps protect the moisture-sensitive barrier polymer.

With regard to design of a die and mandrel, PP will normally require a longer land length than does HDPE. With PP, satisfactory parisons can be produced using a land length from five to ten times the die gap; the longer lands give better surface smoothness. Formation of a suitable parison is dependent on swell of the parison to the proper diameter and thickness. Die swell is relatable to the PP resin MWD, or the use of high melt strength PP, but can be altered some by changing the die opening, the extrusion rate, or the melt temperature.

Molds are comparatively inexpensive, usually made from cast aluminum. Cooling of the blow molded part is the rate limiting factor. High productivity can only be obtained with well-designed, well-cooled molds. For thin-wall parts like bottles, the areas of highest heat load are the neck, handle, and pinch-off. The polymer is thicker in these areas, thus the cooling capacity in these areas usually establishes the minimum cycle, and special attention is given to providing adequate cooling in these sections.

Polypropylene items should be deflashed with a shearing action. Bending the flash at the pinch-off forms a PP hinge.

9.4.2   Injection Blow Molding

The injection blow molding (IBM) process was developed to produce blown bottles and wide mouth jars with the good neck definition expected of injection molding. The process makes only oval or cylindrical objects, without handles; no tails, tabs or pinch-offs are generated. The essential steps are preform injection, preform blow, and cooling/ejection.

The injection blow molding process replaces the parison with a molded preform, a closed-end tube with a finished neck on the open end. A group of core rods carries the preforms to each station and is designed to open and admit air in the blowing step. The melt for the injection cycle is usually produced by a reciprocating screw injection unit. The molten polymer is delivered through a melt manifold, through gates, and molded onto the core rods using conventional injection molding techniques. The gate vestige left on the bottom of each part is characteristic of this process. Injection molding the preform, in addition to providing a more controllable item, obviates the need for the melt strength characteristics necessary for extrusion blow molding.

Polypropylene is injected at a melt temperature between 200 °C and 225 °C (400 °F to 450 °F). The preform mold has three or more separate zones for cooling. The neck finish area is typically cooled rapidly to crystallize it. The mold temperature for the body is set at up to 121 °C (250 °F) to provide the still molten form at a controlled temperature, depending on the design. When the preform is properly conditioned, the preform mold opens and the manifold indexes the molten preforms to the blowing station and places them into the blowing molds. The indexing manifold contains the core rods and actuators to open the rods.

Air is introduced through the core rod to blow the body while the cooling process of the thread section is taking place. The pressure applied is similar to that required for extrusion blow molding, about 7 bar (100 psi) to blow the melt into the cold mold.

Polypropylene resins would be selected based on the usual end-use requirements and the needs of the injection molding operation. Numerous PP types would be suitable.

9.4.3   Injection Stretch Blow Molding

Injection stretch blow molding (ISBM) is similar in concept to injection blow molding, but biaxially orients the PP preform in the solid phase so that less material is needed for the item, usually a bottle, to function. The crystallized injection molded preform is moved to the blow mold, conditioned at a temperature of about 150 °C to 160 °C, stretched lengthwise by a moving rod, and blown with air. This produces biaxially oriented containers that have higher clarity, impact, and barrier properties compared to similar unoriented containers.

Two types of ISBM process are practiced, the single-stage and the two-stage process. The difference is that the preform is blown without being fully cooled in the single-stage process, and is reheated from room temperature in the two-stage process.

In the single-stage process, the preform step is similar to the IBM process except that the mold and core rod temperatures are usually near room temperature to crystallize the preform before the blowing phase. Some types of ISBM machine will then return to about 160 °C entirely in the preform mold, while others use a conditioning station before the blowing station. When the material reaches the suitable temperature, the preform is elongated by a rapid movement of a core element while air is introduced to inflate the parison, resulting in a biaxially stretched container.

In the two-stage process, also referred to as re-heat blow (RHB), cooled preforms are fed to a conditioning oven and blowing station. In processing PP, the principal challenge is reliable preform temperatures control within a small processing window (about 7 °C or 13 °F). The stretch ratio must be high (above 15:1) to obtain high clarity and improved toughness with PP. Clarified random copolymers with a MFR between 10 g/10 min and 35 g/10 min perform well in this process.

Containers made by ISBM have superior clarity over those from other blow molding processes due to the biaxial orientation. Orientation also improves the mechanical and barrier properties of PP. Bottles made by this process exhibit high gloss, low bottle weight variation, and precise neck finish tolerances.

9.5   Other Processes

9.5.1   Compression Molding

Polypropylene has been compression molded, a process we shall not bother to describe, in special situations where the conventional methods are not adequate. Very thick filter press plates, for example, have been prepared with this technique. The process is slow and labor intensive. In some instances, combining a melt feeding extruder with a cold compression mold, known as a transfer process, has been used to effect some economies. One line of beverage closures is manufactured in this manner with competitive economics.

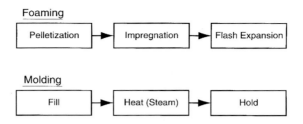

Figure 9.21 Foamed PP bead formation and molding processes

9.5.2   Foamed Bead Molding

Foamed PP beads display a unique characteristic: the ability to absorb large impact loads over a short distance. The process, shown schematically in Fig. 9.21, involves preparing the foamed beads and molding. Foaming the beads involve, first, pelletization of the appropriate polymer, typically a random copolymer, into particles of a precise pellet size. Second, the pellets are impregnated batchwise with the foaming solvent, under heat and pressure. Finally, flash expansion causes the beads to foam to the desired density, depending on the amount of solvent and the temperature. With proper impregnation conditions, considering that flash expansion is adiabatic, the evaporation of the foaming solvent cools the PP down to the point where crystallization rapidly takes place in the expanded foam cell walls.

Molding takes place using moderate steam pressure, about 2 bar (30 psig), where the final bead expansion occurs to fill the mold. The molded part is held in the mold for several hours at elevated temperature to achieve dimensional stability in the part.

Parts molded of PP beads have exceptional impact absorbing capability, and are used in auto bumper inserts and computer packaging.

References

1. *Schrenck, W.J.:* Pol. Eng. Sci 18 (1978) 620
2. J. Comm. (Sept. 28, 1983) 22b
3. Sampling and Analysis of Emissions Evolved During Thermal Processing of Polypropylene Resin Mixtures, Battelle Laboratories, April 1995
4. Polypropylene 1994, Phillip Townsend Associates Inc., 1993
5. *Samuels, R.J.:* Structrd Polymer Properties, John Wiley and sons, New York, 1974
6. *Butler, T.I., Veazey, E.W.,* Eds.: Film Extrusion Manual, TAPPI Press, 1992
7. Permeability and Other Film Properties, Plastics Design Library, 1995
8. *Nash, J.L.:* Poly. Eng. Sci. 28 (1988) 862–870; *Eustance, J.W., Hobbs, S.Y.:* U.S. Pat 4 287 249 (1981) General Electric Co.
9. *Bradley, M., Phillips, E.M.:* SPE ANTEC, Dallas, TX, 1990
10. Bulletin 500–752C, Guide for Injection Molding Pro-fax PP, Himont USA Inc (Now Montell), 1990
11. *Beren, J.R., Capellman, C.:* SAE Int'l Congress & Exposition, Detroit MI, 1994

10   Applications

Charles G. Oertel

10.1   The Evolution

Polypropylene (PP) is one of the best kept secrets in the plastics industry. Ask your neighbor whether he or she has ever used PP or even heard of it, and chances are you will be greeted with a blank stare. That same neighbor will acknowledge at least having heard of polyethylene, polyester, nylon, and perhaps even phenolic: other generic plastics whose secrets are less well kept. Even the trade names that producers of PP have collectively spent millions of dollars to register and promote are barely recognized beyond those individuals in the industry who make, transport, and purchase it.

The irony of this lack of recognition is that PP is everywhere. It quietly goes about protecting the food we eat, the medicine we take, and the cables that bring life to our telephones and computers. We protect our floors, dress our bodies, cover our furniture, and keep our babies dry with fibers made of PP. We are surrounded by PP when we drive our cars or watch a soccer game. We depend on it to clean up oil spills, prevent erosion, and protect medical personnel from infectious waste. We even use it to transport our pets, our tools, our cold drinks, and our belongings on trips. In view of the fact that it is one of the most ubiquitous plastics ever developed, it is amazing how PP can be so hard working and so little recognized.

What is it about this versatile material that makes it ideal for so many uses? To begin with, PP is lightweight: a mere 0.9 g/cc. It is lighter than water and lighter even than its first cousin polyethylene, which means it can be used for applications that require a low-density plastic material. Its flexural modulus and melting point are both relatively high. Those two properties set it apart from other olefin polymers and permit its use, for example, in the fabrication of bottles that are filled with hot substances.

Polypropylene also exhibits excellent chemical resistance. This inertness makes it ideal not only for exposure to hostile environments but also for applications requiring compliance with FDA regulations, such as food packaging and medical delivery systems. It can be copolymerized with other monomers or alloyed with other polymers to yield final products custom-designed for specific applications. All this from a relatively inexpensive and readily available monomer. From this, one can understand why PP has enjoyed its exceptional growth, but it is puzzling how the secret of this success has been so well kept.

This chapter illustrates the versatility of PP by highlighting many of the applications for which it has become the resin of choice. Some applications were awarded to PP from the very beginning because no other plastic resin was capable of performing; the living hinge being an example. Most applications, however, evolved over time as PP demonstrated improved economics or enhanced performance over other thermoplastic resins. Applications will be presented in the approximate order of market size, although there will be minor exceptions to facilitate comparisons and to highlight trends.

10.2   Fibers

According to the Society of the Plastics Industry (SPI), the largest single use for PP in the United States is in the manufacture of fibers, although in some tabulations injection molding is recorded as being a larger segment because it includes much of the SPI category of sales to compounders (see Fig. 9.1). The fiber industry was not always a large consumer, however. When PP was first proposed to the fiber industry as a new raw material, the reaction was basically negative. It could not be dyed with existing procedures, and there was simply no overwhelming consumer demand for a new synthetic fiber. Nylon was doing very well, thank you.

The first commercial PP fiber facility was brought on stream in the U.S.A. in 1961 by the then Hercules Powder Co. at Covington, VA, when it bought a fiber spinning facility from Industrial Rayon Corporation. The first fibers, quite crude by today's standards and available in limited colors, were sold primarily for cordage and industrial applications. Early efforts to penetrate the carpet fiber market were unsuccessful due to PP's lack of resilience compared with both natural fibers and nylon. Polypropylene fibers in deep pile carpets, the preferred carpet structure for home use, remained matted down in high traffic areas. This shortcoming, when added to the lack of vibrant colors, which at that time were attainable only through post extrusion dyeing, was a distinct handicap.

10.2.1   Carpets

To be sure, PP offered several distinct advantages for carpet face yarn; it possessed excellent stain resistance, and its lower specific gravity meant more fiber volume (or bulk as it is known in the industry) per given weight of carpet. After all, if a carpet fiber refuses to accept dyes, it follows that it is also likely to resist the staining effects of ketchup, mustard, bleaches, peroxides, and other household items that are often spilled on carpets. The negatives, however, won out, and the residential carpet market opted for resiliency and bright colors over stain resistance and higher bulk.

However, the commercial carpet market is a different story. Most commercial carpet is short pile, produced generally in subdued colors and subjected to considerable staining and soiling in offices and in commercial traffic areas such as airports and retail stores. In airports, for example, the electric carts that transport passengers from gate to gate often leak battery acid, which attacks nylon carpets but does not affect PP. Since PP fiber is pigmented during extrusion (as opposed to dyed), the color is more light-fast and resistant to fading. When PP's color fastness and cleanability are combined with its low cost per surface yard, a compelling case is made for its use in commercial carpeting.

At this writing, it is appropriate to mention that considerable work is continuing toward perfecting the design of the dies used in the extrusion of PP fibers. Die design and the resulting fiber cross section is important in many areas, including crush resistance, luster, feel, wearability, and soil resistance. The results of this work together with the advent of newer polymers and new carpet constructions, has enabled PP to grow dramatically over the past eight years in residential carpets, particularly Berber and cut pile Saxony construction.

Polypropylene has replaced natural fibers, primarily jute, as the material of choice in nearly all carpet backing throughout the world. This is covered in the next section. However, the use of PP face yarn with PP primary and secondary backing, combined with the use of a special PP adhesive to secure the tufted fibers in place, yields a carpet made entirely from one polymer. This construction facilitates the recycling of used carpet, allowing the entire carpet to be reprocessed efficiently and economically.

10.2.2   Slit Tape

Although fabrics made from slit tape have widespread uses, and its volume sales are spread across many different market areas, it is presented here because of its historic affiliation with carpet construction and the fact that it is still a vital part of the carpet industry. In fact, the use of PP in the slit tape market exceeds its use in the bulked continuous filament (BCF) carpet market.

The term "slit tape" derives from fibers made by slitting wide webs of extruded sheet into very narrow tapes. These, then, are not fibers in the sense that they do not consist of polymer strands each extruded through a separate and discrete die opening. The advantage of producing fibers via the tape process is the ability to produce a low-cost product that can be used in less demanding applications. This led to its early use as a replacement for jute and other natural fibers in both primary and secondary carpet backing.

Primary carpet backing is the backbone of the carpet, even though it cannot be seen in the finished carpet. The primary backing must accept not only the onslaught of needle punctures during the tufting operation but must withstand the abuse of subsequent dyeing, steaming, drying, and other harsh process treatments without changing dimension or losing strength. After tufting, an adhesive emulsion is applied to the reverse side to secure the tufted fibers and to provide an adhesive layer for the secondary backing.

Secondary carpet backing protects the underside of the tufted fibers and provides added strength to the carpet. It is the secondary backing that is visible on the back of the finished carpet, as shown in Fig. 10.1. The moisture resistance of PP improves longevity of the carpet when exposed to conditions of high humidity. Mold growth is reduced, and inherent swelling, caused by moisture absorption, is held to a minimum. Natural fibers, the alternative material for carpet backing, lose strength after prolonged exposure to high humidity and add appreciably to the weight of the carpet. Also, the availability and price of natural fibers, jute for example, are not constant, being subject to the vagaries of uncertain crop yields and to unpredictable political occurrences in producing countries.

Fabrics woven from slit tape are also used in tarpaulins, erosion abatement screens, sand bags, fertilizer and feed bags, swimming pool covers, and other similar heavy-duty products. A quite impressive show of strength is the intermediate bulk container (IBC) bag, shown in Fig. 10.2. The same properties that are important in carpet backing—moisture resistance, high tensile strength, light weight, ease of manufacture, and low cost—support its use in these products, as well. For exterior applications, it is necessary to stabilize PP because it is vulnerable to photochemical oxidative breakdown, initiated by UV light. Various light stabilizers are regularly incorporated in these products to counter this phenomenon, and carbon black is often added to help screen out UV light, a technique that explains why most of these fabrics are black in color (UV stability is discussed in more detail in Section 4.3.2). An

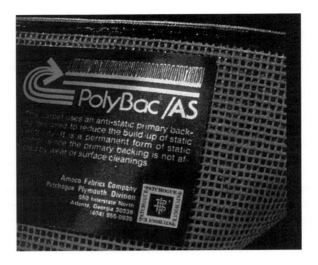

Figure 10.1   Secondary carpet backing, made from PP slit tape, provides support and protects the underside of the carpet. Its resistance to moisture prolongs carpet life, minimizes mold formation, and improves the dimensional stability of the carpet

Figure 10.2   Intermediate bulk container (IBC) bag used to ship intermediate-sized quantities of various bulk commodities. Bags are lightweight, durable, and can be collapsed for convenient return to the shipper

example is the recent use of slit tape fabrics in pond liners that protect the environment by preventing ground contamination from evaporating ponds. The chemical and moisture resistance of PP, together with its light weight and low cost, make it ideally suited for this type of application.

The high strength, low cost, and moisture resistance of slit tape fabrics have encouraged growing use in geotextile applications, where the fabric is used to stabilize difficult soil conditions. It is particularly effective where high ground water is present and textiles of natural fabrics would deteriorate rapidly. An example of its use appears in Fig. 10.3.

In some instances the tapes, after slitting, are fibrillated and used as face yarn in synthetic turf and outdoor carpets. Again, the low density and the colorfastness combine to yield high bulk, long lasting ground covers at attractive prices. The same fibrillated tape, when twisted, is widely used for tying twine, where the high strength and low cost again win the day.

10.2.3 Nonwoven Fabrics

The largest single fiber application for PP is in nonwoven fabrics. There are three distinct types, differing in the method of fabrication: spunbonded, melt blown, and thermobonded carded web from staple fibers. The three methods yield fabrics that differ in appearance and physical properties, thereby expanding the markets served. Spunbonded fabrics exhibit high strength, whereas melt blown fibers produce softness and bulk. Composites of both spunbonded and melt blown fabrics, generally referred to as SMS fabrics (spunbonded-melt blown-spunbonded), are routinely used to yield products with special properties. This versatility has enabled nonwovens to enjoy exceptional growth, and all predictions are that this will continue because of the growth markets they serve. Thermobonded carded web is a

Figure 10.3   Geotextile, made from woven slit tape, is used to stabilize soil prior to construction

two-step procedure resulting in fabrics that differ slightly from either spunbonded or melt blown fabrics but which are used in similar applications. This method of constructing diapers involves the use of short-cut staple PP fibers that are matted, embossed, and heat set to form a continuous sheet of nonwoven fabric. The fabric thus made is converted to diaper linings in a manner similar to that employed with the spunbonded products. A more detailed explanation of the fiber processes can be found in Chapter 9, Fabrication Processes.

The fabrics are produced in different basis weights. This is the weight per area, generally expressed in grams per square yard. Fabrics with low basis weights are used in applications such as diaper liners, whereas higher basis weights are used in heavy-duty applications like tarpaulins and tent fabrics. In many cases, an SMS laminate is used to enhance strength while improving softness.

The largest single market for PP nonwoven fabric is disposable diapers, as illustrated in Color Plate 10.1. The baby diaper market has changed considerably during the past two decades. It is now universally dedicated to disposable products, many of which are intricate engineering marvels combining a snug elastic fit, simple fasteners, soft comfortable linings, and a super-absorbent filler. The liners, as mentioned earlier, are made on high-speed lines that employ spunbonded, melt blown, and thermobonded carded web technologies. Polypropylene is the resin of choice for lining diapers because it is nonhygroscopic and serves to keep the surface of the diaper, adjacent to the skin, dry. All parents are quick to recognize the value of this feature and how it contributes to the quality of life for both infant and parent. Disposable diapers are the norm in developed countries, and as less developed countries evolve toward this convenience, the worldwide market is expected to grow rapidly. The comfort of diaper liners is also employed in feminine hygiene products and adult diapers. All three areas are expected to continue growing, especially in the developing countries.

The high costs associated with sterilizing and laundering hospital garments has led to the widespread use of disposables. Polypropylene nonwoven fabrics are ideally suited for this application, as shown in Fig. 10.4. The fabrics are lightweight, nonabsorbent, chemically resistant, nonallergenic, and breathable, and can be disposed of using readily available procedures such as incineration. Many garments employ an SMS construction in which added barriers are incorporated in the melt blown center portion to inhibit the passage of blood-borne pathogens and other disease-producing microbes. The nearly perfect balance of properties for medical applications leads one to think that PP nonwovens were discovered and developed solely for this use.

The ease with which PP can be spun into fibers, its low specific gravity, its water resistance, and its ability to entrap aliphatics makes it ideal for fabricating the floating booms that are used to control oil spills. Fibers making up the filler in the oil containment booms are produced using the melt blown process, the same as for disposable garments. This unique process produces extremely fine fibers, adding surface area and bulk to the final product.

10.2.4   Apparel

The apparel market has tempted the producers of PP fibers for decades. The size of the market is extremely attractive, and the properties of PP, at least on paper, appear to closely fit its needs. Numerous attempts in the past, however, have been met with only modest success.

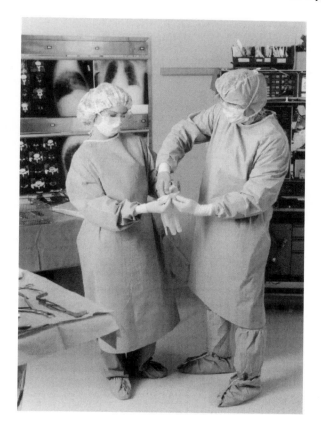

Figure 10.4   Disposable surgical garments, made from nonwoven PP fabrics, protects medical personnel, are lightweight, comfortable to wear, and can be disposed of easily and safely. Photo courtesy Kimberly Clark Corporation

Recent developments suggest that this waiting period may be over and that PP may gain a substantial position in the apparel market.

It was the military that pioneered the use of PP in apparel, having first recognized its utility in underclothing, where it was effective in keeping the body dry. Prolonged periods of dampness, not unusual in military operations, can be very damaging to the skin and can compromise the ability of military personnel to complete their mission. This is most noticeable in cold weather operations, and it is here that PP is being used today in socks, T-shirts, and other similar underlayer garments.

Pigmented PP fiber is color-fast and stain resistant. It does not absorb moisture, thereby allowing perspiration to evaporate from its surface or pass through it to an absorbent outer layer; in either case serving to keep the skin dry. Polypropylene fibers also resist mildew, provide thermal insulation, resist static buildup, minimize odor development, and have excellent abrasion resistance. To date, PP garments are manufactured and sold commercially for many clothing items, including bike shorts, sweat bands, football undershirts, hiking

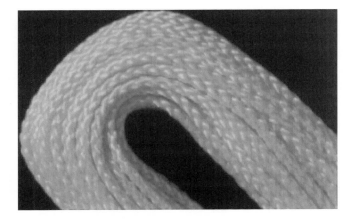

Figure 10.5   Polypropylene monofilaments produce lightweight, high-strength, moisture resistant cordage and twine, much of which is used in marine applications

socks, and outerwear for many other sport activities, as seen in Color Plate 10.2. As texturizing and fabric finishing procedures improve, PP will see ever-increasing use in apparel fabrics.

10.2.5   Cordage

Polypropylene cordage, shown in Fig. 10.5, is widely used aboard ship, where its low density keeps the mooring and tow lines on top of the water in constant view of the crew, and where its low moisture absorption keeps them from becoming water logged and heavy after continued exposure to the marine environment. The ability to pigment the fibers also yields bright, light-stable colors, thus making the lines more visible, a feature that adds to both safety and convenience. Nearly all ships today are outfitted with "poly" lines for many of the on-board chores. Polypropylene lines are also evident in many water sport activities, where they separate the swimmers during races, connect water skiers to their tow boats, and are used for rescue activities when things go wrong. Polypropylene cordage has also enabled the average home owner to purchase and use inexpensive ropes and cords that do not rot or embrittle with age, rendering them useful over a long period of time.

10.2.6   Netting

Polypropylene netting is one of those special products made from this versatile plastic that has created a niche for itself in areas unseen or unnoticed by most people. Some applications, like the safety fences that protect skiers during races, snow fences, and the temporary containment barriers at many construction sites, are quite visible. Other applications are less visible, such as the use of netting to reduce the settling of fill materials on soft soil during construction. These strong nets, referred to as geogrids, are an alternative to the use of geotextiles in reinforcing the construction base in soft soil areas. It is used as a base in the building of levees

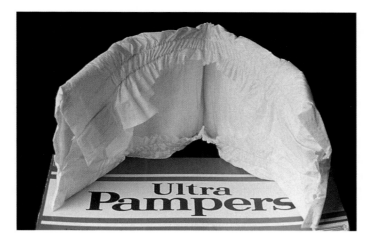

Color Plate 10.1 Disposable diapers, as pictured here, are universally replacing cloth diapers for infants. Variations of these products are available for incontinent adults

Color Plate 10.2 Lightweight outerwear, woven from PP fiber, is easy to care for and offers protection from wind and water

and roads, and as a reinforcing agent in the construction of retaining walls. The use of PP netting shortens the construction time and reduces the amount of fill needed, thereby reducing construction costs.

10.3   Injection Molded Consumer Products

From the very beginning, PP has been used to injection mold consumer products. Early attempts produced items like combs, key cases, tumblers, and other similar products that did not require a great deal of sophistication with respect to resin capabilities or mold design. From that humble beginning, PP has grown to become the resin of choice in many intricately molded parts for appliances, automobiles, electronics, and household goods.

10.3.1   Appliances

Possibly the most visible appliance application in which PP has been solidly entrenched over the years is the interior liner in automatic dishwashers, shown in Fig. 10.6. There are not many environments in the home more hostile than a dishwasher interior, which requires cycling through hot water, high detergent concentrations, dry heat, and physical abuse from dropped silverware and dishes. Polypropylene alone provides the necessary chemical resistance, rigidity, appearance, and durability to hold up through the expected life of the product, and to allow its manufacture at sufficiently low cost to render the final appliance affordable.

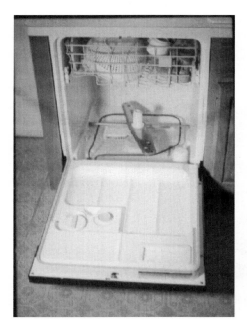

Figure 10.6   Automatic dishwasher liners of PP withstand hot water, detergents, dry heat, and physical abuse, while maintaining an attractive appearance for many years

Figure 10.7   Many small applications incorporate PP molded parts for consumer appeal. Its light weight, low cost and high performance add value to the final product

Small electrical appliances also contain numerous PP parts. Here its light weight, rigidity, ease of molding, and excellent dielectric properties enhance the value of the appliance product. One can hardly pick up an electric drill, blender, mixer, can opener, coffee maker, or humidifier without coming in contact with PP in one of its many forms. The coffee maker shown in Fig. 10.7 is an example of the use of PP in small appliances.

For reasons identical to those that support the use of PP in dishwashers, this versatile polymer is also used in automatic clothes washers. The most apparent component is the agitator, most of which are molded from PP. Other parts include soap dispensers, inlet valves, and internal parts designed to protect motors, switches, and the like.

10.3.2   General Consumer Products

Rigid luggage, represented by the photo in Fig. 10.8, is another major end use for PP. Once again, light weight is a major reason for its selection, but the resin must also display excellent impact resistance, be easily molded, and have acceptable aesthetics when molded in color. Polypropylene fills these requirements, and does so at low cost.

The use of PP to mold outdoor furniture is becoming commonplace. Figure 10.9   illustrates a typical design. Modification with fillers provides a range of physical properties that are needed to make durable, attractive outdoor furniture. Good mold design is essential to prevent induced stresses, especially in the large parts required in lawn and garden furniture. While these furniture pieces exhibit excellent resistance to humidity, acid rain, and other environmental hazards that cause premature failure in metal and cloth components, they must be properly stabilized and formulated to avoid polymer degradation. Improved stabilizer

Figure 10.8   Luggage must be both light and durable. Polypropylene offers both of these important properties and is widely used in rigid luggage

systems, which protect the polymer during exterior applications such as this, are discussed in Chapter 4.

Although not necessarily a consumer product, the design and manufacture of stadium seats is related, in a sense, to that of outdoor furniture. Polypropylene is selected for both applications for many of the same reasons. Stadium seats have been molded in PP for decades, and are depicted in Fig. 10.10.

The widespread use of child car seats is steadily increasing, thanks to mandates handed down by various government bodies and to a general recognition that their use reduces infant

Figure 10.9   Polypropylene, compared with metal and cloth, offers freedom of design in outdoor furniture, resulting in attractive contemporary designs that will not rust or corrode and do not require painting

Figure 10.10 Stadium seats can be molded in color to produce attractive functional seating that requires little maintenance

injuries. Polypropylene is lightweight, can be easily molded into relatively large components, is impact resistant, rigid, and has sufficient heat resistance to maintain this rigidity even when left inside a closed automobile, where temperatures can approach 90 °C (200 °F). Molded from impact copolymers, car seats have become very sophisticated, possess many special features, and can be broken down easily for transporting when not in use. Polypropylene's light weight makes transporting easier, and its strength and moldability make it ideally suited for this application.

The small, portable ice cooler has become as commonplace as the lunch pail in much of the industrial world. It comes in all sizes and shapes, shown in Color Plate 10.3, and can be seen at construction sites, recreation areas, factories, offices, sporting events—nearly everywhere people gather. Because of its excellent resistance to stress cracking and impact, and of course, its light weight and high flexural modulus, PP was selected to mold the lids, covers, and liners of many of these coolers. In fact, today most coolers utilize PP in some part of the construction. Most coolers contain a sandwich layer of molded-in expandable foam to provide insulation, but the PP structure itself assists in retarding heat transfer, thereby helping to keep the contents cool. The stiffness of the liner also contributes greatly to the rigidity of the finished cooler.

Homeowners who care for their yards and gardens have used PP and unknowingly thanked its light weight and rugged durability. Rakes, hose reels, planters, spreaders, and hose nozzles are all examples of applications where PP delivers outstanding performance. Other olefins tend to stress crack, while other generic polymers add weight and cost to an

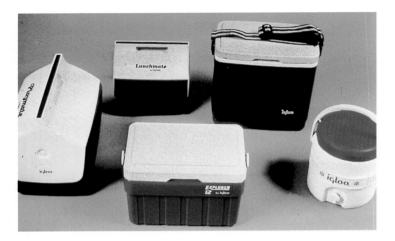

Color Plate 10.3 Nearly everyone can identify with portable coolers, many of which contain key PP components. These components contribute both stiffness and light weight to the product

Color Plate 10.4 The low water absorption of PP means that part dimensions remain relatively stable, a requirement in products that meter and/or dispense water such as the sprinklers and sprayers shown here

application that desires neither. Also, PP's ability to maintain dimensional stability during constant contact with water has led to its use in lawn and garden sprinklers and sprayers, indicated in Color Plate 10.4. As with all injection molded items, PP's low color and its compatibility with all common pigments enables the manufacturer to present a final product in bright attractive colors. This feature enhances the "shelf appeal" of highly competitive products such as yard and garden tools, thereby delivering a market advantage to the manufacturer.

10.3.3   Medical Applications

Polypropylene became the resin of choice for most of the previously discussed general injection molded applications because of its light weight, low cost, or both. Several medical applications, however, go beyond these two important characteristics and draw on unique properties of PP. It is possible, for example, to formulate PP molding compounds to enable them to undergo steam or radiation sterilization after molding and still retain sufficient physical properties to perform the intended application. The most notable such application is the disposable syringe.

Most syringes today, like those shown in Color Plate 10.5, are disposable for reasons of both cost and safety. Environmental considerations have all but eliminated the use of ethylene oxide to sterilize medical devices, leaving irradiation as the most cost-effective method available. Most plastics, when subjected to the levels of radiation necessary for sterilization, become brittle and unusable. As stated above, PP, specifically polymerized for medical use, and especially formulated for exposure to radiation, can withstand this exposure and still retain a high percentage of its original strength. Details regarding stabilization against radiation sterilization appear in Section 4.6.3.

It is important in medical syringes for the barrel to be transparent enough for the technician to ascertain its contents and rigid enough to keep its shape, allowing the plunger to dispense its contents evenly and completely. Gradations must be bold and visible throughout the dispensing operation, calling, in some cases, for printing on the exterior of the barrel. Also, there is often a considerable delay between the molding of the syringe and its ultimate use. The physical properties of its components must not deteriorate during this "shelf time".

Polypropylene fills this need extremely well. It can be precision-molded in large economical family molds to yield the proper dimensions, it is clear enough to view the contents, it can be printed if necessary and, most important, it can be irradiation sterilized and still perform its intended function.

In addition to syringes, PP is also used in other laboratory and hospital devices. Examples are petri dishes, intravenous bottles, specimen bottles, food trays, pans, and other behind-the-scenes objects that are less apparent. One such object is the container that is used to collect used syringes and other contaminated medical waste, and is often referred to as the "sharps container." This container, usually pigmented a bright color, is designed to accept used syringes through a cap that allows passage of items in one direction only; it is illustrated in Color Plate 10.6. It is blow molded or injection molded from a resin that has a high flexural modulus and high hardness so as to resist puncturing from the syringes within. Finally, it is disposable, generally by incineration. Polypropylene provides all of these features and is widely used for this application.

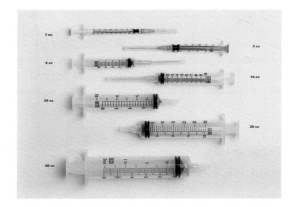

Color Plate 10.5 Nearly all syringes in use today are disposable, a feature that reduces cost and prevents the spread of disease. Polypropylene syringes can be radiation sterilized prior to sale and enjoy nearly all of the international markets for disposable syringes

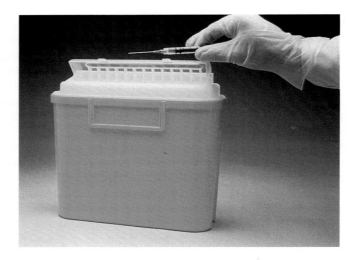

Color Plate 10.6 "Sharps" containers of PP protect medical workers from discarded hazardous implements

The other unique feature of PP that makes it ideal for medical use is its ability to be processed into nonwoven fabrics. The use of nonwovens in medical applications is large and growing and is covered in Section 10.2.3.

10.3.4   Rigid Packaging

Rigid packaging is a term used to describe items such as margarine tubs, yogurt containers, trays, bottles, boxes, and closures of many types. The containers come in all sizes and shapes and are fabricated by three major processes: injection molding, blow molding, and thermoforming. They protect hundreds of different products, most of which are food products, and have been doing so for many years. Polypropylene is widely used for this application throughout the world and enjoys favorable status with the food and drug regulatory agencies in all developed countries. Polypropylene is by far the resin of choice for bottle closures, and has been for many years. Its stiffness and resistance to stress cracking make it ideal for this use. Some closures incorporate the living hinge principle, as shown in Fig. 10.11. This property is unique to PP and serves to produce a closure that can be resealed easily and conveniently.

Until recently, the resins of choice to mold rigid containers were polyethylenes because of the limited life required and the relative low cost of the resin. However, the advent of more restrictive environmental laws, particularly in the U.S.A. and Europe, has focused more interest on PP. In some U.S. states, for example, the use of packaging materials is being restricted by legislative decree. The package must be recycled at a specified recovery rate, be reduced in total weight, or have 25% post-consumer content to reduce the load on available land fills. The strength of PP enables the manufacturer to achieve a source reduction of around 10% to 30%.

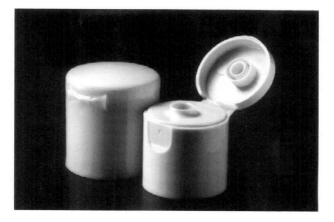

Figure 10.11 A feature unique to PP is its ability to forma "living hinge." This concept is widely used in resealable closures, such as those shown here, to produce closures that can be easily and cleanly resealed. Photo courtesy Seaquist Closures

Polypropylene can be post-consumer recycled and is already being recovered to the extent of 200 million pounds annually from automobile batteries in the U.S.A. alone. Recyclability is volume sensitive; the larger the volume of PP in packaging, the more economically it can be recycled. More is better in this sense, and more is exactly what PP has been enjoying in rigid packaging. The third route to environment compliance, reducing the volume of the package, is one for which PP is well suited. Polyethylene, the largest volume resin used in rigid packaging, has a lower flexural modulus, requiring a greater wall thickness. The same basic container can be molded with thinner walls using PP, thereby complying with the source reduction option in the environmentally oriented regulations.

Thin walls, however, require resins with high flow characteristics. Generally, high flow resins are low molecular weight polymers that display poor physical properties. General acceptance of this phenomenon has kept PP from capturing this market in the past. Recently, however, thanks to newly designed polymers, thin walls with excellent physical properties are possible. This development is enabling PP to capture more thin-wall, rigid container markets like those shown in Color Plate 10.7.

Polypropylene enjoys excellent resistance to moisture vapor transmission (MVT) but is not effective in inhibiting the passage of oxygen. To protect foods or other products that are adversely affected by oxygen, PP is coated or extrusion laminated with a material that provides this protection. The multilayer ketchup bottle is an example of this technique. It consists of five coextruded layers: two PP layers to give rigidity and MVT resistance, a polyvinyl alcohol layer to provide oxygen protection, and two layers of a special adhesive to bond the polyvinyl alcohol to the PP layers. This composite is blow molded to produce the final bottle. Polypropylene is also used to blow mold syrup bottles, an application that requires the bottle to remain rigid during hot filling. Examples of these important PP applications are shown in Color Plate 10.8.

In recent years, "ready to eat" meals became available in sealed PP containers that do not require refrigeration and that can be heated, after opening, in a microwave oven. These containers, shown in Fig. 10.12, are particularly popular as the main food item in prepackaged lunches. Polypropylene is the resin of choice for this because it has the necessary rigidity, can withstand the heat of retort cooking as well as the heat applied to the container prior to consumption of its contents, is classified as GRAS (generally recognized as safe) in the U.S.A. with respect to FDA compliance, and protects the contents from both moisture and oxygen during its stay on the store shelf.

Clarifying agents are commercially available that contribute good see-through and contact clarity to injection molded PP containers. This feature, combined with PP's excellent impact resistance and heat resistance (dishwasher temperatures), have resulted in its wide-spread use in food storage containers, and is now expanding rapidly into home, office, and workshop bulk storage containers.

New injection stretch blow molding techniques combined with new clarifiers for PP are producing bottles that rival PET in appearance. These clarified resins are not only lighter in weight than PET but also cost less per pound, a double savings. The cost/performance advantage of PP has led to its use in commercial bottles, including those for carbonated water, hot filled juices, teas, and sport drinks.

In addition to injection molded rigid containers, it is important to point out that recent success in thermoforming PP via solid phase pressure forming has led to increased interest because of the potential for high productivity and source reduction. Polypropylene can now

Color Plate 10.7 The development of high flow PP resin led to its use in thin wall injection molded containers. Its stiffness permits thinner walls. thereby reducing the total package weight, a feature that not only reduces the cost of shipping but also reduces the amount of packaging material mandated for recycling

Color Plate 10.8 Multilayered blow molded bottles contain two or more layers of PP to provide stiffness and to serve as a barrier to moisture vapor. Ketchup bottles utilize this construction. Polypropylene is also used to blow mold bottles that are hot filled, such as the syrup bottle also pictured

Figure 10.12 Containers of PP hold meals in a ready-to-eat condition until heated at mealtime, usually in a microwave oven

be processed at speeds competitive with polystyrene, and the orientation created by this process yields clear parts with improved stiffness and toughness. Drinking glasses, deli containers, and other formed packages can be produced via this process.

10.3.5   Transportation

Without question, the largest single application for PP in this market is the molding of interior and exterior parts for automobiles and light trucks. Although a number of plastic materials, most notably phenolics, polystyrene, and cellulose acetate butyrate, were used in automobiles as far back as the 1950s, the vast majority of plastic components were developed subsequent to the early 1970s when a worldwide need to reduce unit weight accelerated their development. Early targets were metal, rubber, and glass components, all of which contributed heavily to the weight of the vehicle. Replacing these parts with a lighter material like PP provided immediate weight savings with no loss in performance.

The development of PP impact copolymers provided resins with the required balance of impact resistance and stiffness to satisfy most of these early applications. Polypropylene was also the lightest of all candidate resins, low in cost, and readily available worldwide from a number of suppliers. It is no surprise that it became the resin of choice in so many automotive applications. A diagram showing many of the current PP automotive applications is presented in Fig. 10.13.

Probably the most widely known PP automotive application is the battery case (more properly, but rarely, called a storage cell). Previously molded in hard rubber, the switch to a PP copolymer resulted in a significant reduction in weight and cost. The ability to mold PP battery cases in bright colors, as depicted in Color Plate 10.9, or simply to produce an attractive translucent case by omitting pigment altogether, added to its appeal when contrasted to the black, hard rubber products. Today, almost all batteries for automobiles, light trucks, motorcycles, aircraft, and boats are made with cases and covers molded from PP.

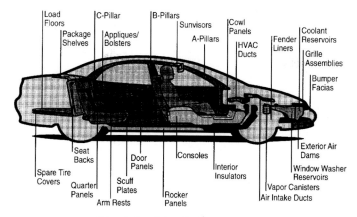

Polypropylene Automotive Parts

Figure 10.13 Today's automobiles and light trucks rely heavily on PP. This cut-away highlights many of the automotive components, both interior and exterior, that are made from PP. Its use grows annually

10.3.5.1   Interior Uses

Among the many applications for PP in automotive interior trim are door panels, kick panels, quarter panels, angel wings, arm rests, pillar covers, consoles, and cowl panels. Except for fabrics, these trim parts represent most of the components that are visible inside the vehicle. Polypropylene has captured a major portion of this market.

Early in their development, these molded parts were colored to be as close to the color of the final product as possible and were subsequently painted to provide the exact color and to mask mold imperfections and weld lines. When the paint was scratched or scuffed, and the substrate became visible, it was thought to be close enough to the paint color to be little noticed. This technique allowed rather broad specifications on the molded parts, allowing the manufacturer to enjoy the resulting low costs which, in turn, helped to offset the added cost of painting. In time, it was realized that painting was not the answer because painted parts began to show their age prematurely, especially in high scuff areas such as door panels, kick panels, and consoles.

Consequently, today more and more interior trim parts are molded-in-color, eliminating the need for painting. This requires more precise molding which, in turn, requires newer resins. Today's resins flow more easily throughout the mold, forming fewer molded-in stresses and less obvious weld lines. In fact, in many cases these resins negate the need for multiple gates, effectively eliminating visible weld lines altogether. The result is interior trim parts that do not require painting, that are excellent color matches for interior trim parts made of other materials, and that hold up well in high scuff areas.

One aspect of the use of molded thermoplastic parts for automotive interior trim that is not generally recognized is the need for heat resistance. The interior of a closed automobile in the hot summer sun can reach temperatures approaching 90 °C (200 °F). In a no-load application, PP exhibits superior resistance to distortion compared with other resins commonly used to mold interior parts, a feature that helps make it the resin of choice for such applications.

Modern automobiles are built for quiet comfort, and today's advertisements extol these benefits to all who will listen. Polypropylene interior parts help to create this quiet environment because they do not "ring," an undesirable property that many other polymers exhibit, much to the dismay of design engineers and passengers alike.

In today's world, with its global emphasis on recycle, the automobile presents a real challenge because of the multitude of generic plastic resins currently in use. Polypropylene is versatile enough to assume a large number of these applications, thus simplifying the job of recycling expired vehicles. For example, the instrument panel in many cars is constructed using three different plastic resins, one with a very high modulus to serve as the skeleton, another to make the instrument display attractive, and a third, very soft material to cover those areas that are likely to be impacted by the occupants in the event of an accident. Polypropylene can be tailored to perform each of these functions without sacrificing performance. The entire instrument panel is then recyclable without first requiring the labor-intensive chore of identifying and separating plastic components. This concept, pioneered in Europe, is generating interest throughout the western world. A typical PP instrument panel appears in Fig. 10.14.

10.3.5.2   Exterior Uses

The past twenty-five years have seen major changes in the way automobiles are designed and built. Computer assisted design and computer assisted manufacture (CAD-CAM) have shortened the design cycle for new models and minimized the troubling "glitches" that affected new model start-ups. Integral to this change is the growing use of plastic components that require less lead time to produce and provide the designer with an almost limitless range of geometric shapes to enhance styling and improve aerodynamics. What were once

Figure 10.14 Several automobile manufacturers, primarily European based, have selected PP to mold portions of the instrument panel. This not only reduces weight but also assists in recycling when the vehicle is eventually committed to salvage

considered one-of-a-kind concept cars are now mass produced, thanks, in part, to PP exterior parts.

Much of the change resulted from government mandates imposed to reduce weight, improve fuel economy, and minimize the damages resulting from low-speed impacts. Substituting plastic for metal certainly reduced the weight of the vehicle. The redesign of the entire bumper system to pass the five mile per hour impact test eliminated huge chrome bumpers in favor of a complex energy absorbing hydraulic system or an energy absorbing honeycomb and/or foam system, each of which was covered with a facia molded from plastic resin. Many of the early facias were molded using the reaction in mold (RIM) resin systems, but negative customer reaction to the ripples resulting from the different thermal expansion properties of RIM resins relative to the surrounding metal resulted in an eventual switch to thermoplastic olefin (TPO) resins.

First the end caps, and then the entire bumper facia converted to TPO. The PP facia was, and still is, painted to provide an exact color match to the remainder of the vehicle. An outstanding example of a high-style painted PP bumper fascia appears in Color Plate 10.10. Recently some TPO facia have been molded directly in accent colors, thereby avoiding the need for an exact color match while at the same time eliminating the costly painting step.

Early TPO resins were produced by compounding PP with certain elastomeric resins (see Chapter 5) and, in fact, this technique is still in use today. Recent advances, however, enable some resin producers to tailor make the final TPO in the reactor, thus eliminating the compounding step and producing a more uniform product.

In addition to bumper facia, TPOs are used to mold air scoops, side body claddings, rocker panels, and, more recently, the grills themselves. In fact, the use of chrome grills has all but disappeared from light trucks and will most likely disappear from automobiles, as well, in the near future. Grills of TPO, like those on the light truck shown in Color Plate 10.11, absorb moderate impact, will not rust or corrode, and can be produced in attractive colors.

It was recognized early that the molds used to injection mold and thermoform plastics are far less expensive than the massive dies needed for metal stamping. Also, the variety of resins available enabled the materials engineer to select those with physical properties that directly addressed the specific need. A case in point was the replacement of metal fender liners with liners thermoformed using a PP copolymer, a change that not only protected the engine compartment from road debris and provided structural integrity to the front end assembly, but also reduced overall weight, improved corrosion resistance, and lowered costs.

10.4   Film

Early on, it was learned that PP could be extruded into sheet and film (sheet defined as > 10 mil, film as < 10 mil). Techniques to orient the film were later employed which provided considerable strength in the oriented direction. When it was oriented in two directions (machine and cross), the film became very strong and very clear. The film products resulting from this latter technique, known as biaxially oriented PP film (BOPP) could be prepared in a single extrusion step and eventually replaced cellophane as the most widely used clear packaging film in the world. Details of the orientation processes are outlined in Chapter 9.

Color Plate 10.9 Polypropylene battery (storage cell) cases were one of the earliest and most identifiable automotive applications. Light weight, stiffness, and acid resistance are requisites for this demanding use, three properties generic PP. The fact that PP cases could be produced in attractive colors was an added plus.

Color Plate 10.10 This shows the freedom of design that PP bumper facia provides the automotive designer. Not only is the bumper functional, it is also beautiful

Color Plate 10.11 Injection molded TPO grills are replacing chrome plated metal grills in light trucks because they are capable of taking more abuse than their metal counterparts and can be produced in attractive colors

Color Plate 10.12 BOPP film protects snack foods and other food products that are adversely affected by UV light. The opaque film blocks UV while producing an attractive package that appeals to potential customers

10.4.1   Biaxially Oriented Film

In many ways PP is an ideal polymer for packaging film. It is resistant to grease and oil, resists moisture permeation, is abrasion resistant, provides high tensile strength even at elevated temperatures, possesses good impact and flexibility at very low temperatures, and its stiffness is an asset on the converting line. Aesthetically, PP film displays excellent clarity and gloss, while its low density reduces the cost per unit area of film when compared to most other film polymers.

Biaxially oriented film can be made via two distinctly different processes: tubular (bubble) and tenter frame (see Chapter 9). Both processes were used early in commercial production of BOPP film, and both are still in use today. The bubble process is favored to produce very thin films. The tenter process, however, is the most widely used process, offering improved economics, particularly in somewhat thicker films. Both processes yield exceptionally clear films that can be coated, heat sealed, or metalized to accommodate today's sophisticated converting lines.

Biaxially oriented PP films are selected according to the needs of the converting line and the level of protection required by the contents of the package. The converting lines generally require that one or more surfaces be heat sealable which, in turn, requires that heat seal coatings adhere well to the surface of the film. While BOPP film provides good moisture barrier, coatings must be applied if oxygen barrier properties are required to protect the contents. Most foods, for example, must be protected from both oxidation and moisture absorption while in the package. Some also require protection from UV light, in which case the film is often metalized to provide complete opacity. Obtaining adhesion of coatings and inks was a technical breakthrough without which the use of BOPP film would not have grown beyond a few specialty applications.

Food packaging applications were early targets for BOPP film, with applications dating back to the early 1960s. Today, it is the dominant film packaging material in the snack food, bakery, and candy industries.

Snack food packaging is the largest single use of BOPP film. It is used because of its excellent moisture barrier properties, stiffness, gloss, printability, and crispness. When needed, special coatings provide excellent oxygen barrier properties, as well. Snack foods that are potato-based are adversely affected by UV light, a condition that requires an opaque package. Opaque BOPP films or clear BOPP films that are metalized address this need.

Snack food packages consist of more than one layer. At the very least, a heat seal layer is required to seal the package. Other layers include slip films to facilitate processing through the converting lines, oxygen barrier layers for contents protection, and adhesive layers to hold it all together. The introduction of highly flavored snack foods adds still another requirement to the package: fragrance retention. The packaging of food products today requires a sophisticated array of specially engineered films designed specifically for the products they are chosen to protect.

Bakery packaging is slightly less demanding than snack food packaging because bakery products generally have a shorter shelf life. The key requirement here is keeping the baked goods fresh and soft by preventing the loss of moisture, a feat that BOPP films perform very well. Clarity and printability are also important to enhance shelf appeal.

The packaging of sweet (candy) products is the third major food packaging market for BOPP. Here, protecting the fragrance and blocking out oxygen are the two primary requirements made difficult by the long shelf life experienced by many candy products. Opaque films are often used in this application, where the attractive pearlescent background, printability, crispness, and gloss add to its suitability for packaging these products, as shown in Color Plate 10.12.

Opaque films are also used to label soft drinks and other beverages. They produce an attractive package, do not rip, provide some abrasion resistance, and do not come off when the bottle is chilled, for example, in ice water. Examples of these labels can be seen in Color Plate 10.13.

Capacitors, widely used in the electronics industry, are made using a special BOPP film to provide the necessary electrical insulation. Moisture absorption negatively affects the ability of a plastic to provide insulation. Since PP offers low moisture absorption and has inherently good insulating properties, it is ideal for this application. Capacitors are ubiquitous in today's electronic world, yet little notice is ever paid to them or to how they are constructed. Polypropylene is an essential component of many such unheralded products.

10.4.2   Unoriented Film

The rapid chilling of extruded PP film produces an unoriented film with excellent clarity. The film produced in this manner lacks the stiffness of BOPP and, while clear, is not as clear as BOPP. However, it is less costly to make and serves certain competitive markets where soft clear films are desired.

Stationery products consume much of the cast film manufactured today. This includes clear overlays, dividers, and ancillary film products, such as photo albums and baseball card protector pages, that proliferate in today's homes and offices. The environmental concerns surrounding PVC have accelerated the use of cast PP in these applications, many of which were previously served by PVC film.

Figure 10.15 Polypropylene film, oriented in the machine direction, is used to produce "tensile tape," a tape exhibiting extremely high linear strength and commonly used for securing packages and for other similar household applications

The positioning of a PP nonwoven fabric next to the skin in disposable diapers to keep the skin dry by facilitating the passage of moisture was covered previously. Cast PP film, on the other hand, is often used as the outer protective layer in the diaper construction, its purpose being to keep the moisture inside the diaper. One advantage of cast PP film is that it reduces "crinkle," a disturbing sound made when a film is flexed. This is especially important when used in diapers for adult incontinence, a market that is gaining importance as the world population ages. In this area, lower modulus PP products, such as the new high alloy copolymers, mentioned in Section 6.3.4, are even more attractive.

Cast film is also used in various tapes and pressure-sensitive labels. Some tapes are made from film that is oriented in the machine direction and are appropriately referred to as high tensile tapes, or just packaging tapes, examples of which can be seen in Fig. 10.15. Pressure-sensitive labels are made from both cast and BOPP film, although cast film is generally used when the surface is not truly flat. The softness of the film allows it to conform better to the surface on which it is applied.

10.5   Wire and Cable

Although some PP has been used over the years for insulating power cable, its primary use has been in telephone "singles;" that is, the individual wires used for telephone transmission. In this role, PP yielded the necessary colors, resisted softening by the jelly used to waterproof underground cables, resisted stress cracking, and provided the necessary dielectric properties. Special stabilization prevents the copper wire from causing premature degradation of the polymer. Although this is an interesting application and PP performs its function very well, the future in telephone transmission is with optical fiber, and the wire and cable market is indeed limited.

10.6   Miscellaneous Applications

Strapping made from plastic resin is routinely used to secure packaged merchandise during shipping, having replaced steel strapping in many areas. Polypropylene is one of several resins currently used. When oriented in the machine direction, PP displays excellent tensile strength, a property essential for secure strapping. It also resists moisture pickup, a phenomenon that causes hygroscopic resins to swell and subsequently loosen. Polypropylene, as well as other plastic resins used for strapping, can be easily captured and recycled.

The use of BOPP film/paper laminates in packaging is widespread. This is usually accomplished by incorporating a low-density polyethylene (LDPE) adhesive layer to bond the two materials. The BOPP film in a laminated structure can be used to serve two major purposes: it can protect the printed paper from damage caused by abrasion or moisture, or it can be used on the inside to create a barrier between the ink and the package contents. Products that require chilling often become wet from condensation, and the labels on these packages benefit from the integrity that the moisture-resistant BOPP layer provides. Other products, examples being lawn and garden products, are often stored for extended periods in humid areas and the containers in which they are packaged also benefit from PP's added moisture resistance. Suppliers like the improved aesthetics provided by the BOPP layer, a phenomenon alternately described as "depth of finish" or "improved richness." These are added benefits, directly attributable to the PP overlay [see Color Plate 10.13].

New PP polymers are being developed that can be processed at high speeds in extrusion coating equipment, resulting in a single-step paper/PP composite. This extrusion coating technique eliminates the lamination step, thereby reducing the cost of the package. Although not yet widely used, extrusion coated paper is already replacing some BOPP/paper laminates, and this trend is sure to continue, given the cost savings inherent in this approach.

An interesting PP development resulting from new technology is the ability to design reactor particles that are extremely porous. This high porosity, and the resultant increase in surface area, enables this form of PP to absorb a large amount of liquid and remain a free-flowing powder. The benefits of this feature are enjoyed most by compounders, who are able to use this type of concentrate to precisely meter liquid additives into extruders and other compounding devices without the use of metering pumps and without the side effects associated with nonuniform distribution of liquid additives.

Most everyone has, at one time or another, sent or received a package wrapped with decorative ribbon. Chances are this ribbon was produced from a foamed, pigmented PP sheet that was oriented in the machine direction (see Chapter 9) to produce the pearlescence that gives these ribbons their special appeal. The ribbons, shown in Fig. 10.16, are extremely strong, colorful, resistant to moisture, and relatively inexpensive, and demonstrate again the versatility of PP applications.

Another small but growing use for PP is in the manufacture of corrugated board. These boards are lightweight and completely printable and are widely used for signage and light storage containers; see Color Plate 10.14. Unlike paper board, the PP product is unaffected by water, which means the items fabricated from it maintain their strength even in the wettest

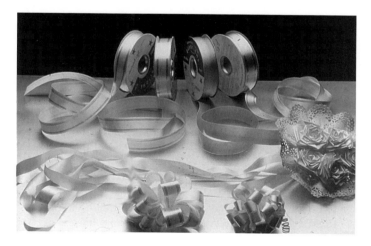

Figure 10.16 Decorative ribbon, used on special occasions throughout the world for gift wrapping, is made by orienting foamed PP sheet. Its colorful pearlescent appearance is quite attractive

Color Plate 10.13 Bottle labels, like those shown, are printed on opaque BOPP film to prevent removal of the label when the bottle is subjected to wet conditions, such as from condensation when the bottle is chilled or when the entire bottle is submerged in ice water

Color Plate 10.14 Polypropylene corrugated board is unaffected by moisture, and its rigidity and durability make for excellent signage and light storage boxes. Photo courtesy Coroplast Corp.

Figure 10.17 Australian currency takes advantage of the durability of PP

environment. Signs don't wilt and boxes don't collapse. The U.S. Post Office uses a large number of PP corrugated boxes to transport mail.

While PP has clearly provided added value in many of its applications, the ultimate in that category has now been reached. It is the material, in a strong nonwoven form, on which Australian currency is being printed; see Fig. 10.17. However, the promise that it will make the dollar last longer probably does not refer to how long any individual will be able to keep it in his wallet!

11   Regulations and Approvals

Catherine E. Ruiz, Richard T. LeNoir

11.1   Introduction

Industry and consumer consciousness continues to be elevated with respect to safety, environmental, and health concerns. As more is learned about the effects of chemicals and polymers and their manufacturing, use, and disposal, more efforts are made to identify and minimize the associated potential hazards. The impetus to do so comes from many sources including consumer groups, industry, and government. This chapter highlights some of the organizations and mechanisms used to classify safety and/or health hazards associated with plastic resins in general, and PP in particular.

The organizations which develop and promulgate the mechanisms which allow classification of plastics materials with respect to health and safety include government, third-party certifiers, and direct users of the resins. There are two primary protocols utilized. The first can be termed "self-certification," where there exists an established series of standards or requirements against which a resin manufacturer measures its product. Any testing required is the responsibility of the resin manufacturer. The resin manufacturer then determines which, if any, of the standards their material meets. It is the responsibility of the resin manufacturer to insure that enough evidence exists to support any claims made with regard to the classification of its resin against the standards. The self-certification protocol is typically associated with government-sponsored health and safety initiatives, such as the Food and Drug Administration regulations for food contact in the United States and the European Union Directives for food contact in Europe. Self-certification is also the typical method for accommodating customer-imposed specification related to health and safety.

The second protocol, which is utilized to classify resins, is third-party certification. In this case, an outside or "third party" determines the resin's performance relative to the standard. The third-party certifier then grants recognition to the resins. Such recognition is usually accompanied by agreements between the certifier and the resin manufacturer for follow-up service. As part of the follow-up service, the certifier conducts audits of various types to provide continuing evidence that the resin remains the same as when it was originally certified and/or that it continues to meet the standards to which it was recognized. The third-party certifiers do not assume any liabilities of the resin manufacturer.

Each type of polymer and each unique end-use application may have specialized standards, requirements, and organizations to which it must conform or respond. The remainder of this chapter will provide examples that are commonly encountered by manufacturers of PP. The examples are representative of the types of relevant classifications. Each country or economic group may have their own version of a given generic type of classification, although there are significant moves to establish cooperative agreements between similar organizations in different countries.

11.2   Hazard Communication

In the spirit of educating the worker, many laws have been established around the world to address the use of chemicals and the hazards associated with them. The key aspect of this legislation is to communicate the known hazards of the chemical substance to the employees working with that chemical. The United States has the Occupational, Safety and Health Act's Hazard Communication Standard (HAZCOM) [1], Canada has the Workplace Hazardous Materials Information System (WHMIS) [2], and the European Union has Directives 67/548/EC and 88/379/EC. Many other countries have similar pieces of legislation. Most of these laws contain a requirement for Material Safety Data Sheets (MSDSs) to be provided, if not on all chemical substances, at least for those chemical substances which meet hazardous definitions as established by the laws and regulations [3].

11.2.1   Material Safety Data Sheets (MSDSs)

The most accepted means of conveying health, safety, and environment (HSE) information about a product is the MSDS. Many countries have requirements for providing MSDSs, preferably in the native language. For instance, in Europe, recent legislation made it mandatory to provide the MSDS in the language of each EU member. There are laws and regulations that establish the requirements for the content of the MSDSs [4]. Information such as supplier name and address, hazardous chemical identification, physical property data, fire and explosion data, reactivity data, toxicology data, environmental data, first-aid measures, personal protective equipment needs, and storage and handling information are required in a MSDS. No standard format has been mandated except in Europe. Countries like the United States and Canada have suggested formats. In the U.S.A., the Chemical Manufacturers Association (CMA) worked with the American National Standards Institute (ANSI) to develop a standard for MSDS preparation [5]. ANSI Standard Z400.1-1993 was developed to provide guidance on MSDS preparation to comply not only with the U.S. HAZCOM Standard but also with the requirements of Canada and Europe. The format is designed to put the required information into a sixteen-section MSDS which is very similar to the format dictated by the EU [6].

11.2.2   PP and PP Copolymers

Polypropylene and PP copolymers with no additives are not hazardous materials by any known definition, regulation, or law. What can make PP polymers hazardous are the ingredients used in formulating the final product mixture. For instance, fiberglass is used to reinforce PP and give it enhanced physical properties. Fiberglass is considered a hazardous material because it is a skin irritant. By blending it with PP at levels exceeding 1%, the PP mixture is considered a hazardous material. Other ingredients, such as flame-retardants and mineral fillers like talc, can also make PP formulations hazardous. If a PP mixture containing a hazardous ingredient is tested and it is shown there are no adverse health, safety, or environmental effects from the use of the mixture, then the PP mixture can be considered a nonhazardous substance. However, in Europe, a hazardous mixture must be labeled according to Directives 88/379/EC and 93/112/EC.

11.3   Chemical Registration

Before a chemical substance can be imported, manufactured, or processed in a country, the use of that chemical substance must be in compliance with that country's chemical registration legislation. Chemical registration usually involves petitioning for the use of a chemical substance by providing enough information for the government to make a health, safety, and environmental assessment of the chemical substance, and usually requires some registration of manufactured quantities. With the exception of specifically identified confidential information, these facts become part of the public record. Most chemical registration procedures do not require registration of mixtures, only the components of the mixture. For polymer formulations, each ingredient of the formulation must be registered on the chemical substance inventory.

There are approximately thirteen countries that require the listing of all chemical substances used within their borders (see Table 11.1). More countries are in the process of formulating their chemical registration requirements (see Table 11.2). As can be seen from the following examples, the requirements of chemical registration vary from country to country. The following briefly summarizes the registration requirements in the U.S.A., Canada, and Europe.

11.3.1   Toxic Substances Control Act (TSCA)—United States

All chemical substances used industrially in the United States must comply with TSCA legislation. The TSCA Inventory lists the chemicals currently covered; it is continuously

Table 11.1 Countries with Existing Chemical Regristration Requirements

Country	Inventory
Australia	AICS
Austria	
Canada	DSL
China	ICCS
European Union	EINECS/ELINCS
Finland	
Japan	MITI
Korea	ECL
Norway	
Philippines	PICCS
Sweden	
Switzerland	
United States	TSCA

Table 11.2 Countries Proposing New Chemical Registration Requirements

Country
India
Malaysia
Mexico
New Zealand
South Africa
Russia
Taiwan
Thailand

updated. Registration of chemical substances requires the filing of a Premanufacture Notice (PMN) with the Environmental Protection Agency (EPA). Information to be filed on the PMN form includes chemical identity; chemical abstract services (CAS) number; prospective uses of the chemical substance; any toxicity information whether it be health, safety, or environmental; manufacturing information; and any potential exposure problems [7].

Once the petition is filed with the EPA, the chemical substance undergoes a 90-day review. At the end of the 90-day period, if the EPA has no questions concerning the information submitted, a chemical substance can be manufactured or imported into the United States. Once the chemical substance is produced commercially for the first time, a manufacturer or importer has 30 days to file a Notice of Commencement (NOC) of commercialization, which includes the first commercial manufacturing date and justification for any confidential business information that might have been claimed in the original PMN filing [8].

There are exemptions to filing of the 90-day PMN, such as the R&D exemption and the polymers exemption. The R&D exemption allows chemical substances not on the TSCA Inventory to be used in research and development activities, but they cannot be sold commercially in the U.S.A. [9]. The polymers exemption allows the use of low-risk polymers without going through the PMN process [10]. Under recently published polymer exemption rules [11], polymers that meet specific criteria are exempt from EPA notification prior to commercial manufacturing. Those rules require maintaining manufacturing records, describing the new polymers, and reporting the production volume for three years.

These records must be kept at the manufacturing sites. In January of the year following first-time manufacture of the polymer, the EPA must be notified regarding the number of polymers that were made. One important requirement concerning polymers is that a monomer incorporated into or charged at more than 2% must be used in the name of that polymer. An example would be a propylene homopolymer that would have more than 2% ethylene incorporated into the polymer matrix. This no longer could be called a PP homopolymer, but would have to be called a propylene/ethylene copolymer.

Finally, it should be noted that TSCA involves much more than simply a list of chemicals. There are many other areas of chemical regulation, such as import certification, export notification, significant new uses of chemicals, just to name a few, that fit under the TSCA umbrella [12].

11.3.2   European Inventory of Existing Chemical Substances (EINECS)/European List of New Chemical Substances (ELINCS)

In the last few years, European countries have made efforts to consolidate their regulatory actions under one governing body, which is the European Union (EU). By doing this, the EU has chosen the EINECS and ELINCS lists and procedures for their chemical registration [13]. New chemical substances must be listed on one of these lists to be used in Europe. The EINECS list is a fixed list of chemical substances that were in commercial use in Europe in the early 1980s [14]; ELINCS is the list of new chemical substances notified since that time.

Notification takes place in the manufacturer's country of residence. A new chemical substance is exempted from notification and can be used for research and development purposes, provided the amount manufactured does not exceed one metric ton. To manufacture more than one ton, the first notification of the chemical substance must take place. This includes information concerning the identity of the chemical substance and a base set of toxicity testing to allow a health, safety, and environmental evaluation of the chemical substance. To exceed each higher magnitude level (i.e., 10 tons/yr or 50 tons total, 100 tons/yr or 500 tons total), more toxicity work must be performed, as specified by the chemical registration rules. Once toxicity testing is complete, the chemical substance is listed on ELINCS and can be used throughout the EU countries.

One major difference between new chemical substance registration in the EU and the U.S.A. is that new chemicals can be registered in the EU on ELINCS under a trade name rather than the chemical name. Therefore, someone who may make the same chemical substance would have to file for new chemical registration, even though the chemical may already be listed under a different trade name.

Polymers are not listed on either EINECS or ELINCS. As long as the monomers used to manufacture the polymers are listed on either list, then the polymer is said to be in compliance with the chemical registration rules of the EU. However, the 7th Amendment of Directive 67/588/EC establishes new rules related to polymers.

11.3.3   Domestic Substances List (DSL) and Nondomestic Substances List (NDSL)—Canada

In July 1994, the chemical registration rules in Canada became effective. The official list of chemical substances allowed to be used in Canada is the DSL. The Canadian government included in the first DSL those chemical substances that were in commercial production from 1984 to 1986. The NDSL is defined as the list of chemical substances commercially used in the rest of the world, but is in fact the chemical substances on the TSCA Inventory minus those on the DSL. The NDSL has been legislated to be updated approximately every six months starting in 1995 using the 1990 TSCA Inventory.

A new chemical substance can be added to the DSL by the process of chemical registration. The Canadian approach to chemical registration has elements of both the European and the U.S. versions. Canada has established different categories of registration such as research and development, product development, export only, and site-limited intermediates. Each of the categories has its own schedule of notification involving yearly quantities manufactured and/or total accumulation of the chemical substance in Canada, and information required for each quantity [15]. To exceed the quantities listed in the regulations, one must provide the information required for producing that quantity. Physical properties and toxicity information are usually required.

This approach to the development of toxicity and physical property information at various target quantity levels is similar to the European form of registration. In addition, more conventional to chemical substances, polymers are also registered using a similar series of notification and information requirements. This varies from the new U.S. and existing European methods in that polymers are/will not be listed in either of those inventories.

11.4   Food Contact

Polypropylene homopolymers and propylene/ethylene copolymers are used in many food contact applications. These range from simple beverage closures to retortable pouch applications. There are several countries and regions that have established significant food contact regulations in the world. These include the U.S.A., Canada, European Union, Australia, and Japan. Each has a different way to regulate food contact applications, although the U.S.A. and Australia have some similarities. In the following sections, the food contact regulation methods of these countries and regions will be discussed.

11.4.1   United States: Food and Drug Administration (FDA)

The FDA is the government agency that regulates the food area in the United States. The United States Department of Agriculture (USDA) has jurisdiction over meat, fish, and poultry plants. However, the USDA refers to the FDA regulations for food contact to clear materials for use in meat, fish, and poultry plants. Therefore, the FDA is looked upon as the U.S. experts in matters related to food.

11.4.1.1   FDA Petitions

Polypropylene resins and the additives and colorants used in these resins are considered indirect food additives. The FDA utilizes a premarketing petition process to clear indirect food additives. The first step of the petition process is to test the indirect additives under the conditions of use in contact with certain food simulants [16]. The amount of extractables from the polymers is determined, then toxicity data must be developed on the extractable material. All of this information is put into a petition and submitted to the FDA for approval of the particular indirect additive. In addition, a proposal for the regulation of the indirect additive is submitted as part of the petition. After FDA review and approval, the new regulation is officially published in the U.S. Federal Register. This process can be time-consuming, but once completed, a regulation is established which specifies how the indirect food additive can be used. The regulations formally published in the Federal Register for food additives are found in the Code of Federal Regulations under Title 21.

11.4.1.2   FDA Regulations for PP Homopolymers and Copolymers

The specific FDA statute that regulates PP and its derivatives for food contact applications is found in the Code of Federal Regulations, Title 21, Part 177.1520. This is known as the "Olefin Polymers Regulation." There are other applicable FDA regulations which are called end-use regulations because they apply to the final articles used in the food contact application. These include under Title 21, Part 175.105, Adhesives; Part 175.300, Resinous and Polymeric Coatings; Part 176.170, Components of Paper and Paperboard in Contact with Aqueous and Fatty Foods; Part 177.1210, Closures with Sealing Gaskets for Food Containers; and Part 177.2600, Rubber Articles Intended for Repeated Use. These end-use regulations have requirements for the resins used in their applications and, in addition, require testing of the final article prior to FDA certification. If our resins are in compliance with Part 177.1520, they will qualify as resins under the aforementioned end-use regulations. However, to fully comply with the end-use regulation, a manufacturer of the food contact article must test that article and make the certification on it.

11.4.1.3   Title 21, Part 177.1520—Olefin Polymers Regulation

The following will discuss in a little more detail Part 177.1520 as it pertains to PP homopolymer and propylene/ethylene copolymers. There are four sub paragraphs under Part 177.1520 labeled (a) (b) (c) and (d) (see Table 11.3).

Sub paragraph (a) provides definitions for olefin polymers. For example, sub paragraph (a)(1) defines PP homopolymer as "the catalytic polymerization of propylene." Part 177.1520 (a)(3)(i) defines olefin copolymers as "the catalytic copolymerization of two or more of the one-alkenes having two to eight carbon atoms."

Sub paragraph (b) provides for the use of various additives in olefin polymers. These include specific references in sub paragraph (b), as well as references to additives covered by FDA regulations, specifically parts 170 through 189 (in Title 21 of the Code of Federal Regulations).

Sub paragraph (c) provides the specifications for the olefin polymers defined in sub paragraph (a). For instance, 1.1 under subparagraph (c) gives the specifications for PP homopolymer (see Table 11.4). Specifications for olefin copolymers such as propylene/ethylene copolymers are listed under sub paragraph (c) in 3.1a and 3.2a. There are two specifications for olefin copolymers because FDA distinguishes between cooking and noncooking applications for utilizing these resins. The difference between the two specifications is the hexane extractables. For noncooking applications, the maximum hexane extractable is 5.5% at a temperature of 50 °C. For cooking applications, specified in 3.2a, the maximum hexane extractables is 2.6% at 50 °C.

Table 11.3 Olefin Polymers Regulation—21 CFR 177.1520

Sub Paragraph	Topic
(a)	Definitions of olefin polymer types
(b)	Additives that can be used in olefin polymers
(c)	Specifications for olefin polymer types described in sub paragraph (a)
(d)	Test method for specifications listed in sub paragraph (c)

[Refs. on p. 400]

Table 11.4 Specifications For Certain Olefin Polymers

Polymer types	Density (g/cm³)	Melting point (°C)	Max. hexane extractables	Max. xylene solubles	Type food contact application
Polypropylene homopolymer	0.88–0.913	160–180	6.4% @ reflux temp	9.8% @ 25 °C	All
Polyethylene homopolymer	0.85–1.00		2.6% @ 50 °C	11.3% @ 25 °C	All
Polyethylene homopolymer	0.85–1.00		5.5% @ 50 °C	11.3% @ 25 °C	Non cooking only
Propylene/ethylene copolymers	0.85–1.00		2.6% @ 50 °C	30% @ 25 °C	All
Propylene/ethylene copolymers	0.85–1.00		5.5% @ 50 °C	30% @ 25 °C	Non cooking only

Table 11.5 Conditions of Use—21 CFR 176.170(c)

Conditions of use	Description	Cooking/ noncooking
A	High temperatures heat-sterilized (e.g., over 212 °F)	Cooking
B	Boiling water sterilization	Cooking
C	Hot filled or pasteurized above 150 °F	Noncooking
D	Hot filled or pasteurized below 150 °F	Noncooking
E	Room temperature filled and stored (no thermal treatment in the container)	Noncooking
F	Refrigerated storage (no thermal treatment in the container)	Noncooking
G	Frozen storage (no thermal treatment in the container)	Noncooking
H	Frozen or refrigerated storage: ready-prepared foods intended to be reheated in container at time of use	Noncooking

To understand the difference between these two specifications, note that FDA defines "cooking" as temperatures of 212 °F and above. These are referred to as "Conditions of Use" A and B, defined in Title 21, Part 176.170 (c), Table 2 (see Table 11.5). Noncooking applications are referred to as conditions of use C through H (see Table 11.5). For further clarification, FDA has gone so far as to define "microwave cooking" versus "microwave reheating." Microwave cooking is precisely that: cooking of raw food in a container. This corresponds to the "Conditions of Use" A and B stated above. The FDA has defined microwave reheating as a noncooking application covered under "Conditions of Use" C through H. This means that reheating previously cooked food in a microwave is not considered a cooking application and, therefore, propylene/ethylene copolymer resins used in microwave reheating applications are subject to the specifications of 3.1a listed above.

Finally, subparagraph (d) includes test procedures referred to in sub paragraph (c) specifications. The test procedures include specific gravity, melting point, hexane extractables, and xylene solubles.

11.4.1.4   Food Types

It has been previously mentioned that the FDA has defined "Conditions of Use." FDA has also defined food categories in 21 CFR 176.170(c), Table 1 (see Table 11.6). All foods can be put into one of these categories. Some of the end-use regulations require testing on the final food contact article, depending on the type of food to be in contact with that article. Table 11.7 gives examples of common foods and how they are categorized in the FDA regulations.

11.4.2   Canada: Health and Welfare Department—Health Protection Branch (HPB)

In Canada the regulation of food contact materials is much different than in the U.S.A. The HPB in Canada is sanctioned to review food contact materials and issue letters of "no objection" for their use. In other words, each resin mixture or formulation is reviewed by the HPB to insure that no adverse health effect will occur with the use of that resin. The HPB has developed a data base of information on many plastic resins and additives and colorants used

Table 11.6 Types of Raw and Processed Foods

Type	Sub-type	Description
I		Nonacid, aqueous products; may contain salt or sugar or both (pH above 5.0)
II		Acid, aqueous products; may contain salt or sugar or both, and including oil-in-water emulsions of low or high fat content
III		Aqueous, acid or non-acid products containing free oil or fat; may contain salt, and including water-in-oil emulsions of low or high fat content
IV		Dairy product and modifications
	A	Water-in-oil emulsions, high- or low-fat
	B	Oil-in-water emulsions, high- or low-fat
V		Low moisture fats and oil
VI		Beverages
	A	Containing up to 8% of alcohol
	B	Nonalcoholic
	C	Containing more than 8% alcohol
VII		Bakery products other than those included under Types VIII or IX
	A	Moist bakery products with surface containing free fat or oil
	B	Moist bakery products with surface containing no free fat or oil
VIII		Dry solids with the surface containing no free fat or oil
IX		Dry soilds with the surface containing free fat or oil

in plastic resin formulations. The process to gain a letter of "no objection" from the HPB is very simple. One must provide information concerning the resin formulation to the HPB. In addition, it must be specified what type of food contact application and the types of foods that will be in contact with the resin. If it passes HPB review, the letter of "no objection" will be issued. If the HPB does not have enough information to issue the "no objection" letter (i.e., a

Table 11.7 FDA Categories [17, 18, 19, 20, 21, 22]

FDA food types	Examples of food products
I	Raspberries, maple syrup, consommé, ripe olives
II	Vinegar, mayonnaise, organge juice, cream dressing
III	Crab, caviar, lobster, oysters, trout, salmon, beef loin, ground beef, lamb leg, mutton chop, ground pork, bacon, Canadian bacon, ham (lean), liver sausage, wieners, dried beef, chicken, duck, goose, turkey, oleo margarine
IV-A	Cheddar cheese, Roquefort cheese, swiss cheese, butter
IV-B	Milk, buttermilk, ice cream, cottage cheese, cream cheese, sweet cream (18%), sweet cream (40%)
V	Lard, peanut oil
VI-A	Soda pop
VI-B	Beer
VI-C	Distilled spirits
VII	Wheat bread (toast), devil's food cake, angel food cake, doughnuts, waffles, macaroon cookies, sugar cookies, high protein doughnuts, soda crackers, mince pie, biscuits
VIII	Macaroni, puffed rice, shredded wheat, corn meal, coffee
IX	Potato chips, Fritos, cheese curls, french fried potatoes, popcorn, broiled beef rib steaks, broiled pork chops, broiled trout, fried beef rib steak, fried pork chops, fried trout, broiled chicken, fried chicken

new additive is used in the formulation), they will request the resin manufacturer to do additional test work to show the safety of the resin in contact with food. Please note that some of the letters of "no objection" can be very specific and this depends on exactly what the petitioner requested from HPB.

11.4.3   European Union

The European Union is still undergoing harmonization of their food contact regulations. Directive 89/109/EC established the basic requirements for all food contact materials. This means materials and articles in their finished state must not transfer their constituents to foodstuffs in quantities which could endanger human health or bring about an unacceptable change in the composition of the foodstuffs.

11.4.3.1   PP and PP Copolymers

Directive 90/128/EC specifically relates to plastic materials and articles intended to come in contact with foodstuffs. Commonly known as the "Monomers Directive," it regulates the use of PP and PP copolymers in food contact applications. The monomers that are allowed to make food contact polymers are specified.

There are two lists of monomers: Section A is the "List Of Authorized Monomers And Other Starting Substances;" Section B is the "List Of Monomers And Other Starting Substances Which May Continue To Be Used Pending A Decision On Inclusion In Section A." When final harmonization takes place, only the Section A monomers list will exist. The EU has established a time frame for providing the proper information to get the Section B monomers onto the Section A list.

To put new monomers on the Section A list, a procedure has been established in Directive 89/109/EC. Some of the monomers in Section A and B have specific migration limits (SMLs). This means that polymers made from the specific monomers must be tested with food simulants under the intended conditions of use to check for extraction of the monomer into the food. Both propylene and ethylene are listed in Section A of the "Monomers Directive," and neither has a SML. The further requirement to determine compliance with the directive is to determine the overall migration from the food contact article. There are overall migration limits specified in this directive. The overall migration specifies that plastic materials and articles shall not transfer their constituents to foodstuffs in quantities exceeding 10 milligrams per square decimeter of surface area of material or article. In certain cases, this limit is expressed as 60 milligrams of the constituents released per kilogram of foodstuff (see Table 11.8). This means that the final article in contact with food must be tested with food simulants under specific conditions of use according to Directive 82/711/EC and 85/572/EC for testing migration of constituents of plastics.

11.4.3.2   Additives

Recently the EU adopted the third amendment to Directive 90/128/EC. The third amendment contained a list of approximately 277 additives which can be used without restrictions in plastics in contact with food. However, this is not a complete list of additives.

Table 11.8 Cases Where 60 mg Constituents Released/kg Foodstuffs is Applicable

Case	Description
(1)	Articles which are containers or which can be filled, with a capacity of not less than 500 mL and not more than 10 L
(2)	Articles which can be filled and it is impracticable to estimate surface area in contact with food
(3)	Caps, gaskets, stoppers or similar devices for sealing

Where additives are not listed, one must still review each EU member's regulations for additives used in food contact applications.

11.4.3.3   *Certifications for Food Contact Compliance*

The directive states that each company will self-certify the compliance status of the materials used in food contact applications. As previously stated, the polymers are governed by Directive 90/128/EC and this certification is made in the compliance letter. As for the additives, those listed in Directive 90/128/EC can also be certified to be in compliance with this directive. However, for those additives that are not covered by the directive, a statement of compliance per each member country's regulations must be made.

11.4.4   Japan: Japan Hygienic Olefin and Styrene Plastics Association (JHOSPA)

The JHOSPA was established September 26, 1973. As of June 1989, there were 750 members comprising additive producers, color material producers, resin manufacturers, molders, and firms and related businesses such as trading companies and food manufacturers. Its focus is on food containers, packaging materials, and utensils of polyethylene, PP, polymethylpentene, polybutene-1, butadiene resin, polymethylmethacrylate, nylon, polyethylene terephthalate, polycarbonate, polyvinyl alcohol, polyacetal, polyphenylene-ether, polyacrylonitrile, fluoro-carbon resin, polymethacrylstyrene, polybutyleneterephthalate, polyarylsulfone, polyarylate, hydroxybenzoic acid polyester, or any combination of the above-mentioned plastics.

   The JHOSPA was established to further the knowledge and observance of Japan's Food Sanitation Law and hygienic regulations on food containers, packaging, and utensils made of the plastics mentioned above. In addition, they are charged with doing research and collecting data information on hygienic matters related to food containers, packaging, and utensils made of plastics; establishing voluntary standards on hygienic matters related to food containers, packaging, and utensils made of plastics; issuing and registering certificates of compliance with voluntary standards and regulations; insuring that raw materials meet the JHOSPA voluntary standards and regulations; and inspecting containers, packaging, and utensils registered to JHOSPA.

   The regulatory basis for articles used in contact with food is the Japan Food Sanitation Law, which was enacted in 1947. Article 10 of this law stipulates the specification standards for materials used in contact with food. The voluntary standards (PL) established by JHOSPA in 1974 have taken on a more significant role in the certification of food contact materials than the Food Sanitation Law specifications, because the JHOSPA process review is more extensive and accepted by organizations representing consumers.

Only members of JHOSPA can make application to gain a certificate of compliance. An application form must be completed containing information such as the type of material, its trade name, the formulation for the product, and the results of specific testing that is dictated by the voluntary standards. Once the application has been reviewed by the JHOSPA committee and approved, a certificate of compliance is issued to the manufacturer of the material or the food contact article [23].

11.4.5   Australia

Plastic materials for food contact use are regulated under Australian standard 2070. In particular, PP and certain PP copolymers are regulated under Part 5 of this standard. Part 5 outlines the requirements for PP plastic materials for use in the manufacture of plastic items for food contact use. Under the general requirements in the standard, PP is produced by polymerizing propylene alone or polymerizing propylene with ethylene and/or any of the alkene-1 hydrocarbons, provided that the alkene-1 hydrocarbons do not contain more than eight carbon atoms and that those containing four to eight carbon atoms do not comprise more than 15% by mass of the polymerization mix. In addition, PP blends can be manufactured under this standard. These include blends of PP homopolymers and copoly- mers, as specified earlier, and blends of PP homopolymers and copolymers with polyethylene, ethylene vinyl acetate copolymer, polyisobutylene, and polystyrene, or mixtures thereof, provided that the polystyrene does not exceed 10% by mass of the resultant polymer blend. For the polymer to be considered PP, the resultant polymer must not contain less than 50% by mass of propylene units. Catalysts and the metal residues from the catalysts, emulsifying agents, suspension agents, colorants, and other miscellaneous additives are specified in the standard. Table 2 of the standard contains the list of additives that may be used in PP formulations. Similar to the U.S. FDA, there are extraction test requirements for PP using n-hexane and xylene (see Table 11.9). Test procedures are listed in the standard. Unlike the U.S. FDA, these extractions can be done either on the base resin or on the formulated polymer. Finally, materials that are used for food contact must be marked according to the standard [24].

Table 11.9 Limits of Extractable Substances—AS 2070, Part 5

Polymer type	Max. n-hexane extractables	Max. xylene solubles
Polypropylene homopolymer	6.5%, reflux temp.	10%, 25 °C
Polypropylene copolymer (as defined by the regulation)	5.5%, 50 °C	30%, 25 °C

11.5   Potable Water

Another regulatory area applicable to PP manufacturers is the consideration of the polymeric material and its compositional components as indirect additives when used in potable water applications. This aspect of a material's contribution as a potential contaminant to drinking water is addressed by organizations such as NSF International, based in the United States. Other organizations concerned with potable water components include the Water Research Council, based in England, and KIWA, based in the Netherlands. NSF International is used here to illustrate an example of the types of evaluations which may be conducted when considering materials for potable water applications.

In the United States, NSF International can be considered to be to public health safety and environmental quality what Underwriters Laboratories is to fire and electrical safety. For over fifty years, NSF has been developing and recognizing numerous standards for potable water applications. In the late 1980s, a consortium, lead by NSF International, was formed to develop voluntary, third-party consensus standards and a certification program for all direct and indirect drinking water additives. The initiative was prompted by a request from the U.S. EPA with the intent of replacing the EPA Additives Advisory Program for drinking water system components. Other members of this consortium included the American Water Works Association, the Association of State Drinking Water Administrators, and the Conference of State Health and Environmental Managers.

One of the outcomes of the EPA request was Standard 61: Drinking Water System Components—Health Effects. This standard is intended to evaluate the potential for any adverse health effects due to contact of the component material with potable water. It does not address product performance issues, although these are often considered in end-product standards. As applied to PP-based products, Standard 61 requires that a specimen of a particular surface area be exposed to an aqueous solution for a period of time at a certain temperature. The surface area, the composition of the aqueous solution, and the exposure protocol are determined by the intended end use of the product. Details of exposure protocols can be found in Standard 61. Following the exposure, the extractant solution is analyzed for the presence of contaminants. The contaminants targeted are determined by a formulation review.

11.6   Medical Applications

Polypropylene and PP copolymers are used in various medical applications such as drug packaging (e.g., bottles) and medical devices (e.g., syringes, intravenous tubes). There are no specific regulations that can be used to call a resin a so-called "medical grade." However, Europe has criteria contained in the European Pharmacopeia for "Polypropylene For Containers For Preparations For Parenteral Use" [25]. In addition, the EU has passed Directive 93/42/EC, which lays out the rules for medical applications; however, it is not fully implemented by all EU members, with some still using their internal rules.

Most countries (including European countries where applications are not covered by the European Pharmacopeia) have a regulatory agency which reviews petitions to clear drugs and medical devices and formally gives the approval to market the product. Data must be developed to show the compatibility and safety of the product to be used in the medical application. Testing, like the United States Pharmacopeia (USP) tests for a Class VI plastic [26], can be one measure to show a plastic's safety in medical applications. However, the manufacturer of the drug or medical device is usually the one who has to prove the safety of the consumer product. The resin manufacturers can only provide information to support the submission to the government agency. In many cases, this support entails the revealing of confidential information about the resin (i.e., formulation). Some countries, such as Canada and the U.S.A. have provisions for maintaining confidential information in a file that is kept at the government agency called a Drug Master File (DMF). The EU is in the process of establishing a DMF information system. Information is put in a DMF by the sponsor company and includes items such as formulation of the resin, toxicology data developed (such as USP Class VI testing), manufacturing process, and resin release specifications, to name a few. The government agency, with the permission of the sponsor company, can use the DMF when reviewing petitions for new drugs or medical devices.

11.7   Fire and Electrical Safety Certifications

Fire and electrical safety certification is a well-known tool applied to classify materials, including PP. There are numerous organizations which grant recognitions based on performance relative to fire and electrical testing standards. These organizations are considered to be third-party certifiers. They include: Underwriters Laboratories (UL), based in the United States, perhaps the most well known worldwide, Canadian Standards Association (CSA), British Standards Association (BSI), Verband Deutscher Elektrotechniker (VDE, Germany), and Association Francaise de Normalisation (AFNOR, France), among others. Underwriters Laboratories is the world's largest independent safety and testing organization, and its specific tests will be utilized to demonstrate the type of testing conducted in the area of fire and electrical safety certification.

The purpose of the evaluations and recognitions conducted by UL on resins is to provide preselection data to potential users. It is considered a preselection technique because the testing is conducted, in theory, without regard to a specific end product. It is not meant to predict actual performance in an application but rather to indicate inherent material characteristics relative to a set of specific standards. The data is then used to help identify resins which can be considered for use in an end product covered under another UL product standard. It is still up to the manufacturer of that product to establish that the component and, subsequently, the entire product meet the requirements of the corresponding UL end-product standard.

Underwriters Laboratories has hundreds of product standards. Four of those standards relate specifically to material preselection testing and are representative of the kinds of classifications which might apply to a material such as PP. The resin-specific standards are identified in Table 11.10.

Table 11.10 Resin Standards

Standard	Subject
UL94 [27]	Flammability testing
UL746A [28]	Short-term property testing
UL746B [29]	Long-term property testing
UL746C [30]	Use in electrical equipment evaluations

11.7.1   Flammability

The UL94 standard covers classification of a material's tendency to ignite in the presence of a flame and to continue to burn after the ignition source is removed [27]. The primary value of the tests conducted per UL94 is to compare the relative burning characteristics of different materials or to identify changes in any given material. The UL94 standard references many ASTM and ISO test methods covering such areas as molding, calibration of the flame, and oven parameters.

Only the flame test itself and its resulting classification categories are highlighted here. There are three distinct flame tests in UL94 which are most often applied to a PP product. These are presented in Table 11.11 along with their related ASTM and ISO test methods and the appropriate IEC standard. The American Society for Test Methods (ASTM) and International Standards Organization (ISO) are well-known test method standards development organizations. The International Electrotechnical Commission (IEC) is the authority for world standards for electrical and electronic engineering. Its standards are used as the basis for national standards in over 100 countries around the world.

11.7.1.1   Horizontal Burn (94HB)

A classification under UL 94HB implies a maximum burning rate for a bar specimen. The test is called a horizontal burn test because the bar is oriented in the horizontal plane during the procedure. The test consists of applying a 20-mm flame to a molded 125 mm × 12.5 mm × 3 mm bar until the flame front reaches the first of two distance markers. The time it takes to reach the second distance marker, 75 mm away, is recorded. To get a 94HB recognition, the burning rate thus determined cannot exceed 40 mm/min. If the test specimen thickness is less than 3 mm, the burning rate cannot exceed 75 mm/min. Further details of the test can be found in the UL 94 Standard.

Recognition under the UL 94HB flame test does not imply any self-extinguishing character for the resin. Any standard PP should pass the test at 3 mm. Recognition is then

Table 11.11 Flame Testing Categories

Test type	Rating	ASTM method	ISO method	IEC method
Horizontal burn	HB	D635	1,210	707
Vertical burn	V0, V1, V2	D3801	1,210	707
Five inch flame	5VA, 5VB	D5048	10,351	

granted to 1.5 mm. At these thicknesses, the test tends to be a routine but useful way to categorize the resin.

11.7.1.2   20-mm Vertical Burn (94V0, 94V1, 94V2)

The vertical burn test is designed to differentiate between materials which have some self-extinguishing characteristics. The term "self-extinguishing" here means that the material will cease to burn upon removal of the ignition source. In the case of the vertical burn test, the ignition source is a 20-mm flame. It is applied to a bar of the same dimensions used in the horizontal burn test, but, in this case, the orientation of the bar is vertical.

The classifications in this category, as noted above, include 94V0, 94V1, and 94V2. The rating of a resin is a function of its self-extinguishing efficiencies, its tendency to drip, and its tendency to glow. All of these characteristics are observed on five specimens of a given material after each of two sequential ten-second flame applications on each bar. Both the individual performance of any bar and the summary performance of the specimen set is considered in assigning recognition under a flame class. Table 11.12 illustrates the requirements for each flame class. Further details of the test can be found in the UL 94 Standard.

11.7.1.3   125-mm Vertical Burn (94-5VA, 94-5VB)

An alternate vertical flame test developed specifically to look at materials intended for enclosure applications is the 94-5V test series. In this test, a 125-mm flame is applied to 5 bar and 5 plaque specimens in the thickness of interest for a total of 25 seconds via 5 applications of 5 second durations. To achieve a 5V rating, the total flame and glow time for each individual bar specimen after the fifth flame application cannot exceed 60 seconds and any drips cannot ignite cotton placed beneath the specimens. Materials which have been determined to be 5V through flame testing applied to a bar are further differentiated based on whether the flame applications to the plaques result in a burn-through hole. A 5VA rating indicates the flame burned a hole in the plaque; a 5VB rating indicates that no burn-through occurred.

Table 11.12 Vertical Burn Ratings per UL94[a]

Criteria	V0	V1	V2
Burning time after each flame application for each individual specimen	≤ 10 seconds	≤ 30 seconds	≤ 30 seconds
Total flame time for all 5 specimens, including both flame applications	≤ 50 seconds	≤ 250 seconds	≤ 250 seconds
Flame time + glow time for any individual specimen after the second flame application	≤ 30 seconds	≤ 60 seconds	≤ 60 seconds
Burning/glowing to the clamp in which the specimen is mounted	No	No	No
Flaming, dripping particles which ignite cotton located beneath the specimens	No	No	Yes

[a] Adapted from Table 8.1 in UL94 [27]

Table 11.13 Short-Term Property Evaluations Typical for PP

Test	ASTM test method	ISO test method
Tensile strength	D638	527
Tensile or Izod impact	D1822 or D256	180 (Izod only)
Dielectric strength	D149	243
Volume resistivity	D257	167
High voltage, low current high arc resistance*	D495	—
Comparative tracking index*	D3638	112
High voltage arc tracking rate*	UL test method	
Hot wire ignition*	D3874	—
High current arc ignition*	UL test method	
High voltage arc resistance to ignition*	UL test method	
Glow wire resistance to ignition*	UL test method	

* Results reported as Performance Level Categories

11.7.2   Short-Term Property Evaluations

The UL746A standard evaluates short-term properties of polymer materials [28]. The data are intended to provide guidance for the manufacturer and users of the materials with respect to certain physical, electrical, ignition, and flammability characteristics. The tests most likely to be conducted on PP-based products are summarized in Table 11.13, along with applicable ASTM and ISO test methods. The data developed on the electrical and ignition properties indicated by an asterisk in Table 11.13 are reported by UL as "Performance Level Categories" or "PLCs." The use of PLCs effectively group materials according to their relative performance, assisting the end user and safety engineer in making material selections. In addition, all of the data developed under UL746A can be used to identify potential replacement materials in the event that the originally selected resin becomes unavailable.

11.7.3   Long-Term Property Evaluations

UL746B is designed to work in union with, and as an extension to, UL746A. Whereas UL746A investigates short-term properties such as tensile and dielectric strength, UL746B studies changes in such properties over time and at elevated temperatures [29]. The test program consists of exposing molded specimens to a series of four temperatures and testing samples until failure is observed. Because PP has the fairly unique characteristics that it experiences rapid deterioration upon the onset of degradation and that it exhibits visual signs of degradation simultaneously, a unique version of the thermal aging test program has evolved specifically for PP.

Typically, the aging temperatures for PP are $130\,°C$, $140\,°C$, $150\,°C$ and $160\,°C$. The samples tested include tensile strength bars, tensile impact bars, and dielectric plaques. The test program consists of aging the samples along with additional samples which have been placed in the oven on a delayed schedule. When the original samples placed in the oven show signs of visual degradation, the delayed samples are removed from the oven and tested to make sure they continue to maintain at least 50% of their property value as determined on unaged samples. If a material has been recognized as a UL94V2 or better flame class, then samples are also aged to insure that they do not lose their flammability properties after aging.

A control of "known" performance is always aged along with the material being evaluated. The data developed from aging at four temperatures is then compared to the control's performance in this test, and the control's performance is compared to its performance in its original evaluation. Underwirters Laboratories then assigns a Relative Thermal Index (RTI) based on all these considerations. A different assignment may be made for "Mechanical without Impact" (based on tensile bar performance), "Mechanical with Impact" (based on tensile impact bar performance), and "Electrical" (based on dielectric plaque performance).

Details of the test can be found in the UL746B standard. It is important to keep in mind that a Relative Thermal Index (RTI) assigned under this standard does not imply any specific performance or acceptability of use at a given temperature for a resin, but only indicates its relative thermal performance when compared to a "known" reference resin. Typical RTI values for PP-based resins which have been well stabilized for long-term heat aging performance are in the $100\,°C$ to $115\,°C$ range, although some PP resins have achieved RTIs as high as $125\,°C$. In the absence of testing, UL assigns a generic rating of $65\,°C$ to PP products.

11.8   Customer Specifications

As stated in previous sections, there are many government regulations that we must be aware of concerning our products. In addition, there are nongovernment organizations, like Underwriters Laboratories, which have developed standards in health, safety, and environment that are recognized around the world as if they are law.

Some PP customers are developing their own Health, Safety, and Environmental (HSE) standards, establishing criteria for purchase or use of chemical substances. These standards are usually related to the use of certain chemical substances or whether certain chemical substances appear in the products that they use. Hazardous materials normally targeted are heavy metals (i.e., lead, cadmium, chromium and mercury), carcinogens, chloroflurocarbons (CFCs) or ozone depleting chemicals (ODCs), and other unwanted chemical substances. Examples of these standards are Ford's Engineering Material Specification WSS-M99P9999-A1; General Motors Restricted and Reportable Chemicals Engineering Standard, GM1000M; and Lego's Product Safety Certificate. Such customer specifications should be reviewed carefully to understand the specific supplier obligations that are assumed upon signing certificates of compliance with those standards. In some cases, confidential information is requested to be revealed to the customer, which may not be a normal business practice without secrecy agreements being established.

References

1. Code of Federal Regulations, Title 29, Part 1910.1200
2. Hazardous Products Act, the Controlled Products Regulations, Ingredients Disclosure List, Federal and Provincial Occupational Safety and Health Legislation, Hazardous Materials Information Review Act
3. U.S.: Code of Federal Regulations, Title 29, Part 1910, 1200. Canada: "WHMIS Core Material: A resource manual for the application and implementation of WHMIS"—August 1988—Workers Compensation Board of British Columbia, Richmond, British Columbia. Europe: Directives 67/48/EC and 88/379/EC
4. U.S.: Ref. [3]. Canada: Ref. [3]. Europe: Directive 91/155/EC
5. "American National Standard for Hazardous Industrial Chemicals—Materials Safety Data Sheets—Preparation", ANSI Z400.1, 1993
6. Directive 91/155/EC
7. Code of Federal Regulations, Title 40, Part 720
8. Code of Federal Regulations, Title 40, Part 720.102
9. Code of Federal Regulations, Title 40, Part 720.36
10. Code of Federal Regulations, Title 40, Part 723.250
11. U.S. Federal Register, 60, (60) (Wednesday, March 29, 1995) 16316–16336
12. U.S. Toxic Substances Control Act, Code of Federal Regulations, Title 40, Parts 700–799
13. European Union–7th Amendment
14. Council Directive 67/548/EC
15. Guidelines For the Notification and Testing of New Substances: Chemicals and Polymers March, 1993. Copy may be obtained from: Environment Canada; New Substances Division; Commercial Chemicals Branch, Conservation and Protection; 14th Floor, Place Vincent Massey; Ottawa, Canada K1A 0H3
16. "Recommendations for Chemistry Data for Indirect Food Additive Petitions," Chemistry Review Branch, Office of Premarket Approval, Center for Food Safety and Applied Nutrition, Food and Drug Administration, Washington, DC 20204, June 1995
17. "Handbook of Chemistry and Physics". Chemical Rubber Publishing Co., Boca Raton, 1960, p. 1954–1967
18. *Davis, C.E., Oakerman, H.W., Cahill, V.R.:* Food Technology 20 (Nov. 1966) 1475.
19. *Rusoff, I.I., Goodman, A.H., Sommer, J., Cantor, S.M.:* Food Technology 18 (1964) 1789
20. Discussions with Professor S.S. Chang, Rutgers University, November 13, 1970
21. *Strock, H., Ball, C.O., Chang, S.S:* Food Technology 21 (1961) 163–166
22. *Chung, Mackay and Raney:* Food Technology (1966) 692
23. "Legal Requirements for Synthetic Resin Products In Japan, Japan Tupperware, April 1993
24. Australian Standard 2070, Part 5–1981, "Plastics Materials For Food Contact Use: Part 5—Polypropylene"
25. European Pharmacopeia, Part VI.1.2.2.3
26. United States Pharmacopeia XXIII, 1995
27. Standard for Safety UL94, "Tests for Flammability of Plastic Materials for Parts in Devices and Applications," Underwriters Laboratories Inc., Fourth Edition, June 18, 1991
28. Standard for Safety UL 746A, "Polymeric Materials—Short Term Property Evaluations," Underwriters Laboratories Inc., 3rd Edition, August 2, 1990
29. Standard for Safety UL 746B, "Polymeric Materials—Long Term Property Evaluations," Underwriters Laboratories Inc., 3rd Edition, June 4, 1979
30. Standard for Safety UL 746C, "Polymeric Materials—Use in Electrical Equipment Evaluations," Underwriters Laboratories Inc., 3rd Edition, May 19, 1989

Part III

Polypropylene: The Future

12   Specialty Types and Developments

Edward P. Moore, Jr.

12.1   Introduction

If the future of the polypropylene (PP) business is anything like past history, those associated with it are sure to find it exciting and rewarding. As any business matures, the growth rate begins to level off, and, eventually, shrink. In this chapter, it is not our intention to predict the future course of PP but to illustrate two developments that, like similar developments described earlier, could sustain the growth and expansion of the PP property envelope and range of applications. They are PP from metallocene catalysts, which includes syndiotactic PP, and nonolefinic alloy copolymers.

12.2   Metallocene Catalysts

The discovery of metallocene catalysts has been one of the more exciting developments in recent times. Although little interest followed Breslow's 1955 work, due to low activity, in the 1970s interest was briskly renewed with the discovery by Kaminsky of the accelerating effect of methylaluminoxane cocatalyst. Efforts and progress in the last decade have been increasingly intense, and, with the development of supported metallocenes and the "constrained geometry" systems, the potential for propylene polymerization has improved, and PP has received increasing attention. The technical details of metallocenes have been well documented in many publications. Three major references [1, 2, 3] and an excellent review article [4] are suggested for more details. While the science has grown explosively, and the mechanisms are now well understood, the business has been slow to develop.

    Most of the work on metallocene catalysts has been aimed at PE, and commercialization of those efforts is proceeding rapidly [5]. However, there is also great potential for PP. Isotactic PP (iPP), syndiotactic PP (sPP), atactic PP (aPP), and propylene-based copolymer rubbers are candidates for production by metallocenes, as well as a range of new copolymers that could significantly expand the properties achieved with conventional PP polymers.

12.2.1   Technology

As the details of these catalysts were discussed in Chapter 2 and may be found in the referenced publications, we will address the capabilities of the catalysts here, rather than the chemistry. We will consider the metallocenes relative to all polymers, then focus on their impact on PP. Some of the advantages of the metallocene catalysts deal with areas not even considered in our conventional polymers.

The following are some of the major advantages of metallocene catalysts [4, 6]:

1. Many more vinyl monomers, even with bulky and polar side groups, can be polymerized successfully. This not only enables more polymers to be prepared, but a wider range of copolymers are consequently possible, due to the more compatible reactivity ratios between comonomers.
2. Extremely uniform polymers are obtained. Degree of regularity, molecular weight, and composition fall in very narrow ranges. This is due to the single catalyst site geometry; all sites are essentially identical in performance. In contrast, Ziegler–Natta sites vary between the very nonspecific sites that create atactic PP and the highly specific sites that give stereoregular PP.
3. The regularity of the product may be selected over a wide range. It may be low or high in regularity, and isotactic or syndiotactic.
4. The degree of unsaturation may be regulated. As the normal termination mechanism leaves a vinyl double bond at the chain end, unsaturation for later functionalization may be programmed into the molecule.

12.2.2   Isotactic PP

The iPP from metallocene catalysts differs from conventional PP by often being less than 100% regioregular, while Ziegler–Natta products are normally very high in regioregularity [6, 7]. Consequently, the melting points and crystallization rates from metallocenes can be lower, but the maximum use temperature (heat deflection temperature) can still be equal to or slightly higher than in conventional PP. As catalyst advances have reduced the number of regioerrors in the chain, the melting point has approached that of conventional PP. The properties of typical iPP polymers from metallocene catalysts are listed in Table 12.1. The slower crystallization rates present some problems in processing.

The consistently stereoregular polymer has been described as having a "narrow tacticity distribution." The most practical consequence of this narrow tacticity distribution is the total absence of atactic polymer. Thus, problems associated with the atactic fraction, usually also low in MW, are eliminated or alleviated with metallocene polymers. In addition to the

Table 12.1 Properties of PP from Metallocene Catalysts

Type	% Regio-errors	Melting point °C	M_W/M_n	Flexural modulus MPa	Light transmission %	Extractables %
Metallocene homopolymer	2.5	139	2.2	1,090	56	
Metallocene homopolymer		151	2.3	1,480	44	
Metallocene homopolymer	0.5	160	2.5	1,670	35	
Conventional homopolymer	0	162	5.8	1,230	34	
Metallocene random		140		970	65	1.1
Conventional random		141		640	57	7.9

Source: Hoechst AG, Ref. [7]

elimination of plate-out, fuming, and die drool behavior, the low levels of extractables can be significant for polymers going into food contact and medical applications.

Like the regio- and stereospecificities, the molecular weight and polymer yield of the PP are also determined by the metallocene structure, and have covered a wide range during the history of the catalysts. The improvement of the mid-1980s placed the achievable PP MW in a commercially attractive range, and provided a yield of several thousand kilograms of PP per gram of metal. As with conventional PP, hydrogen regulation of MW is effective with metallocene catalysts.

The molecular weight distribution (MWD) of metallocene PP is very narrow, M_w/M_n of about 2 to 2.5, compared to 6 to 8 for conventional PP. Narrow MWD, which is highly desirable in fine fiber production, is achieved on conventional PP by chemically assisted extrusion degradation, providing a M_w/M_n of about 3 to 4. Thus, metallocene-based PP may have significant advantages in the fiber business [8].

The metallocenes provide very uniform distribution of comonomers, which is particularly important in random copolymers. In conventional copolymers, the comonomer content varies with molecular weight, which, together with the atactic fraction, contributes to stickiness and difficulties in production and handling. Metallocene copolymers show a virtually constant composition with MW. This eliminates the most sticky fraction, the highly substituted low MW end. Consequently, it is possible to prepare copolymers with higher average comonomer concentrations, and therefore lower melting points, without problems with plugging and agglomeration in polymerization. The result is a film layer that will heat seal at a lower temperature and with good hot tack strength.

The metallocene catalysts will also incorporate higher alpha-olefin (HAO) comonomers and other highly substituted comonomers more readily than will Ziegler–Natta catalysts. In PE films, the HAO comonomers have provided enhanced strength and toughness. Comparable property improvements have been shown with HAO comonomers in PP [8].

It is also possible to extend the PP property envelope toward totally atactic polymer. Truly atactic propylene-ethylene copolymers have exhibited superior elastomeric properties, principally improved elastic recovery and better clarity [9].

Some of the more desired properties to be derived from the above materials, and the more likely markets for them, are listed in Table 12.2. Polypropylenes from metallocene catalysts are expected to serve several specialty businesses, such as fine fibers, heat sealable films, and softer, tougher films and articles, rather than the commodity markets.

The cost of metallocene catalysts is somewhat higher than conventional Ziegler–Natta catalysts, but still does not account for a large part of the polymer cost, and is expected to decrease as developments continue. Because they may be used in existing PP plant

Table 12.2 PP Products from Metallocene Catalysts

Property advantages	Application
Very narrow MW distribution	Fine fibers
Softer, clearer iPP or sPP homopolymers and copolymers, no atactic content	Medical bags and tubing, food containers
Low melting random copolymers, no atactic	Heat sealable films
Clearer, tougher elastomers, better elastic recovery	General elastomeric uses, blends

configurations, major investments will not be needed to begin manufacturing PP from metallocene catalysts.

12.2.3   Syndiotactic PP

Although its existence and structure have been known since the early Natta work, sPP is now approaching commercial status, due to its easier preparation and higher specificity with the metallocene catalysts [10, 11]. Even highly syndiotactic PP provides lower melting, softer, slower crystallizing, clearer PP than conventional homopolymer. Typical properties are shown in Table 12.3. As with iPP from metallocenes, the degree of regioregularity can be lower than conventional PP, giving lower melting points and slower crystallization rates. Further details of the morphology of sPP appear in Chapter 3.

The potential suppliers of sPP are generally those also involved in metallocene catalyst development and commercialization. As with iPP from metallocenes, sPP is expected to be offered for specialty applications, yet to be defined.

12.2.4   Commercialization

The research on metallocenes is a good example of the specialty approach to the business. Several companies have major research programs to develop positions aimed at gaining a share of the future business and associated profits. As of the end of 1994, about 600 patents had been issued worldwide, and disputes over the ownership of contested technical territory had already begun. Clearly, these companies are committed to the business, not just the science.

Although the major players have invested much in the development of patents and technology, the move to commercial operations in metallocene-based PP has been less

Table 12.3 Properties of sPPs

Property	Units	Polypropylene sample			
		sPP1	sPP2	sPP3	Conv. iPP
Melt flow rate	g/10 min	5.3	8.9	2.9	
Melting point	°C	125	126	148	163
Density	g/cm^3	0.87	0.87	0.89	0.91
Crystallinity	%	21	22	29	55
CH$_3$ placement: racemic[b]	%	91.4	91.9	96.5	1.4
CH$_3$ placement meso[b]	%	8.6	8.1	3.5	98.6
M_W/M_n		2.6	2.6	1.7	8
Flexural modulus[a]	MPa	380	415	760	1,170
Notched Izod	J/m	775	670	750	25
Haze[a]	%	20	27	48	—

[a] Comparative values
[b] By ^{13}C NMR; total % in pentads
Source: Fina Oil and Chemical Co. Ref. [11]

dramatic [12]. Two producers have metallocene PE available in commercial quantities, several have prepared large quantities iPP and sPP from metallocenes, and several have announced plans to commercialize PP from metallocenes. However, none were selling PP from metallocene catalysts in commercial quantities in early 1995. However, the level of activity and commitment of the participants indicate that some level of business success is highly likely. Considering its stage of development, this technology still has the potential of fueling another revolution in the PP industry. It is very likely, at least, to extend the PP property envelope well beyond existing limits.

12.3   Nonolefinic Alloy Copolymers

The later fourth generation catalyst advances that permitted the development of Montell's Catalloy process (Section 7.1.8.1), when carried further, opened up additional new possibilities. A key feature of these catalysts is the high, uniform porosity, which is maintained during the polymerization process, combined with structural integrity of the PP particle. The highly porous PP particles enable the polymerization of nonolefinic monomers within them. Properly conducted, both the nonolefinic polymer and a graft copolymer with PP may be formed simultaneously, in micron-scale domains, uniformly distributed within the particle [13]. As illustrated in Fig. 12.1, the even distribution of the nonolefinic component, polystyrene in this

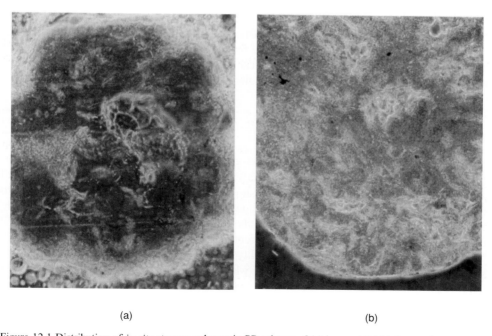

(a)   (b)

Figure 12.1 Distribution of *in situ* styrene polymer in PP spheres of (a) low and (b) high porosity

Table 12.4 Properties of Developmental Hivalloy™ Engineering Resin Alloys

Grade	Specific gravity	Melt flow rate g/10 min	Tensile strength MPa (psi)	Flexural modulus MPa (Kpsi)	Notched Izod impact strength J/m	Heat deflection temperature, @ 66 psi °C
XPA017	1.19	12	37 (4500)	2600 (380)	2	71
XPA019	1.19	10	117 (17000)	12400 (1800)	1.8	140
XPA047	1.18	8	65 (9500)	4300 (625)	6.5	129

Source: Montell Polyolefins, Ref. [2]

case, results from the high porosity of the PP granule. Montell has established a strong patent position on this technology, which is called the "Hivalloy" process.

Normally the reactor product is pelletized, with the addition of stabilizers, impact modifiers, mineral fillers, or reinforcing fillers, according to the desired properties. The effectiveness of the reinforcing or impact modifying additives depends upon the detailed composition and physical nature of the alloy from the reactor. The high dispersion levels needed for the optimum property balance are developed in the polymerization, exceeding the ability to achieve the dispersion by high-shear melt extrusion, and reducing the energy requirement and the exposure of the polymer to high temperature.

The practical result of this intimate alloy is the development of more desirable properties such as higher heat deflection temperature, stiffness, hardness, and creep resistance to enhance the properties inherent in PP: the chemical resistance, low density, easy processability, and inertness to moisture. This approach is employed in PP/PS alloys that display stiffness-impact behavior in the range of engineering plastics. The properties of some developmental compositions, listed in Table 12.4, illustrate the range of materials available in quantity in 1995 [14]. The Hivalloy technology is applicable to a number of polymers and copolymers, including most vinyl polymers, and other addition and condensation polymers [15].

12.4   Summary

It is encouraging to see, 40 years after Natta's first PP preparation, that the industry is still vigorously establishing new technologies that could bring further revolutionary changes to the PP business. Each year, about $900 million is spent just on polyolefin catalyst research, and some 150 patents issue [4]. While the future is always uncertain, the new PP technologies, with the combination of current mysteries and surprising new discoveries, have already set the stage for the possibility of renewed growth of PP into unforeseen segments of the business. The PP business, which has been vigorous and exciting for four decades now, shows few signs of slowing down.

References

1. *Cardin, D.J., Lappert, J.F., Raston, C.L.:* Chemistry of Organo-zirconium and Hafnium Compounds, Hellis Horwood, J Wiley, 1986
2. *Haltermann, R.L.:* Chem. Rev. 92 (1992) 965–994
3. Metallocene Conference (MetCon), published annually, Catalyst Consultants Publishing Co. Springer House, PA
4. *Sinclair, K.B., Wilson, R.B.:* Chem and Industry 21 (7 Nov 04) 857–864
5. Mod. Plast. 70 (June 1994) 48–50
6. Private communication, L. Resconi, Montell Polyolefins, Ferrara, Italy
7. *Spaleck, W., Winter, A., Bachmann, B., Dolle, V., Kuber, F., Rohmann, J.:* New Isotactic Polypropylenes by Metallocene Catalysts, Metcon '93, Houston, TX
8. *McAlpin, J.J., Stahl, G.A.:* Applications Potential of Exxpol™ Metallocene-based Polypropylene, MetCon '94, Houston, TX
9. *Galimberti, M., Martini, E., Sartori, F., Piemontesi, F., Albizzati, E.:* Polyolefinic Elastomers from Metallocenes, MetCon '94, Houston, TX
10. Plast. Tech. 38 (March 1992) 29
11. *Shamshoum, E.S., Sun, L., Reddy, B.R., Turner, D.:* Properties and Applications of Low Density Syndiotactic Polypropylene, MetCon '94, Houston, TX
12. Metallocene Polypropylene, Phillip Townsend Associates Inc., Houston, TX, 1994
13. *DiNicola, A.J.:* HIVALLOY Resin Technology: Reactor Produced Polyolefin Alloys, 2nd Annual North America Symposium on Recent Advances in Polymer Blends and Alloys, Hilton Head, SC, 1994
14. Development Data Sheets, Hivalloy™ Engineering Resin Alloys, XPA Series, Montell Polyolefins, 1995
15. *Galli, P., Haylock, J.C., Albizzati, E., DeNicola, A.J.:* High Performance Polyolefins, IUPAC, Akron, OH, 1994

Subject Index

Thio compou
Third pa
Ti(al)
T